S0-BDS-432

Algebra
and
Trigonometry

Algebra and Trigonometry

REVISED EDITION

Edward A. Cameron
University of North Carolina

HOLT, RINEHART and WINSTON
New York, Chicago, San Francisco,
Toronto, London

Copyright © 1960, 1965 by Holt, Rinehart and Winston, Inc.
All Rights Reserved
Library of Congress Catalog Card Number: 65-14884
21253-1015
Printed in the United States of America

PREFACE

The purpose of this book, as in the case of the original edition, is to give a modern treatment of algebra and trigonometry that exhibits the logical structure of these disciplines and includes those topics essential for subsequent mathematical study. In the revision, the order of some of the topics has been changed, the number of exercises has been increased, several sections have been completely rewritten, and new material has been added.

The first two chapters have been interchanged, and the proofs of the theorems on the real number system (now treated in Chapter 2) have been greatly simplified. The concept of a function is presented in Chapter 1, both as a mapping and as a set of ordered pairs. Many additional exercises on functions are given, and a section on composition of functions is included.

Work on inequalities is based on the order axioms for the real numbers and is of the type needed in the study of the calculus.

In the treatment of equations and systems of equations, emphasis is placed upon equivalent equations and equivalent systems. Reduction to echelon form is the preferred method in the solution of systems of linear equations.

The work on matrices has been greatly expanded to include rectangular (not necessarily square) matrices, expression of a system of linear equations in matrix form, and the concept of inverse of a matrix. The algebra of matrices as well as the algebra of sets are presented as examples of algebraic systems that possess many but not all of the properties of the algebra of real numbers.

Complex numbers are introduced as ordered pairs of real numbers, with the usual notation given later. The relations connecting complex numbers, vectors, and polar and Cartesian coordinates are described, and applications of the trigonometric form are explored.

The chapter on the theory of equations includes those topics needed for later work in mathematics including some theory of factorization, presented in such a manner as to lead naturally into advanced courses in algebra.

The work on trigonometry is concentrated in Chapters 9 and 10, except for applications to complex numbers. This arrangement makes the book readily usable for two categories of students, those who have had some trigonometry and those who have not. Chapter 9 deals with trigonometric functions of angles and their applications to indirect measure and vectors. This chapter as well as most of the chapter on logarithms can be omitted and used for reference by students who have had a traditional trigonometry course in high school. Chapter 10 treats the circular functions of real numbers and the analytic aspects of trigonometry. The relation between circular and trigonometric functions, which permits a dual interpretation of identities and equations, is stressed. The importance of the periodic character of the circular functions is illustrated by applications to harmonic motion and sound.

Chapter 13, Permutations, Combinations, and Probability, is new. In an introduction to probability, concepts are described in terms of sets in such a manner as to generalize readily in a more abstract setting.

Throughout the book, both in algebra and trigonometry, the function concept is emphasized. It is believed that practice in thinking in terms of functions is of great value to the student. The axiomatic approach in Chapters 2, 4, and 11 will give the student some introduction to the nature of modern algebra. A serious attempt has been made to maintain a reasonable level of precision and rigor.

This book is adaptable to courses of different lengths. It can be covered completely in a year course. A three-hour semester course for students with fair training in high-school algebra and some knowledge of numerical trigonometry can be based upon Chapters 1, 2, 4, 5, 6, 7, 10, 11, and 12. Courses of four and five semester hours are also possible.

Answers to most odd-numbered exercises are given in the back of the book. Answers to even-numbered exercises appear in a separate pamphlet.

The author wishes to express his appreciation to colleagues in all parts of the country who have used the original book and have generously offered suggestions for its improvement.

E. A. C.

Chapel Hill, North Carolina
January, 1965

CONTENTS

COS (U-V) = COS U COS V + SIN U SIN V
COS (U+V) = COS U COS V - SIN U SIN V
SIN (U+V) = SIN U COS V + COS U SIN V

Algebra and Trigonometry

Numbers, Sets, and Functions

1

1.1 Number Systems

Algebra is concerned with systems of numbers (or other objects; for example, vectors and matrices) in which one or more operations, such as addition and multiplication, can be performed. One of these number systems is the **integers** (positive, negative, and zero whole numbers). In this system the operations of addition, multiplication, and subtraction can always be performed, but division is not always possible. For example, since there is *no integer* q such that $3q = 7$, the quotient of 7 by 3 does not exist in the system of integers; that is, we cannot divide 7 by 3 in this system. However, in the system of **rational numbers** (integers and fractions), division, except by 0, is always possible. Since also the operations of addition, subtraction, and multiplication can be performed in the rational number system, we say that this system is **closed** under the four operations mentioned. The rational number system gets its name from the fact that each of its members can be expressed in the form a/b as the *ratio* of two integers a and b. The rules for adding, subtracting, multiplying, and dividing rational numbers are assumed to be familiar. The rational numbers suffice for most practical problems involving measure.

There are, however, problems in mathematics for which the rational numbers are inadequate. For example, there is no rational number that expresses exactly the length of the hypotenuse of a right triangle with legs each of length 1 (see Fig. 1–1). This interesting fact is reputed to have been discovered by the Greek mathematician, Pythagoras, in the fifth century B.C. We sketch a proof of it here.

If we denote the length of the hypotenuse of the triangle in Fig. 1–1 by x, the famous Pythagorean theorem in geometry yields

$$x^2 = 1^2 + 1^2, \quad x^2 = 2.$$

Hence, the proof reduces to showing that there is no rational number whose square is 2. To show this, we use the indirect method of proof. That is, we assume the opposite of what we want to prove and demonstrate that this assumption leads to a contradiction. Hence, we conclude that the original proposition must be true.

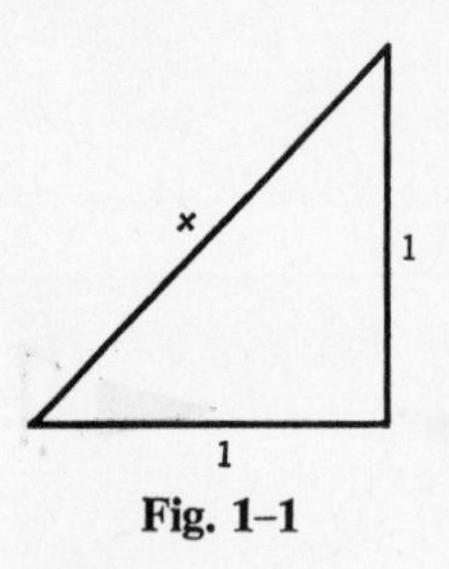

Fig. 1–1

The next step, then, is to assume that there *is* a rational number a/b whose square is 2. A rational number can always be reduced to lowest terms—that is, to a form in which numerator and denominator have no common integral divisor greater than 1. We may assume that this reduction has been done and that a and b have *no common factor greater than* 1. We have

$$\left(\frac{a}{b}\right)^2 = 2, \quad \frac{a^2}{b^2} = 2, \quad a^2 = 2b^2.$$

We now need to use the concept of an *even* integer, which is an integer expressible as two times an integer, the concept of an *odd* integer as one that is *not even,* and the fact that the product of two *odd* integers is *odd.*

The right member, $2b^2$, of the last equation above is an even integer, and hence the left member, a^2, is also an even integer. This means that the integer a itself must be even. For if a were odd, its square, a^2, being the product of two odd integers, would also be odd. Since a is even, we may write $a = 2c$, where c is an integer. Substituting $2c$ for a in the last equation above, we get

$$(2c)^2 = 2b^2, \quad 4c^2 = 2b^2, \quad 2c^2 = b^2.$$

The same type of argument used to show that a is even can be applied to the equation $2c^2 = b^2$ to show that b is even. Since a and b are both even, they have 2 *as a common factor.* This contradicts the fact that *a and b have no common factor greater than* 1. Thus, the assumption that there exists a rational number a/b such that $(a/b)^2 = 2$ leads to a contradiction. We conclude that there is no rational number whose square is 2.

It would be a highly unsatisfactory state of affairs not to have a number to represent the length of a line segment that is to be constructed. To remedy this and other deficiencies, the rational number system was extended to the **real number system,** a system consisting of the rational numbers and other numbers called **irrational.** We assume some intuitive acquaintance with real numbers. In Chapter 2 we give a list of some fundamental properties of the real number system and show that much of elementary algebra is based upon these properties. For the remainder of this chapter we shall rely upon the student's intuitive knowledge of the real numbers.

The following diagram indicates how the various number systems mentioned are related.

- **Real Number System**
  - **Rational Number System**
    - **Integers ($\cdots, -1, 0, 1, 2, 3, \cdots$)**
    - **Fractions ($\frac{1}{2}, \frac{4}{5}, -\frac{2}{3}, \cdots$)**
  - **Irrational Numbers ($\sqrt{2}, \sqrt{5}, \sqrt[3]{11}, \pi, -\sqrt[5]{4}, \cdots$)**

1.2 The Set Concept

Perhaps the most elemental concept in mathematics is that of a **set.** We use the term frequently, as when referring to the *set* of integers, the *set* of points in a line, the *set* of real numbers. The concept is also used in everyday discourse, as, for example, in the expressions: a *set* of golf clubs, a *collection* of stamps, a *flock* of sheep, the *class* of all male adults in the United States. We make no attempt to define the notion of set in terms of anything more elementary; it is usually taken as one of the undefined terms in the foundations of mathematics. In dealing with a particular set, it is important to be able to decide whether a specific object does or does not belong to the set in question. For example, 5 belongs to the set of integers but $\frac{2}{3}$ does not; $\frac{3}{4}$ belongs to the set of rational numbers but $\sqrt{2}$ does not.

We shall use capital letters to denote sets and small letters to denote members of a set. The symbol $x \in A$ will be used to mean "x belongs to A" ("x is a member of A"), and $x \notin A$ to mean "x does not belong to A."

A specific set may be described in various ways. If the set contains only a finite number of elements (members), it may be specified by listing these elements. For example, if P is the set of positive even integers less than 8, we may write $P = \{2, 4, 6\}$. If S is the set of elemental substances discussed by the Greek philosopher Empedocles, then $S = \{\text{earth, air, fire, water}\}$. Another method of denoting a set is to give a property that an object possesses if and only if it belongs to the set, as in the example: T is the set of all triangles that contain two equal angles.

Notation frequently used in denoting a set is illustrated by the following expression, where R is the set of all real numbers:

$$R = \{x \mid x \text{ is a real number}\}.$$

This statement is read "R is the set of all x such that x is a real number." The sets P and T referred to above may be defined in this notation as follows:

$$P = \{x \mid x \text{ is a positive integer, } x \text{ is even, } x \text{ is less than } 8\},$$
$$T = \{t \mid t \text{ is a triangle, } t \text{ contains two equal angles}\}.$$

Two sets A and B are said to be **equal** provided each member of A is a member of B and each member of B is a member of A. That is, two equal sets consist of precisely the same members.

Suppose that the elements of two sets A and B can be paired off so that in the pairing each element of A occurs in exactly one pair and each element of B occurs in exactly one pair. In this case the two sets are said to be in **one-to-one correspondence** and to contain the *same number of elements.* For example, if $A = \{1, 2, 3\}$ and $B = \{a, b, c\}$, a pairing that shows a one-to-one correspondence of A and B is $(1, a)$, $(2, b)$, and $(3, c)$. This pairing may also be denoted as follows: $1 \leftrightarrow a$, $2 \leftrightarrow b$, $3 \leftrightarrow c$.

If A and B are two sets, the set consisting of *all ordered* † *pairs* of elements (x, y), where x belongs to A and y belongs to B, is called the **Cartesian product** of A and B, and is denoted by $A \times B$. In the example given above, the Cartesian product consists of the following nine ordered pairs:

$$\{(1, a), (1, b), (1, c), (2, a), (2, b), (2, c), (3, a), (3, b), (3, c)\}.$$

The set $A \times B$ can be denoted by $\{(x, y) \mid x \in A, y \in B\}$.

1.3 Subsets

We recall that every rational number is a real number. This fact can be expressed by saying that the set of rational numbers is a *subset* of the set of real numbers. As another example, the set of all squares is a subset of the set of all rectangles. In general, if every member of a set B is a member of a set A, then B is called a **subset** of A. When this is the case, we write $B \subseteq A$; read "B is a subset of A" or "B is contained in A." In particular, a set is a subset of itself. For example, the set of integers is a subset of the set of integers. Notice that if $B \subseteq A$ and $A \subseteq B$, then $A = B$; and conversely, if $A = B$, then $B \subseteq A$ and $A \subseteq B$. A is called an **improper** subset of itself. All other subsets of A are called **proper.**

In connection with a particular problem, we may be concerned with the subsets of a definite fixed set. This fixed set may be referred to as the **universal set** and denoted by the letter U. Notice that the concept of a universal set is relative; a universal set for one problem is not necessarily universal for another. Included among the collection of all the subsets of a given set U is U itself and the **null set,** denoted by ϕ. The latter is defined as the set that does not contain any members. The null set (also called the **void set** and the **empty set)** plays somewhat the same role in the theory of sets that zero does in the theory of numbers. If $U = \{a, b, c\}$, then the collection of subsets of U consists of the following eight subsets:

† The term *ordered pair* means that the order in which the members occur in the pair is significant.

$$U, \phi, \{a\}, \{b\}, \{c\}, \{a, b\}, \{a, c\}, \{b, c\}.$$

This example shows that the number of subsets of a set of three elements is 2^3. In general, if U contains n elements, there are exactly 2^n subsets of U. A proof of this fact can be constructed by observing that a subset S of U is determined by considering in turn each element of U and either choosing it or rejecting it as a member of S. Since there are two choices for each element and there are n elements, it can be argued that altogether there are 2^n ways in which a subset can be selected.

EXERCISES

1. Is the set of even integers closed under addition? Under multiplication? What are the answers to these questions for the odd integers?
2. Prove the answers to the questions raised in Exercise 1 by using the fact that an even integer can be written in the form $2n$ and an odd integer in the form $2n + 1$.
3. Construct a proof for the statement that there is no rational number whose square is 3.
   (*Hint:* Study the proof given in Section 1.1 and use the fact that if $a^2 = 3b^2$, then a must have 3 as a factor.)
4. Apply the usual rules for addition, subtraction, multiplication, and division to the two rational numbers a/b and $c/d \neq 0$, and observe that in each case the result is a rational number.
5. Show by an example that the set of irrational numbers is *not* closed under multiplication.
6. Denote each of the following sets by enumerating the elements:
   (a) The first five letters of the alphabet
   (b) The set of positive integers greater than 5 and less than 12
   (c) The three primary colors
   (d) The positions on a baseball team
   (e) The days in a week
   (f) The presidents of the United States since 1935
7. Denote each of the following sets by the symbolic notation introduced in Section 1.2.
   (a) The set of all rational numbers
   (b) The set of all right triangles
   (c) The set of perfect square integers
   (d) The set of all even integers
   (e) The set of all positive integers divisible by 3
   (f) The set of all positive rational numbers less than 7
   (g) The set of all rectangles that are not squares
   (h) The set of all negative real numbers that are rational

8. If $U = \{2, 4, 6\}$, list all subsets of U.

9. If $U = \{p, q, r, s\}$, list all subsets of U.

10. Of the following sets, which are subsets of which?
R = set of real numbers
J = set of integers
Q = set of rational numbers
F = set of proper fractions
N = set of negative real numbers
H = set of irrational numbers
K = set of squares of rational numbers

11. If R is the set of all real numbers, define two subsets of R such that each element of R is in one but not both of these subsets.

12. If Z denotes the set of integers, define two subsets of Z such that each element of Z is in at least one of these subsets and only one element of Z is in both.

13. If $A = \{\text{John, Henry, Tom}\}$ and $B = \{\text{Mary, Ruth, Alice}\}$, define two different one-to-one correspondences between A and B.

14. If A is the set of integers and B is the set of perfect square integers, does the pairing given by $\{(x, x^2) \mid x \in A\}$ represent a one-to-one correspondence between A and B? What is the answer to this question if A is the set of nonnegative integers?

15. If $A = \{x, y\}$, $B = \{p, q, r\}$, list the elements of the Cartesian product $A \times B$. Is $A \times B = B \times A$?

16. If $S = \{s_1, s_2, s_3\}$ and $T = \{t_1, t_2\}$, list the elements of the Cartesian product $S \times T$. Is $S \times T = T \times S$?

17. Which of the following describe the null set?
(a) The set of men who have run a mile in less than 4 min
(b) The set of women who have been presidents of the United States
(c) The set of living baseball pitchers who have won more than 400 games in the major leagues
(d) The set of positive integers less than 1
(e) The set of irrational numbers

18. If A is the set of positive integers less than 6, write the elements of that subset of $A \times A$ in which the first member of each ordered pair is less than the second.

19. If $A \times B = \{(x, 2x) \mid x \in A\}$ and A is the set of integers, what is the set B?

20. If $X = \{1, 2, 3, 4\}$ and $Y = \{2, 4, 6, 8\}$, what is the set whose members belong to *both* X and Y? What is the set whose members belong to X or Y or to both?

21. Prove that $\sqrt{2} + \sqrt{3}$ is irrational.

1.4 The Algebra of Sets

It is an interesting fact that there is an *algebra* of subsets of a given set that resembles in some respects the algebra of real numbers. We give here a brief indication of the way in which this algebra is developed.

Let U be a set, which we refer to as the universal set. We consider the collection of all subsets of U, including U itself and the empty set ϕ. Two binary operations are defined on subsets; they are called *forming the* **union** and *forming the* **intersection** *of two subsets*. These operations are denoted by $\cup$ and $\cap$, respectively; the expression $X \cup Y$ is read "X union Y," and $X \cap Y$ is read "X intersection Y." The two operations are defined as follows:

$$X \cup Y = \{\text{set of all elements that belong to } X \textit{ or } \text{to } Y \textit{ or } \text{to both}\},$$
$$X \cap Y = \{\text{set of all elements that belong to } \textit{both } X \text{ and } Y\}.$$

For example, if $X = \{2, 4, 6\}$, $Y = \{4, 6, 8\}$, $Z = \{2, 3\}$, we have

$$X \cup Y = \{2, 4, 6, 8\}, \quad X \cap Y = \{4, 6\}, \quad X \cup Z = \{2, 3, 4, 6\},$$
$$X \cap Z = \{2\}, \quad Y \cup Z = \{2, 3, 4, 6, 8\}, \quad Y \cap Z = \phi.$$

The union and intersection of subsets can be represented pictorially by drawings called **Venn diagrams.** The elements of the sets are represented by points interior to closed curves. In Fig. 1–2 the shaded area represents $A \cup B$, and in Fig. 1–3 the shaded area represents $A \cap B$.

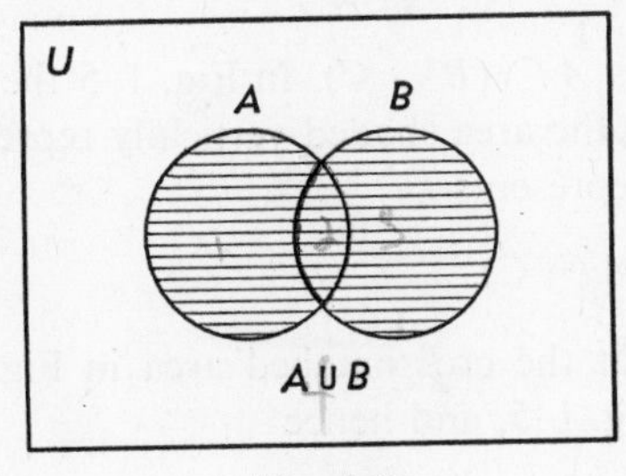

Fig. 1–2

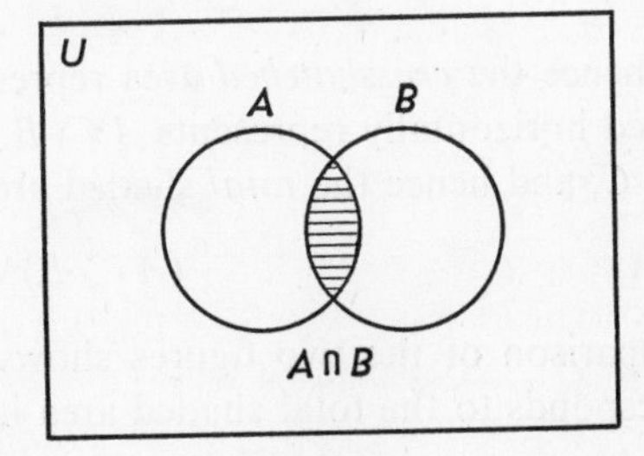

Fig. 1–3

The operations of forming the union and intersection of subsets correspond to adding and multiplying numbers. The parallelism becomes quite striking when we note that many of the fundamental laws governing the addition and multiplication of real numbers, such as the commutative, associative, and distributive laws, are obeyed by the union and intersection operations on subsets. The following properties of these operations can be demonstrated by Venn diagrams:

$A \cup B = B \cup A \qquad A \cap B = B \cap A$ **(Commutative laws)** [1.1]

$\left.\begin{array}{l}(A \cup B) \cup C = A \cup (B \cup C)\\ (A \cap B) \cap C = A \cap (B \cap C)\end{array}\right\}$ **(Associative laws)** [1.2]

$$A \cap (B \cup C) = (A \cap B) \cup (A \cap C) \quad \textbf{(Distributive law)} \qquad [1.3]$$

$$A \cup \phi = A \qquad A \cap U = A \quad \textbf{(Identity laws)} \qquad [1.4]$$

$$A \cup U = U \qquad A \cap \phi = \phi \qquad [1.5]$$

Since

$$A \cup \phi = \phi \cup A = A \text{ for all subsets } A \text{ of } U$$
$$A \cap U = U \cap A = A \text{ for all subsets } A \text{ of } U,$$

ϕ and U are called **identity elements** for the operations of union and intersection, respectively. They play the roles in the algebra of sets that 0 and 1 play in the algebra of numbers.

We construct the Venn diagram for [1.3]. In Fig. 1–4 the area shaded horizontally represents A and the area shaded vertically represents $B \cup C$,

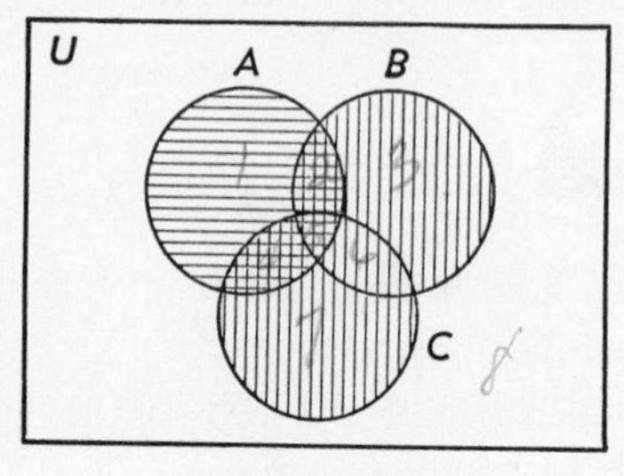

Fig. 1–4

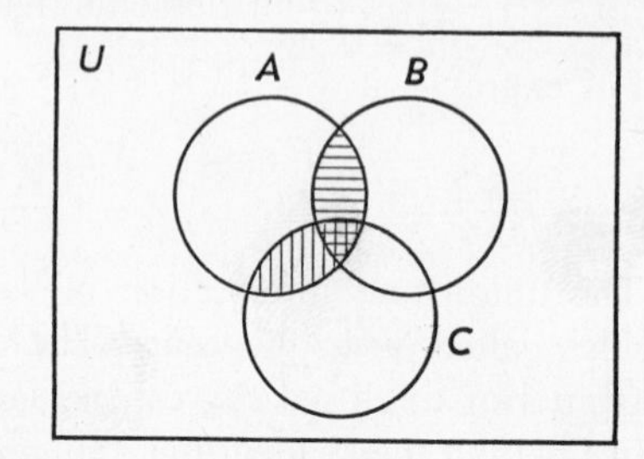

Fig. 1–5

and hence the *crosshatched* area represents $A \cap (B \cup C)$. In Fig. 1–5 the area shaded horizontally represents $A \cap B$ and the area shaded vertically represents $A \cap C$, and hence the *total* shaded area represents

$$(A \cap B) \cup (A \cap C).$$

Comparison of the two figures shows that the crosshatched area in Fig. 1–4 corresponds to the total shaded area in Fig. 1–5, and hence

$$A \cap (B \cup C) = (A \cap B) \cup (A \cap C).$$

If A is a subset of the universal set U, then the set $\sim A$, which consists of all elements of U not contained in A, is called the **complement** of A. From the definition of $\sim A$, the following relations are clear:

$$A \cup (\sim A) = U, \qquad A \cap (\sim A) = \phi. \qquad [1.6]$$

$$\sim(\sim A) = A. \qquad [1.7]$$

By Venn diagrams the following relations, called **DeMorgan's laws**, can be established:

$$\sim(A \cup B) = (\sim A) \cap (\sim B). \qquad [1.8]$$

$$\sim(A \cap B) = (\sim A) \cup (\sim B). \qquad [1.9]$$

Example

Use properties [1.1] to [1.9] to prove

$$(\sim A) \cap (A \cup B) = (\sim A) \cap B.$$

PROOF:

$$\begin{aligned} (\sim A) \cap (A \cup B) &= [(\sim A) \cap A] \cup [(\sim A) \cap B] && [1.3] \\ &= \phi \cup [(\sim A) \cap B] && [1.1] \text{ and } [1.6] \\ &= (\sim A) \cap B && [1.1] \text{ and } [1.4] \end{aligned}$$

Therefore,

$$(\sim A) \cap (A \cup B) = (\sim A) \cap B \qquad \text{Successive substitution}$$

The algebra of subsets is an example of a **Boolean algebra**, a subject that has assumed considerable practical importance in recent years in connection with high-speed electronic computers.

EXERCISES

1. Let $A = \{1, 2, 3\}$ and $B = \{2, 3, 5\}$; find $A \cup B$ and $A \cap B$.
2. If $X = \{a, b, c, d\}$ and $Y = \{b, d, f\}$, find $X \cup Y$ and $X \cap Y$.
3. If $X = \{x \mid x \text{ is a positive integer less than } 10\}$ and $Y = \{y \mid y \text{ is an integer greater than 5 and less than } 15\}$, find $X \cup Y$ and $X \cap Y$.
4. If $X = \{1, 3\}$, $Y = \{1, 5\}$, $Z = \{3, 6\}$, compute $X \cap (Y \cup Z)$ in two ways.
5. If $X = \{p, q, r\}$, $Y = \{q, r, s\}$, $Z = \{s, t\}$, compute $X \cup (Y \cap Z)$.
6. If $R = \{\text{set of real numbers}\}$, $J = \{\text{set of integers}\}$, $Q = \{\text{set of rational numbers}\}$, $N = \{\text{set of negative real numbers}\}$, $H = \{\text{set of irrational numbers}\}$, describe the following sets: (a) $Q \cup H$, (b) $J \cap N$, (c) $Q \cap H$, (d) $R \cup Q$, (e) $N \cap R$, (f) $J \cap H$.
7. If the universal set U is the set of real numbers and Q is the set of rational numbers and P is the set of positive real numbers, find the following sets: $\sim Q$, $\sim P$, $Q \cap P$, $\sim(Q \cap P)$, $Q \cup P$, $\sim(Q \cup P)$.
8. Use Venn diagrams to demonstrate relations [1.1].
9. Use Venn diagrams to demonstrate relations [1.2].
10. Use Venn diagrams to demonstrate relations [1.8].
11. Use Venn diagrams to demonstrate relations [1.9].
12. By use of Venn diagrams show that the following distributive law is true for subsets A, B, and C of a given set U:

$$A \cup (B \cap C) = (A \cup B) \cap (A \cup C).$$

13. By use of Venn diagrams show that

$$A \cap (A \cup B) = A \cup (A \cap B) = A.$$

Prove each of the following by using relations [1.1] to [1.9] as in the case of the example in Section 1.4.

14. $(A \cap B) \cap \sim B = \phi$

15. $(A \cap B) \cup (A \cap \sim B) = A$

16. $A \cup A = A$

17. $A \cap A = A$

18. $\sim[\sim P \cup (P \cap Q)] = P \cap \sim Q$

1.5 Variables

It is often convenient (as in the set notation given in Section 1.2) to let a symbol such as x denote an unspecified member of a set. This is the case, for example, when we say "let x be an arbitrary real number." Such a symbol is called a **variable.** The set referred to is called the **scope** of the variable. It is also called the **replacement set.** For example, if T denotes the temperature during a 24 hr period during which the minimum is 40° and the maximum is 75°, then T is a variable whose scope (or replacement set) is the set of real numbers from 40 to 75. If p is a symbol for an arbitrary positive odd integer less than 12, then p is a variable whose scope is the set $\{1, 3, 5, 7, 9, 11\}$. A variable whose scope is a set consisting of only one object is called a **constant.** The symbol π, which denotes the ratio of the circumference of an arbitrary circle to its diameter, is an example of a constant.

1.6 The Function Concept

One of the most far-reaching and important ideas in the whole of mathematics is that of a **function.** The concept is an abstraction from the many familiar situations in which two changing quantities are related in such a fashion that corresponding to each value of one of them a value of the other is determined.

Example 1

If an object is released at a height of 400 ft above the earth's surface, the distance (s feet) it falls in time (t seconds) is given approximately by the formula $s = 16t^2$, and it will reach the ground in 5 sec. If a value of t is given, then the corresponding value of s is easily computed; for instance, if $t = 2$, then $s = 64$. Here t and s are variables whose scopes are sets of real numbers; the scope of t is the set of real numbers from 0 to 5 and the scope of s is the set of real numbers from 0 to 400.

Example 2

As a second example, suppose that a manufacturer agrees to sell q units of a certain commodity at price p dollars per unit according to the following table.

q	10	20	30	40	50	60	70	80	90	100
p	450	445	445	440	435	425	415	400	385	365

Fig. 1–6

In this example, q and p are variables whose respective scopes are the two sets of numbers listed in the table. For each value of q there is a corresponding value for p: if $q = 10$, then $p = 450$; if $q = 20$, then $p = 445$, etc.

We have here two examples of a *function.* We now define this concept in terms of sets.

Let A and B be sets. Suppose there is a rule that associates with each member of A a definite member of B, and such that each member of B is associated by this correspondence with at least one member of A. (The diagram in Fig. 1–7 illustrates the relationship.) Then *the two sets together with the rule of*

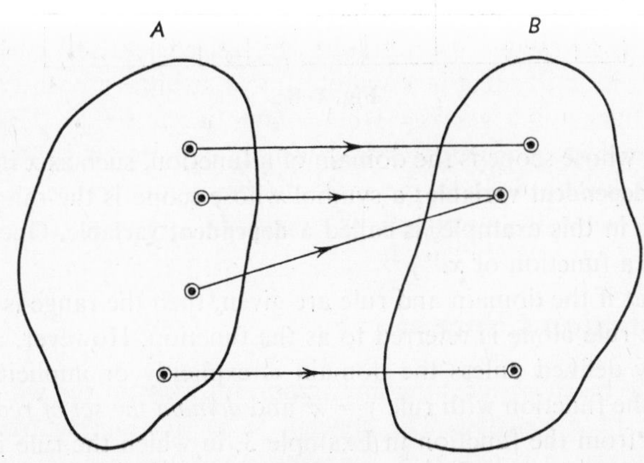

Fig. 1–7

association comprise a **function.** That is, *a function is a correspondence that assigns to each member of one set a definite member of a second set.* The first set is called the **domain** (or **domain of definition**) of the function, and the second set is called the **range** (or **set of values**) of the function, provided each of its members is associated with at least one member in the domain. In this book, except for Chapter 9, the sets will for the most part be sets of numbers. In some cases the domain and the range of a function may be the same set.

In the case of the falling body described above in Example 1, the domain of the function is the set of real numbers from 0 to 5, the range is the set of real numbers from 0 to 400, and the rule of association is given by the formula $s = 16t^2$. In Example 2, the domain is the set of numbers in the first line of the table in Fig. 1–6, the range is the set of numbers in the second line of this table, and the rule is that for any value of q listed in the table the corresponding value of p is listed directly below in the table.

A function is sometimes called a **mapping,** and if x is a member in the domain, the member in the range corresponding to x is called the **image** of x under the function. The range, then, consists of the set of images of the elements in the domain of the function.

Example 3

As another example of a function, let A be the set $\{-4, -3, -2, -1, 0, 1, 2, 3, 4\}$ and B the set $\{0, 1, 4, 9, 16\}$. Let x be a variable with A as its scope and y a variable with B as its scope. Then the equation $y = x^2$ states a rule that associates with each member of A a definite member of B. Thus, we have a function whose domain is A, whose range is B, and whose rule is $y = x^2$. The correspondence can be indicated in the form of a table, as in Fig. 1–8.

x	-4	-3	-2	-1	0	1	2	3	4
y	16	9	4	1	0	1	4	9	16

Fig. 1–8

A symbol whose scope is the domain of a function, such as x in Example 3, is called an **independent variable;** a symbol whose scope is the range of a function, such as y in this example, is called a **dependent variable.** One says in this case that "y is a function of x."

Notice that if the domain and rule are given, then the range is determined. Frequently the rule alone is referred to as the function. However, a function is not completely defined unless the domain is explicitly or implicitly specified. For example, the function with rule $y = x^2$ and *domain the set of real numbers* is quite different from the function in Example 3, in which the rule is $y = x^2$ but the *domain is a set of integers.*

As noted previously, a function is defined when the domain and rule are specified. Further examples of functions follow.

Examples

4. $y = x^3$, x an integer.
5. $y = x^3$, x a rational number
6. $y = \sqrt{25 - x^2}$, x a real number between -5 and 5, inclusive.
7. $y = \frac{1}{x}$, x a nonzero real number.

A function is denoted by a single letter such as f, g, or F.

If the letter f denotes a definite function, then $f(x)$ denotes the element in the range associated with the element x in the domain. It is called the **value** of the function f at x, or the image of x under f. Thus, if in Example 3 we denote the function by f, then $f(x) = x^2$. In particular, $f(-4) = 16$, $f(-3) = 9, \cdots,$

$f(1) = 1, \cdots, f(4) = 16$. The *range* of a function is precisely the set of all values of the function.

Observe that a function assigns to each element in its domain a unique element in the range. But a given element in the range of a function may be the value corresponding to more than one element in the domain. Example 3 gives an illustration, for in the case of this function $f(2) = f(-2)$; each of these values is 4. When each element in the range is a value of the function corresponding to *only one* element in the domain, the correspondence is called **one-to-one.** A one-to-one correspondence was mentioned in Section 1.2.

A function produces a set of **ordered pairs** as illustrated by the table in Fig. 1–8; the first member of the pair is a member of the domain and the second member is the corresponding member of the range. (The term *ordered pair* means that the order in which the members occur in the pair is significant.) Is it true, conversely, that any set of ordered pairs defines a function? The answer is yes, *in case no first member occurs with two different second members.* If this condition is met, there is a function defined whose domain is the set of first members and whose range is the set of second members. Example 2 is an illustration. The rule of correspondence is prescribed by the original pairing. It may not be possible to express the rule by a simple algebraic formula. The table in Fig. 1–9 gives temperatures measured hourly at a certain weather station. This table, which really consists of a set of ordered pairs (1:00, 68), (2:00, 67), etc., defines a function with domain the measures of time and range the measures of temperature.

Time in Hours A.M.	1:00	2:00	3:00	4:00	5:00	6:00	7:00
Temperature in Degrees F	68	67	65	61	60	62	65

Fig. 1–9

If the domain of a function f is D, the corresponding set of ordered pairs is

$$\{(x, f(x)) \mid x \in D\}.$$

Observe that if a function with domain A and range B is given as a set of ordered pairs, this set of ordered pairs is a special kind of subset of the Cartesian product $A \times B$. In order for a subset S of $A \times B$ to be a function of A to B, each element of A must occur in *one* and *only one* of the ordered pairs comprising S, and each member of B must occur in at least one pair. Thus,

$$S = \{(x, x^2) \mid x \text{ an integer}\}$$

is a function from the set of integers to the set of perfect square integers.

$$T = \{(x, \pm \sqrt{x}) \mid x \text{ a positive real number}\}$$

is *not* a function because each first member occurs in pairs with *two different* second members.

Observe that whether a function is defined in terms of a set of ordered pairs or as two sets with a rule of correspondence, the concept is the same. There are advantages in each point of view, and the student should learn both.

1.7 Graph of a Function

A function may be represented pictorially by utilizing a pair of mutually perpendicular lines, each of which has a scale marked on it, as follows (see Fig. 1–10): Choose the length of some segment as a unit; starting at O, the point of

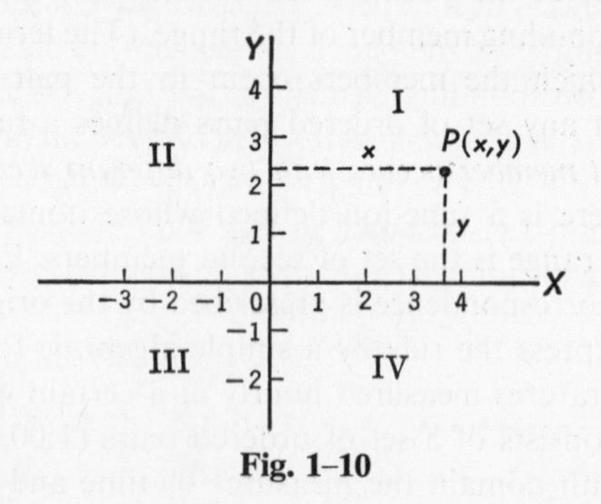

Fig. 1–10

intersection of the two lines, mark off this length repeatedly to the right and also to the left on the horizontal line OX. With the point O associate the number 0, and with the consecutive marks to the right associate the positive integers 1, 2, 3, · · · in order, and with the marks to the left associate in order the negative integers $-1, -2, -3, \cdots$. The points between the marks represent real numbers that are not integers. For example, the point halfway between the points labeled 2 and 3 represents the number 5/2. Indeed, although we cannot prove it here, there is a **one-to-one correspondence** between the points on the line and the set of real numbers. This means that to each real number there corresponds exactly one point, and each point is the partner of exactly one real number in this correspondence. The points and the real numbers are "paired off."

A scale on the vertical line OY is constructed in a similar manner.

The two lines OX and OY are called **coordinate axes** and their point of intersection is called the **origin.** Each point P in the plane of these lines has associated with it two numbers: its *directed* distance from the vertical axis, called the **abscissa** (or **x coordinate**) and denoted by x; and its *directed* distance from the horizontal axis, called the **ordinate** (or **y coordinate**) and denoted by y. The abscissa is measured by the scale on OX and is positive if P is to the right of OY, and negative if to the left. The ordinate is measured by the scale on OY and is positive if P is above OX and negative if below. The abscissa and ordinate of P are called the **coordinates** of P and are usually denoted by (x, y). The four parts into which the plane is divided by the coordinate axes are called **quadrants** and are designated as the first, second, third, and fourth quadrants, as indicated by I, II, III, and IV in Fig. 1–10.

The **coordinate system** described above is called a **Cartesian** coordinate system after the French mathematician and philosopher René Descartes. It establishes a one-to-one correspondence between the points in the plane and ordered pairs of real numbers. Notice that this correspondence exists because of the one-to-one correspondence between the points of a line and the set of real numbers.

Now suppose we have a *numerical* function f, that is, a function whose domain and range are sets of numbers. Thus, we have a set of ordered pairs of numbers; the first member of the pair is an element of the domain and the second member is the corresponding element in the range. The graph of the function is the *set of points in the plane with these ordered pairs as coordinates.* The graph of the function $y = x^2$, x an integer between -4 and $+4$, inclusive, as given in Example 3 of Section 1.6, is shown in Fig. 1–11. A part of the graph of the function $y = x^2$, x a real number, is shown in Fig. 1–12; the entire graph is a curve of infinite extent.

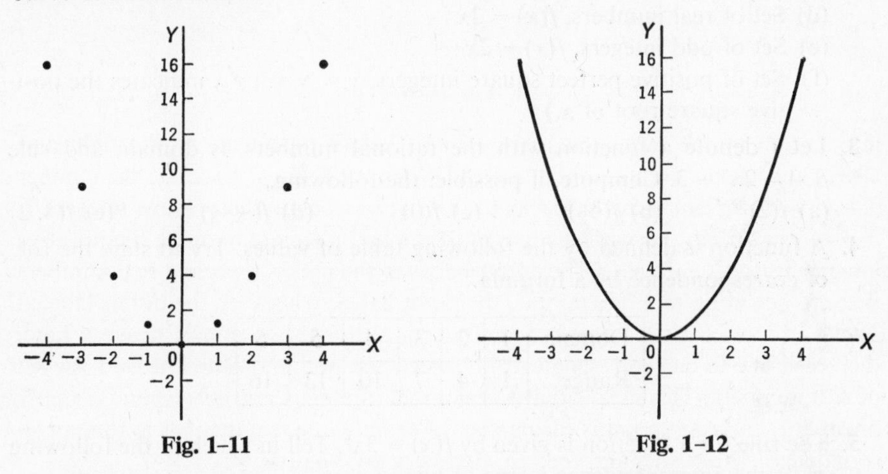

Fig. 1–11 **Fig. 1–12**

In plotting a graph of a numerical function given by a rule and the domain, a table of ordered pairs of corresponding numbers is first constructed and points are plotted with these number pairs as coordinates. If the domain contains only a finite number of members, the points plotted from the table may constitute the entire graph. If the domain consists of all real numbers within a certain interval, and the rule is given by an algebraic formula, usually the graph consists of a smooth curve drawn through the plotted points.

The correspondence between pairs of real numbers and points in a plane, which is established through the medium of a coordinate system, is the basis of **analytic geometry.** In this subject, geometry is studied by algebraic methods.

Points, which are *geometric objects*, are identified with number pairs, which are *algebraic objects. Geometric* curves are identified with *algebraic* equations.

EXERCISES

1. Tell the scope of the variable in each of the following cases:
(a) x is an arbitrary positive integer less than 30 and divisible by 6.
(b) x denotes the total number of days in a calendar month.
(c) x denotes the total number of days in February.
(d) x denotes the number of cents in a dollar.
(e) x denotes number of degrees Fahrenheit in the measure of temperature of a quantity of water as it changes from boiling to freezing.

2. Tell the range of each of the following functions whose domains and rules are given; determine whether or not the function is one-to-one.
(a) Set of integers, $f(x) = x^2$
(b) Set of nonzero integers, $f(x) = 1/x$
(c) Set of nonzero rational numbers, $f(x) = 1/x$
(d) Set of real numbers, $f(x) = 2x$
(e) Set of odd integers, $f(x) = 2x$
(f) Set of positive perfect square integers, $y = \sqrt{x}$. ($\sqrt{x}$ indicates the positive square root of x.)

3. Let f denote a function with the rational numbers as domain and rule $f(x) = 2x^3 - 3$. Compute, if possible, the following:
(a) $f(2)$ (b) $f(3/2)$ (c) $f(0)$ (d) $f(-2/3)$ (e) $f(\sqrt{2})$

4. A function is defined by the following table of values. Try to state the rule of correspondence by a formula.

Domain	1	2	3	4	5	6
Range	1	4	7	10	13	16

5. The rule for a function is given by $f(x) = 3x^2$. Tell in which of the following cases the correspondence is one-to-one.
(a) Domain the set of all integers
(b) Domain the set of positive integers
(c) Domain the set of nonnegative rational numbers

6. The symbol $[x[$ means the largest integer not greater than x. If f is a function with the positive real numbers as domain and rule $f(x) = [x]$, what is the range of f?

In each of Exercises 7 through 14 a function is defined as a set of ordered pairs of numbers. In each case, state the domain, range, and rule of correspondence, and whether or not the function is one-to-one.

19 F F F F

7. $\{(0, 0), (1, 2), (2, 4), (3, 6), (4, 8), (5, 10)\}$
8. $\{(2, 1), (4, 2), (6, 3), (8, 4), (10, 5)\}$
9. $\{(0, 1), (1, 3), (2, 5), (3, 7), (4, 9)\}$
10. $\{(-3, 2), (-2, 2), (-1, 2), (0, 2), (1, 2), (2, 2), (3, 2)\}$
11. $\{(x, x^2) \mid x \text{ an integer}\}$
12. $\{(x, 2x) \mid x \text{ a rational number}\}$
13. $\{(x, f(x)) \mid x \text{ a real number}, f(x) = 3x\}$
14. $\{(x, f(x)) \mid x \text{ a positive real number}, f(x) = \sqrt{x}\}$

For each of Exercises 15 through 20 state whether the set of ordered pairs is a function and, if so, tell its domain and range, and state whether or not it is one-to-one.

15. $\{(0, 3), (1, 5), (2, 3), (3, 4), (4, 7)\}$
16. $\{(-2, 4), (-1, 3), (0, 2), (1, 3), (2, 4)\}$
17. $\{(-3, 5), (-2, 1), (-1, 3), (-2, 7), (0, 3)\}$
18. $\{(1, 3), (2, 6), (3, 9), (2, 8), (4, 10)\}$
19. $\{(x, x^3) \mid x \text{ a positive integer less than } 12\}$
20. $\{(x, \frac{1}{2}x) \mid x \text{ a real number}\}$

Plot a graph of each of the functions in Exercises 21 through 28.

21. $f(x) = 2x - 3$, domain the set of real numbers
22. $y = 1/x$, x a positive real number
23. $y = 3x^2$, x a real number
24. $f(x) = x^2 - 5$, x a real number
25. $y = \dfrac{x + 5}{x - 4}$, domain the set of integers from -3 to $+3$, inclusive
26. $f(x) = \frac{1}{3}x^3$, x an integer
27. $f(x) = [x]$, x a positive real number (see Exercise 6 for definition of $[x]$)
28. $s = 16t^2$, domain the set of real numbers from $t = 0$ to $t = 5$
29. The electrostatic force F between two electric charges q_1 and q_2 is related to the distance r (r being any positive real number) between the charges by the formula

$$F = \frac{q_1 q_2}{r^2}.$$

What is the domain of the function defined by this formula? If both q_1 and q_2 are fixed negative numbers, what is the range of the function? Also, express r in terms of F, and tell the domain of the function defined by the new equation.

30. The pressure P and the volume V of a certain mass m of hydrogen gas in a cylinder is related by the formula

$$PV = km,$$

where k is a positive constant. Express P in terms of V. In this case we say that P is a function of V. Assuming that the maximum pressure the cylinder can withstand without breaking is 10 km, what is the domain and range of the function? Find V as a function of P. What is the domain and what is the range of this function?

31. The potential energy V of a spring fixed at one end and connected to a mass M at the free end is related to the distance x of the mass M from the equilibrium position (the point where the spring exerts no force on the mass M) by the formula $V = \frac{1}{2}ax^2$, where a is a positive constant. Assuming that the spring cannot be stretched or compressed more than 5 ft from equilibrium position, what is the domain of the function defined by this formula? Range? When is the potential energy V a maximum? A minimum?

32. The period T of a simple pendulum is related to its length L by the formula

$$T = 2\pi\sqrt{\frac{L}{g}},$$

where T is measured in seconds, L in feet, and $g = 32$. If it is impractical to build pendulums of lengths greater than 8 ft, what is the maximum period of such a pendulum? Under this restriction on pendulum lengths, what is the domain and what is the range of the function defined by the given formula?

1.8 Composition of Functions

We now describe by means of examples an important way of combining two functions to obtain a new function, called a **composite** of the original pair.

Let f denote the function defined by $f(x) = 3x + 6$ with the set of all integers as domain, and let g be the function defined by $g(x) = \sqrt{x}$ with the set of positive integers as domain. The rule for a new function, called the *composite* of g by f and denoted by $g(f)$, is

$$g(f)(x) = g(f(x)) = g(3x + 6) = \sqrt{3x + 6}.$$

Notice that the image of x under $g(f)$ is obtained by first finding the image of x under f, namely, $f(x)$, and then finding the image of $f(x)$ under g, as indicated in the following diagram:

$$g(f)\colon x \xrightarrow{f} f(x) \xrightarrow{g} g(f(x)).$$

-3

In order for x to have an image under $g(f)$, that is, to be in the domain of $g(f)$, it is necessary that x be in the domain of f and that $f(x)$ be in the domain of g. In the particular example we are considering, since f has the set of all integers as domain and rule $f(x) = 3x + 6$, and g has the set of *positive* integers as its domain, the domain of $g(f)$ consists of those integers x such that $3x + 6$ is a positive integer, that is, the set of all integers greater than -2.

As another example, let f be the function with set of real numbers as domain and rule $f(x) = x^2$, and g be the function with the set of integers as domain and rule $g(x) = 2x + 1$. Then $g(f)(x) = g(f(x)) = g(x^2) = 2x^2 + 1$, and the domain of $g(f)$ consists of those real numbers whose squares are integers, namely, all square roots of nonnegative integers, $0, \pm 1, \pm\sqrt{2}, \pm\sqrt{3}, \pm 2 \cdots$. On the other hand, the function $f(g)$, the composite of f by g, is defined by

$$f(g)(x) = f(g(x)) = f(2x + 1) = (2x + 1)^2,$$

with domain the set of integers.

EXERCISES

Obtain the rule and domain for the function $g(f)$ in each of Exercises 1 through 4.

1. $f(x) = 2x + 1$, domain the set of all integers
$g(x) = x^3$, domain the set of all positive integers

2. $f(x) = x - 3$, domain the set of all integers
$g(x) = 1/x$, domain the set of all nonzero integers

3. $f(x) = \sqrt{x}$, domain the set of all nonnegative integers
$g(x) = 5x^2 - 7$, domain the set of all integers

4. $f(x) = 2x$, domain the set of all real numbers
$g(x) = \dfrac{5x + 2}{x^2 + 1}$, domain the set of all rational numbers

Obtain the rule and domain for each of the functions $g(f)$ and $f(g)$ in each of Exercises 5 and 6.

5. $f(x) = \sqrt{x}$, domain the set of nonnegative real numbers
$g(x) = -2x$, domain the set of real numbers

6. $f(x) = x^2$, domain the set of real numbers
$g(x) = \sqrt{x}$, domain the set of nonnegative real numbers

7. A circular metal plate is being heated for 1 hr in such a manner that its radius r, of initial value 4 in., is increasing at the rate of 0.01 in. per min. Express r in terms of time t, the area A of the plate in terms of r, the area A in terms of t. Interpret these results in terms of composition of functions, giving the domain of each of the three functions.

$V = f(t) = 4t$
$D = f(V) = \frac{V}{100}$
$D = f(t) = \frac{t}{25}$

8. An empty rectangular tank has a square base 10 ft on a side and is 8 ft deep. At a certain instant water starts to flow into the tank at a constant rate of 4 cu ft per min. Describe by giving rules and domains the three functions relating (a) volume of water in tank to time, (b) depth of water to volume of water, (c) depth of water to time. Observe that the function in (c) is the composite of the other two.

9. A baseball diamond is a square 90 ft on a side. A ball is batted along the third base line at the rate of 60 ft per sec. Describe three functions, one of which is the composite of the other two, using the three variables: time, distance of the ball from home plate, and distance of the ball from first base.

10. In a certain chemical experiment the rate R (grams per hour) at which a substance is produced depends upon centigrade temperature T according to the formula $R = 0.01T + 3$. The temperature is regulated to increase at a constant rate from 0° to 100° C in 5 hr. Find the domain and the rule for the function with domain the set of values of time t and range the corresponding values of the rate of production R.

11. Let the function f be defined by $\{(1, 2), (2, 3), (3, 4), (4, 5), (5, 6)\}$ and the function g be defined by $\{(2, 5), (4, 9), (6, 13), (8, 17)\}$. Find the set of ordered pairs comprising the function $g(f)$.

12. Let the function f be defined by $\{(-3, 4), (0, 2), (3, -1), (6, -4)\}$ and the function g be defined by $\{(-2, 0), (-1, 3), (0, 6), (1, 9), (2, 12)\}$. Find the set of ordered pairs comprising the function $f(g)$.

The Real Number System ◄ 2

2.1 Axioms for the Real Number System

In Chapter 1 we introduced the real number system and its various subsystems in examples illustrating the concepts of sets and functions. Certain properties of these number systems were tacitly assumed and used. In this chapter we take a closer look at the real number system and the fundamental principles that determine its structure.

The structure of any branch of mathematics ultimately rests upon assumptions—statements called **axioms** and accepted without proof. In this chapter and in Chapter 4 we state as axioms those properties of the real number system upon which its algebraic characteristics are based. Since much of elementary algebra is concerned with the real number system, these axioms form a foundation upon which most of this subject rests. In particular, the manipulative maneuvers of algebra can be justified on the basis of our set of axioms. The axioms we give here together with those stated in Chapter 4 constitute a definition of the real number system.

We shall use small Latin letters to denote real numbers. The statement $a = b$ (read a equals b) will mean that a and b are names for the same number. Thus, if $a = b$, a may be substituted for b (or vice versa) in any mathematical expression. One observes immediately that the following statements are true.

E_1. $a = a$ **(Reflexive law)**

E_2. If $a = b$, then $b = a$. **(Symmetric law)**

E_3. If $a = b$ and $b = c$, then $a = c$. **(Transitive law)**

There are relations besides equality which obey these three laws; any such relation is called an **equivalence relation.**

By direct substitution, we obtain the following:

$$\text{If } a = a' \text{ and } b = b', \text{ then } a + b = a' + b' \text{ and } ab = a'b'.$$

The last result is sometimes expressed by saying that if equals are added to equals, the results are equal; and if equals are multiplied by equals, the results are equal.

The fundamental operations in the real number system are addition and multiplication. The operation of addition is a function that associates with each ordered pair (a, b) of real numbers a real number denoted by $a + b$ and called the **sum** of a and b. Similarly, multiplication is a function that associates with each ordered pair (a, b) of real numbers a real number denoted by ab and called the **product** of a and b. The axioms given in this chapter are stated in terms of these operations.

▶ Properties of Addition

A_1. The set of real numbers is **closed under addition.** (That is, corresponding to each ordered pair (a, b) of real numbers is a real number $a + b$, called the **sum.**)

A_2. The **associative law** holds for the addition of real numbers. (That is, $(a + b) + c = a + (b + c)$ for all real numbers a, b, and c.)

A_3. There is a real number **zero** (0) such that

$$a + 0 = 0 + a = a \qquad \text{for every real number } a.$$

(Zero is called an **identity element** for addition.)

A_4. Corresponding to each real number a there is a real number $-a$, called the **negative** of a, such that

$$a + (-a) = (-a) + a = 0.$$

($-a$ is also called the **additive inverse** of a.)

A_5. The **commutative law** holds for the addition of real numbers. (That is, $a + b = b + a$ for all real numbers a and b.)

▶ Properties of Multiplication

M_1. The set of real numbers is **closed under multiplication.** (That is, corresponding to each ordered pair (a, b) of real numbers is a real number ab, called the **product.**)

M_2. The **associative law** holds for the multiplication of real numbers. (That is, $(ab)c = a(bc)$ for all real numbers, a, b, and c.)

M_3. There is a real number **one** (1), such that $1 \neq 0$, and

$$a \cdot 1 = 1 \cdot a = a \qquad \text{for each real number } a.$$

(1 is called an **identity element** for multiplication.)

M_4. Corresponding to each *nonzero* real number a, there is a real number $1/a$, called the **reciprocal** of a, such that

$$a\frac{1}{a} = \frac{1}{a}a = 1.$$

($1/a$ is also called the **multiplicative inverse** of a.)

M_5. The **commutative law** holds for the multiplication of real numbers. (That is, $ab = ba$ for all real numbers a and b.)

▶ THE (LEFT) DISTRIBUTIVE LAW

D. If a, b, and c are real numbers, then $a(b + c) = ab + ac$.

The properties stated here for real numbers are no doubt familiar to the reader. The significance of this set of properties is that most of the manipulative maneuvers of elementary algebra can be justified on the basis of these properties. For example, the various devices for factoring depend upon the distributive law. Thus, the subject of elementary algebra can be made into a logical structure (similar in form to Euclid's geometry) if one takes a set of statements such as A_1 to A_5, M_1 to M_5, and D as axioms and proves the rules and theorems of algebra from them. We shall shortly illustrate this procedure by a few examples.

First we remark that any mathematical system with two operations having properties A_1 to A_5, M_1 to M_5, and D is called a **field.** Thus, the real numbers form a field. Drawing upon his experience, the reader can convince himself that the set of rational numbers also possesses all the properties mentioned above, and thus is another example of a field. The complex numbers, to be studied in Chapter 11, also form a field. The study of fields in general is an important part of advanced modern algebra.

The following examples illustrate the use of the basic properties of the real numbers to perform some algebraic manipulations. The reason justifying each step is listed in the column at the right. Recall that the substitution of a letter symbol for its equal is permitted in an expression formed by taking sums and products. No reason will be listed when such substitutions are made.

Example 1

Prove: $(a+b)c = ac + bc$. (This statement is called the **right distributive law.**)

PROOF: $(a+b)c = c(a+b)$ (M_5)
$= ca + cb$ (D)
$= ac + bc$ (M_5)

Example 2

Prove: $a(b+c) + bc = ab + (a+b)c$.

PROOF: $a(b+c) + bc = (ab + ac) + bc$ (D)
$= ab + (ac + bc)$ (A_2)
$= ab + (a+b)c$ (Right distributive law)

EXERCISES

1. Prove: $(a+b)+c = (a+c)+b$
2. Prove: $(ab+cd)+ac = a(b+c)+cd$
3. Prove: $(ab+cd)+ac = ab + c(a+d)$
4. Prove: $ab + (a+b)c = (a+c)b + ac$
5. Prove: $b(a+1) + [a+(-b)] = a(b+1)$
6. Prove: $(a+b)(c+d) = (ac+bc)+(ad+bd)$
7. $(x+a)(x+a) = x^2 + 2ax + a^2$
8. $(x+a)(x+b) = x^2 + (a+b)x + ab$
9. To compare the algebra of real numbers with the algebra of sets, let the operations of addition and taking the union correspond, and the operations of multiplication and taking the intersection correspond; state in symbols the properties, such as the commutative laws, that hold in both types of algebras. Also, list some properties of real numbers that do not hold for sets, and vice versa.
10. If S is a proper subset of the set of real numbers R, which ones of the properties A_1 to A_5, M_1 to M_5, and D does the set S inherit by virtue of being a subset of R?
11. A set with one operation having properties analogous to A_1 to A_4 is called a **group.** Name some other groups besides the real numbers.
12. A set with two operations having properties A_1 to A_5, M_1, M_2, and the left and right distributive laws is called a **ring.** Name some other rings besides the real numbers.

2.2 Some Further Properties of Real Numbers

In Section 2.1 some properties (A_1 to A_5, M_1 to M_5, D) of the real numbers were stated and applied to a few simple exercises. These properties form an axiomatic foundation for most of elementary algebra. That is, most of the processes and theorems of elementary algebra can be justified or proved by deductive reasoning on the basis of these fundamental properties. In this section we shall prove a few theorems to illustrate further how the subject of elementary algebra can be developed logically from a set of axioms—that is, from a set of statements assumed to be true. The structure of any branch of mathematics is based upon a set of statements whose truth is assumed.

The formulation of proofs in algebra is probably somewhat unfamiliar to the reader, and he may become impatient with the details involved in writing out a proof—especially when he has known the conclusion for a long time. However, proof is an indispensable part of mathematics, and the practice secured here will help to acquaint the reader with the true nature of mathematics as a logical structure. We invite him to enter into the spirit of what is being attempted.

At first, in writing out proofs, we take only one step at a time and list the reason for each step, as in the examples in Section 2.1. As one develops skill, several steps may be combined and the reasons not written down; but there must be reasons, and one must be prepared to give them if called upon.

In making proofs we shall frequently need the fact that if $a = a'$ and $b = b'$, then $a + b = a' + b'$ and $ab = a'b'$, results that we have observed to follow at once from the substitution permitted by the meaning of $=$, the equality sign.

▶ THEOREM 1. *If $a + b = a + c$, then $b = c$.*

PROOF:

$$a + b = a + c \qquad \text{(Hypothesis)}$$
$$-a = -a \qquad (A_4)$$
$$-a + (a + b) = -a + (a + c) \qquad \text{(Addition of equals)}$$
$$(-a + a) + b = (-a + a) + c \qquad (A_2)$$
$$0 + b = 0 + c \qquad (A_4)$$
$$b = c \qquad (A_3)$$

▶ THEOREM 2. *If a is a real number, then zero (0) is the only real number such that $a + 0 = a$.*

PROOF: Suppose x is any real number such that

$$a + x = a.$$

By A_3 we have

$$a + 0 = a.$$

Hence, by substitution, we have

$$a + x = a + 0.$$

Then, by Theorem 1, $x = 0$, and the proof is complete.

From Theorem 2 we conclude that the additive identity for the system of real numbers is *unique*—that is, there is only *one* additive identity.

▶ THEOREM 3. *If a is a real number, there is only one real number with the property that its sum with a is zero. (That is, the additive inverse of a real number is* unique.)

PROOF: Suppose x and y are any real numbers such that

$$a + x = 0 \quad \text{and} \quad a + y = 0.$$

Then, by substitution,

$$a + x = a + y.$$

Therefore, by Theorem 1,

$$x = y.$$

Thus, $-a$ is the only number that gives zero when added to a.

▶ THEOREM 4. *If a is a real number, then* $a \cdot 0 = 0$ *and* $0 \cdot a = 0$.

PROOF: $a \cdot a + a \cdot 0 = a(a + 0)$ (D)

$a \cdot a + a \cdot 0 = a \cdot a$ (Substituting a for $a + 0$)

Therefore, $a \cdot 0 = 0$. (Theorem 2)

This proves the first part of the theorem. The second part follows from this part by the fact that $0 \cdot a = a \cdot 0$.

▶ THEOREM 5. *If a and b are real numbers, then* $a(-b) = -(ab)$ *and* $(-a)b = -(ab)$.

PROOF: Since $-(ab)$ denotes the *unique* additive inverse of ab, we have merely to show that the sum of ab and $a(-b)$ is 0 and that the sum of ab and $(-a)b$ is 0.

$ab + a(-b) = a[b + (-b)]$ (D)

$ab + a(-b) = a \cdot 0$ (A_4)

$ab + a(-b) = 0$ (Substituting 0 for $a \cdot 0$)

Hence, $a(-b) = -(ab)$. (Theorem 3)

The proof of the second part of the conclusion can be made in a similar manner and is left to the reader.

▶ THEOREM 6. *If a and b are real numbers, then* $(-a)(-b) = ab$.

PROOF:

$(-a)(-b) + [a(-b) + ab] = [(-a)(-b) + a(-b)] + ab$ (A_2)

$(-a)(-b) + a[-b + b] = [-a + a](-b) + ab$ (Distributive laws)

$(-a)(-b) + a \cdot 0 = 0 \cdot (-b) + ab$ (A_4)

$(-a)(-b) + 0 = 0 + ab$ (Theorem 4)

$(-a)(-b) = ab$ (A_3)

▶ THEOREM 7. *If* $ab = 0$, *then* $a = 0$ *or* $b = 0$.

PROOF: If $a = 0$, the proof is complete. If $a \neq 0$, then $1/a$ exists by M_4, and we make the following argument:

$ab = 0$ (Hypothesis)

$\frac{1}{a}(ab) = \frac{1}{a} \cdot 0$ (Multiplication by $1/a$)

$\left(\frac{1}{a} \cdot a\right) b = 0$ (M_2 and Theorem 4)

$1 \cdot b = 0$ (M_4)

Therefore,

$b = 0$ (M_3)

The method of solving quadratic equations by factoring depends upon Theorem 7.

EXERCISES

1. Prove: If $a + c = b + c$, then $a = b$.
2. Prove: If $ab = ac$ and $a \neq 0$, then $b = c$.
3. Prove: If $ac = bc$ and $c \neq 0$, then $a = b$.

4. Prove: If a is a real number different from 0, and $ax = a$, then $x = 1$. (Thus, the multiplicative identity for the real number system is unique.)
5. Prove: The multiplicative inverse of a nonzero real number is unique.
6. Prove: $[a(b + c)]d = a(bd) + (ac)d$
7. Prove: $-(a + b) = (-a) + (-b)$
8. Prove: $-(-a) = a$
9. Prove: $(-a)b = -(ab)$
10. Prove: $(-1)a = -a$
11. Prove: $[a + b][a + (-b)] = a^2 + (-b^2)$
12. Prove: $a[b + (-1)] + a = ab$
13. Prove: $a[b + (-c)] = 0$ if and only if either $a = 0$ or $b = c$
14. If $(x - 2)(x + 3) = 0$, justify the statement that either $x = 2$ or $x = -3$.
15. Compute $(a + b)(1 + 1)$ in two ways. Use the left distributive law first in one way, and use the right distributive law first in the other. What does your result show about the commutative law for addition?

2.3 Subtraction and Division

The operation of **subtraction** is defined in terms of addition. To subtract b from a is to find a number c such that $b + c = a$. For any pair of real numbers a and b, there always exists such a number, namely, $a + (-b)$, as can be seen by adding $a + (-b)$ to b.

$$b + [a + (-b)] = b + [(-b) + a] = [b + (-b)] + a = 0 + a = a$$

Give reasons for the work in the line above.

Thus, we have shown that $a + (-b)$ added to b does give a as a sum. Hence, we agree to denote $a + (-b)$ by $a - b$ and call it ***a* minus *b*.** Subtraction is called the *inverse* operation to addition because adding b to a and then subtracting b from the sum results in retrieving a.

Similarly, division can be defined in terms of multiplication. To divide a by b is to find a number d such that $bd = a$. If $b \neq 0$, then $a \cdot 1/b$ is such a number, for

$$b\left[a \cdot \frac{1}{b}\right] = b\left[\frac{1}{b} \cdot a\right] = \left[b \cdot \frac{1}{b}\right] a = 1 \cdot a = a.$$

We agree to write $a \cdot 1/b$ as a/b and call it the **quotient** of a by b.

Since 0 has the property that $0 \cdot x = 0$ for any real number x, if $b = 0$ and $a \neq 0$, there is *no* real number d such that $bd = a$. On the other hand, if $b = 0$ and also $a = 0$, then for *any* real number d, we have $bd = a$. In the first case, *no* number can serve as quotient; and in the second, *all* numbers serve as quotients. Hence, division by zero is excluded from operations on real numbers.

▶ THEOREM 8. *The equation $b + x = a$, where a and b are real numbers, has a unique solution.*

PROOF: We have observed that the sum of b and $a + (-b)$ is a, and hence $a + (-b)$ is one solution of this equation. Suppose there are two solutions, say, u and v. Then

$$b + u = a \quad \text{and} \quad b + v = a.$$

Hence,

$$b + u = b + v.$$

Therefore, by Theorem 1,

$$u = v.$$

Theorem 8 is a statement that subtraction in the field of real numbers always leads to a unique result.

Example

Prove: $a(b - c) = ab - ac$

PROOF:

$a(b - c) = a[b + (-c)]$	(Definition)
$= ab + a(-c)$	(*D*)
$= ab + (-ac)$	(Theorem 5)
$= ab - ac$	(Definition)

EXERCISES

1. Prove: $(a - b)c = ac - bc$
2. Prove: $(a - b) + (c - d) = (a + c) - (b + d)$
3. Prove: $a - (b + c) = (a - b) - c$
4. Prove: $ab - a(b - c) = ac$
5. Prove: The equation $ax = b$, $a \neq 0$, has a *unique* solution.
6. Prove: $(a + b) - (b - c) = a + c$
7. Prove: If $a = a'$ and $b = b'$, $b \neq 0$, $b' \neq 0$, then $a/b = a'/b'$.
8. Prove: $(x + y)(x - y) = x^2 - y^2$
9. Prove: $(x - y)^2 = x^2 - 2xy + y^2$
10. Prove: $x^3 - y^3 = (x - y)(x^2 + xy + y^2)$
11. Prove: $(x + y)(x^2 - xy + y^2) = x^3 + y^3$
12. Prove: $(x - a)(x - b) = x^2 - (a + b)x + ab$
13. Does subtraction of real numbers obey the associative law? The commutative law?
14. Is division of real numbers an associative operation? Is it commutative?

Equations ◄ 3

3.1 Introduction

Expressions such as $x + 2 = 7$, $3x = 2$, $x^2 = 2$ are called **equations** in the variable x. They are not statements of fact such as, for example, $16 - 9 = (4 + 3)(4 - 3)$. They are "open" statements in the sense that they may be true when x is replaced by some numbers and false for other numbers. Compare with the open sentences: "x was president of the United States," "x won the Kentucky Derby in 1964." The first sentence becomes a true statement if x is replaced by *Jefferson*, a false statement if x is replaced by *Caruso*, and nonsense if x is replaced by *oxygen.* The second sentence becomes a true statement if x is replaced by *Northern Dancer*, a false statement if x is replaced by *Hill Rise*, and nonsense if x is replaced by $\sqrt{2}$. In considering open sentences or equations involving a variable, the scope of the variable is usually limited to those values for which the sentence or equation makes sense. We would not substitute *cabbage* for x in $x + 2 = 7$ or π for x in "x was president of the United States." The scope of x in the case of the equation would be some set of numbers, and the scope of x in the case of the open sentence concerning presidents would be a set of names of people. In each case, the subset of the scope consisting of elements for which the equation (or open sentence) becomes a true statement is called the **solution set** and its members are called **solutions.** The solution set for the equation is $\{5\}$; for the open sentence the solution set is the set of names of all men who have been president of the United States.

In the case of the equation $x + 2 = 7$, we have observed that we obtain a true statement if x is replaced by 5. Thus, 5 is a **solution** or **root** of the equation.

Hence, if the scope of x is the set of integers, the equation has a solution. On the other hand, the equation $3x = 2$ does not have a solution if the scope of x is restricted to integers. However, a solution does exist in the set of rational numbers, namely $\frac{2}{3}$. As was shown in Chapter 1, there is no rational number whose square is 2, and hence $x^2 = 2$ does not have a solution in the set of rational numbers. But it does have a solution, $\sqrt{2}$, in the set of real numbers. In determining whether an equation has any solutions and, if so, what they are, the scope of the variable must be taken into account. In this chapter, unless otherwise stated, we shall understand in our work with equations that the scope of the variables is the set of real numbers.

3.2 Solving an Equation

Equivalent equations are equations that have exactly the same solution sets. For example, $x - 2 = 0$ and $x = 2$ are clearly equivalent.

Solutions of an equation are frequently found by obtaining a chain of equivalent equations. That is, a sequence of equations, all of which have the same solutions, is obtained such that the solution set of the last member of the sequence is easily specified. This set is also the solution set of the original equation.

Example 1

Solve the equation $2x + 3 = 8$.

SOLUTION:

$$2x + 3 = 8,$$
$$2x = 5,$$
$$x = \frac{5}{2}.$$

Let us analyze this work carefully. The reasoning goes like this: *If* there is a number x such that $2x + 3 = 8$, then adding -3 to both sides yields $2x = 5$, a second equation, which also has x as a solution. Finally, upon multiplication of both members of this second equation by $\frac{1}{2}$, we obtain $x = \frac{5}{2}$. What this reasoning really shows is that *if* $2x + 3 = 8$ has a solution, then the solution is $\frac{5}{2}$. We have not established that $\frac{5}{2}$ actually is a solution.

To show that $\frac{5}{2}$ *is* a solution, we can, of course, substitute it for x in $2x + 3 = 8$ and observe that the true statement $8 = 8$ results. It is more instructive, however, to start with the equation $x = \frac{5}{2}$, multiply by 2 to get $2x = 5$, and then add 3 to both sides to get $2x + 3 = 8$. Thus, if x is $\frac{5}{2}$, then $2x + 3 = 8$, so that $\frac{5}{2}$ is indeed a solution of $2x + 3 = 8$. The *two* lines of reasoning establish the *equivalence* of the three equations displayed above.

Indeed it can be verified at each step that the equation obtained is equivalent to the preceding equation. Sometimes it is convenient to use the symbol $\Longleftrightarrow$

to indicate equivalence. This symbol may be read "implies and is implied by" or "if and only if." Thus, we may write

$$2x + 3 = 8 \iff 2x = 5 \iff x = 5/2,$$

which shows that $5/2$ is the *unique solution* of the equation $2x + 3 = 8$.

Example 2

Solve: $$\frac{2x}{x-1} = 5 + \frac{2}{x-1}.$$

SOLUTION:

$\frac{2x}{x-1} = 5 + \frac{2}{x-1}$		[3.1]
$2x = 5(x-1) + 2$	(Multiplying by $x - 1$)	[3.2]
$2x = 5x - 5 + 2$	(Distributive law)	[3.3]
$-3x = -3$	(Subtracting $5x$)	[3.4]
$x = 1$	(Dividing by -3)	[3.5]

If we check by substituting 1 for x in the original equation, we find that the denominators become zero. Since division by zero is not defined, 1 is *not* a root. What is wrong with our work? Upon examination, we see that the equations in lines [3.1] and [3.2] are *not* equivalent, since to obtain [3.1] from [3.2] we must divide [3.2] by $x - 1$, and this is not permissible if $x = 1$.

This illustrates the fact that multiplication of the members of an equation by an expression containing the variable may produce an equation with a root that is not a root of the original. Thus, when such an operation is performed, it is necessary to check by substitution in the original equation. The equation in Example 2 does not have a root.

Operations on equations that are reversible and hence lead to equivalent equations include: addition or subtraction of the same expression, and multiplication or division by a *nonzero constant.*

The same types of operations used in Examples 1 and 2 above are employed in the cases of formulas involving several letters to express some designated letter in terms of the remaining ones.

Example 3

If $Ft = m(v - v_0)$, express v in terms of the other letters.

SOLUTION:

$Ft = m(v - v_0)$	(Given)
$Ft = mv - mv_0$	(Distributive law)
$mv - mv_0 = Ft$	(E_2)
$mv = Ft + mv_0$	(Adding mv_0)
$v = \frac{Ft + mv_0}{m}$	(Dividing by m)

EXERCISES

Solve each of the equations in Exercises 1 through 16 and give the reason for each step.

1. $6x + 5 = 2x - 7$

2. $5y - 8 = 6 - 3y$

3. $4(3 - x) - 5(x + 2) = 0$

4. $5(y - 7) = 3(3 - 2y)$

5. $\frac{1}{2}x - \frac{3}{4} = 2$

6. $\frac{2}{3}x + 5 = \frac{1}{6}x$

7. $\frac{3}{4}y - 2 = \frac{5}{8}y + \frac{3}{2}$

8. $\frac{5}{12} - \frac{1}{6}x = \frac{3}{4}x + 2$

9. $\frac{3 - 2x}{4} = \frac{5}{3} + \frac{3x - 1}{6}$

10. $\frac{5}{6} - y + 2 = \frac{4 + 3y}{3}$

11. $\frac{17}{10} + \frac{2z - 5}{5} = \frac{7}{2} + z$

12. $\frac{15}{8} - \frac{2w + 1}{4} = \frac{5w - 6}{2}$

13. $1.24w - 3 = 0.44w - 2.20$

14. $0.85 + 2.4y = 2.34 - 0.12y$

15. $0.14y + 0.39 = 0.02y - 0.09$

16. $9.82x - 12.8 = 3.78 + 1.8x$

Solve Exercises 17 through 32 and check the results.

17. $\frac{4}{3x} + \frac{3}{2x} = \frac{17}{12}$

18. $\frac{5}{4x} - \frac{3}{2x} = -\frac{1}{2}$

19. $\frac{3}{y - 5} = \frac{4}{y + 2}$

20. $\frac{5}{2x + 3} + \frac{1}{x - 6} = 0$

21. $\frac{3x}{x + 2} = 3 + \frac{5}{x}$

22. $\frac{2y + 7}{y - 2} = \frac{6y - 1}{3y + 2}$

23. $\frac{3}{x + 1} = \frac{7}{x - 1} + \frac{2}{x + 1}$

24. $\frac{5}{2y + 3} - \frac{3}{y - 2} = \frac{4}{2y + 3}$

25. $\frac{y + 4}{y - 3} - \frac{8y}{2y + 5} + \frac{3y}{y - 3} = 0$

26. $\frac{6y}{2y + 1} + \frac{4}{2y - 1} - \frac{2y + 3}{2y - 1} = 2$

27. $\frac{2x}{2x + 3} = \frac{4x^2 + 1}{4x^2 + 4x - 3}$

28. $\frac{x}{x - 3} = \frac{x^2 + 2}{x^2 - 5x + 6}$

29. $\frac{3x}{x - 3} + \frac{x - 7}{x + 2} = \frac{4x^2 - 5}{x^2 - x - 6}$

30. $\frac{2x + 1}{3x + 2} - \frac{3x - 5}{x - 3} = \frac{12 - 7x^2}{3x^2 - 7x - 6}$

31. $\frac{3x + 2}{2x - 3} - \frac{3x}{2x + 3} = \frac{8}{4x^2 - 9}$

32. $\frac{9}{x + 1} - \frac{2x + 3}{x - 2} = \frac{7x - 2x^2}{x^2 - x - 2}$

Solve Exercises 33 through 68 for the letter indicated in each.

33. $F = ma$ for a

34. $PV = k$ for V

35. $v^2 = 2gh$ for h

36. $s = \frac{1}{2}gt^2$ for g

37. $P_1V_1 = P_2V_2$ for V_2

38. $PV = RT$ for T

39. $v = v_0 + gt$ for g

40. $s = s_0 + vt$ for t

41. $\mathrm{C} = \frac{5}{9}(\mathrm{F} - 32)$ for F

42. $V = E - Ir$ for r

43. $t = \dfrac{\pi m}{Bq}$ for q

44. $Q = \dfrac{2HA}{R}$ for H

45. $s = \frac{1}{2}(v + v_0)t$ for v

46. $F = \frac{5}{9}C + 32$ for C

47. $R = R_0(1 + at)$ for t

48. $A = P(1 + rt)$ for t

49. $E = i(r + r')$ for r

50. $L = L_0(1 + at)$ for t

51. $P_t = P_0(1 + \beta t)$ for β

52. $A = \frac{1}{2}h(b + B)$ for B

53. $\dfrac{1}{R} = \dfrac{1}{r_1} + \dfrac{1}{r_2}$ for r_2

54. $C = \dfrac{Q}{v_1 - v_2}$ for v_1

55. $S = \dfrac{rl - a}{r - 1}$ for r

56. $Q = \dfrac{\phi_2 - \phi_1}{R}$ for ϕ_2

57. $Yu + \dfrac{1}{u'} = \dfrac{2}{r}$ for r

58. $\dfrac{1}{b} = \dfrac{1}{f_1} + \dfrac{1}{f_2}$ for f_1

59. $l = \dfrac{l - M}{Mt}$ for M

60. $\dfrac{n}{b} = \dfrac{m}{M + m}$ for m

61. $\dfrac{a}{f} = \dfrac{b}{u} + \dfrac{c}{v}$ for u

62. $E = I\left(R + \dfrac{r}{n}\right)$ for r

63. $v_1 - v_2 = \dfrac{Q}{K}\left(\dfrac{b - a}{ab}\right)$ for b

64. $\dfrac{e}{Mp} = \dfrac{F}{H - E}$ for H

65. $\dfrac{2e}{M_2} = \dfrac{2F}{He - 2E}$ for E

66. $V = \pi h^2\left(r - \dfrac{h}{3}\right)$ for r

67. $C = 0.0885K\dfrac{(N - 1)S}{t}$ for N

68. $C = 1.112K\left[\dfrac{r_1 r_2}{r_1 - r_2}\right]$ for r_1

3.3 Variation

If the rule of correspondence for a function has the form $y = kx$, where k is a constant, it is said that "y varies directly as x." If the rule has the form $y = k/x$, one says "y varies inversely as x." In each case k is called the *constant of variation*. An especially important scientific law, called the **inverse square law,** has the form $y = k/x^2$, and y is said to "vary inversely as x^2."

If it is known that y "varies as x" in some specified fashion, as illustrated above, a formula relating x and y can be found, provided one pair of corresponding values is known. The process is illustrated in the examples below. In the statement of problems here, as is customary, the same letter will frequently be used to denote both a physical quantity and the number of units in some measure of that quantity. For example, s may denote distance and also the number of feet in the measure of that distance.

Example 1

For a body falling freely from rest, the velocity v varies as the square root of the distance s through which it has fallen. If after falling a distance of 4 ft, an object has a velocity of 16 ft per sec, find the formula connecting v and s, and find the velocity of a body after it has fallen 16 ft.

SOLUTION: The type of formula connecting v and s is $v = k\sqrt{s}$, where k is a constant. Since $v = 16$ when $s = 4$, upon substitution we have $16 = k\sqrt{4}$, or $k = 8$. Hence, the formula expressing v in terms of s is $v = 8\sqrt{s}$. If now we substitute 16 for s, we obtain $v = 8\sqrt{16} = 32$. Hence, the velocity after the body falls 16 ft is 32 ft per sec.

The language of *variation* may be used to describe types of relationships involving several variables. For example, if

$$F = k\frac{M_1M_2}{d^2},$$

k a constant, we say "F varies directly as M_1 and M_2 and inversely as the square of d."

Example 2

The maximum safe load w of a horizontal beam supported at both ends varies directly as the breadth x and the square of the depth y, and inversely as the length z between the supports. If a beam 10 ft long, 2 in. wide, and 4 in. deep can support a load of 800 lb, what is the maximum safe load of a beam of the same material 15 ft long, 3 in. wide, and 6 in. deep?

SOLUTION: The type of formula is

$$w = \frac{kxy^2}{z}.$$

To determine k, we substitute 2 for x, 4 for y, 10 for z, and 800 for w, and obtain

$$800 = \frac{k \cdot 2(4)^2}{10} = \frac{32k}{10},$$
$$k = 250.$$

Hence, the explicit formula expressing w in terms of x, y, and z is

$$w = \frac{250xy^2}{z}.$$

If we now substitute in the formula the values 3 for x, 6 for y, and 15 for z, we obtain

$$w = \frac{250 \cdot 3 \cdot 36}{15} = 1800.$$

Thus, the maximum safe load is 1800 lb.

EXERCISES

Express each of the statements in Exercises 1 through 6 in the form of an equation involving a constant of variation k.

1. z varies directly as the square of x.
2. y varies directly as the cube root of t.
3. V varies inversely as P.
4. V varies directly as T and inversely as P.
5. F varies directly as m and M inversely as the square of d.
6. W varies directly as x and as the square root of y, and inversely as the square root of z.
7. The total surface area A of a cube varies as the square of the edge x. If a cube whose edge is 2 in. has a surface area of 24 sq. in., find the formula for A in terms of x. Then find the surface area of a cube whose edge is 10 in.
8. The volume V of a gas at constant pressure varies as the absolute temperature T (Charles' law). If a certain amount of gas occupies 500 cc when the temperature is 300 A, find the volume when the temperature rises 20°, assuming a constant pressure.
9. For a body falling freely from rest, the distance (s feet) that the body falls varies as the square of the time (t seconds). If $s = 64$ when $t = 2$, find the formula for s in terms of t. How long will it take the body to fall 900 ft?
10. According to Hooke's law, the extension of a spring beyond its natural length varies directly as the force applied. If a weight of 5 lb causes a spring to stretch from 24 to 24.6 in., what weight will be necessary to stretch it to a length of 27 in.?
11. The kinetic energy E of a moving object varies directly as the mass M of the object and as the square of its velocity v. If a body weighing 20 lb and moving with a velocity of 40 ft per sec has a kinetic energy of 500 ft-lb, find the kinetic energy of a 30-lb object moving with a velocity of 20 ft per sec.
12. If V varies inversely as P and if $V = 600$ when $P = 30$, find the formula connecting V and P (Boyle's law for gases).
13. T varies directly as the square of x and inversely as p. A set of corresponding values is $T = 0.01$, $x = 6$, $p = 20$. Find a formula for T in terms of x and p.
14. The intensity of illumination received from a source of light varies directly as the candlepower and inversely as the square of the distance from the source. How far from a 200-cp light would a screen have to be placed in order to receive the same illumination as a screen placed 30 ft from a 50-cp light?
15. The electrical resistance of a wire varies directly as the length of the wire

and inversely as the square of its diameter. If the resistance of a copper wire 30 ft long and 0.02 in. in diameter is 0.8 ohm, find the resistance of a wire 50 ft long and 0.03 in. in diameter.

16. The weight of an object varies inversely as the square of its distance from the center of the earth. If the radius of the earth be taken as 4000 miles, what would be the theoretical weight of a 100-lb object if taken 1000 miles above the surface of the earth?

17. According to Kepler's third law, the square of the time required for a planet to make one complete revolution around the sun varies as the cube of its mean distance from the sun. If the mean distance from the sun of the planet Jupiter is 5.2 times that of the earth, find the number of years required for Jupiter to revolve around the sun.

3.4 Quadratic Equations

A principle used in solving a quadratic equation is the fact that in a number field, $ab = 0$ implies $a = 0$ or $b = 0$ (see Theorem 7, Chapter 2); conversely, if $a = 0$ or $b = 0$, then $ab = 0$.

Example 1

Solve: $2x^2 + x - 6 = 0.$

SOLUTION:

$2x^2 + x - 6 = 0$			
$(2x - 3)(x + 2) = 0$			(Factoring)
$2x - 3 = 0$	or	$x + 2 = 0$	($ab = 0$ implies $a = 0$ or $b = 0$)
$x = 3/2$	or	$x = -2$	(Adding and dividing)

The reasons given show that the assertion in each line implies the assertion in the line below. Starting with the bottom line, the reader can give reasons that each line also implies the line above. Or at each step it can be verified that the new statement is equivalent to the preceding one. Hence, the assertions on the four lines are equivalent, and it is established that $3/2$ and -2 are solutions of the equation $2x^2 + x - 6 = 0$ and that they are the only ones. That is, the solution set is $\{3/2, -2\}$.

To show that the principle referred to in the third line of the solution of Example 1 can be used to solve any quadratic equation, consider the equation

$$ax^2 + bx + c = 0, \qquad a \neq 0, \tag{3.6}$$

which represents all quadratic equations. The trick is first to write the left member as the difference of two squares so that it can be factored. We divide both members by a to obtain the equivalent equation

$$x^2 + \frac{b}{a}x + \frac{c}{a} = 0.$$

We now "complete the square" on the terms $x^2 + \frac{b}{a}x$ by adding $(b/2a)^2$, at the same time subtracting $(b/2a)^2$, and obtain

$$x^2 + \frac{b}{a}x + \left(\frac{b}{2a}\right)^2 + \frac{c}{a} - \left(\frac{b}{2a}\right)^2 = 0.$$

This equation may be rewritten as

$$\left(x + \frac{b}{2a}\right)^2 - \frac{b^2 - 4ac}{4a^2} = 0.$$

Factoring the left member as the difference of two squares, we obtain

$$\left[\left(x + \frac{b}{2a}\right) - \frac{\sqrt{b^2 - 4ac}}{2a}\right]\left[\left(x + \frac{b}{2a}\right) + \frac{\sqrt{b^2 - 4ac}}{2a}\right] = 0.$$

Thus,

$$x + \frac{b - \sqrt{b^2 - 4ac}}{2a} = 0 \quad \text{or} \quad x + \frac{b + \sqrt{b^2 - 4ac}}{2a} = 0$$

$$x = \frac{-b + \sqrt{b^2 - 4ac}}{2a} \quad \text{or} \quad x = \frac{-b - \sqrt{b^2 - 4ac}}{2a}.$$

The two equations in the preceding line may be combined as follows:

$$x = \frac{-b \pm \sqrt{b^2 - 4ac}}{2a}, \qquad [3.7]$$

a result called the **quadratic formula.** The steps taken above are all reversible, so the work shows that [3.7] gives the roots of equation [3.6] in case the right member of [3.7] represents numbers in the scope of x; it also shows that these are the only two roots. Thus [3.7] may be used as a formula to compute the roots of quadratic equations.

If a, b, and c in equation [3.6] are real numbers, then the right member of [3.7] represents two real numbers in case $b^2 - 4ac$ is positive, and only one real number in case $b^2 - 4ac = 0$. If $b^2 - 4ac$ is negative, $\sqrt{b^2 - 4ac}$ is not a real number, and so the right member of [3.7] is not defined in the field of real numbers. In Chapter 11 we introduce some new numbers called (for historical reasons) *imaginary*, in terms of which [3.7] has meaning when $b^2 - 4ac$ is negative. In case $b^2 - 4ac$ is negative, the roots of [3.6], which are still given by [3.7], are called imaginary.

Since the value of the expression $b^2 - 4ac$ gives information about the number and nature of the roots of $ax^2 + bx + c = 0$, it is called the **discriminant** of the latter. We summarize the criteria, it being understood that a, b, and c represent real numbers.

1. If $b^2 - 4ac$ is positive, the equation has two distinct real roots.
2. If $b^2 - 4ac$ is zero, the equation has ~~one real root~~. IDENTICAL ROOTS, two roots
3. If $b^2 - 4ac$ is negative, the equation has two distinct imaginary roots.
4. If a, b, and c are *rational* numbers and $b^2 - 4ac$ is a *perfect square* of a rational number, then the roots of the equation are *rational*.

The truth of statement 4 is clear from the form of [3.7].

If we denote by r_1 and r_2 the roots of [3.6] given by [3.7], we have

$$r_1 = \frac{-b + \sqrt{b^2 - 4ac}}{2a}, \qquad r_2 = \frac{-b - \sqrt{b^2 - 4ac}}{2a}$$

Then, by addition and multiplication, we obtain

$$r_1 + r_2 = -\frac{b}{a}, \tag{3.8}$$

$$r_1 r_2 = \frac{c}{a}. \tag{3.9}$$

Formulas [3.8] and [3.9] can be used to check answers obtained by solving a quadratic equation.

EXERCISES

Solve the equations in Exercises 1 through 9 by factoring left members by inspection.

1. $x^2 - 3x - 4 = 0$ **2.** $x^2 + x - 2 = 0$ **3.** $2y^2 - 7y + 3 = 0$
4. $2x^2 + 3x - 9 = 0$ **5.** $3x^2 + x - 4 = 0$ **6.** $2y^2 - y - 1 = 0$
7. $2x^2 - 5x - 7 = 0$ **8.** $2x^2 - 7x + 5 = 0$ **9.** $10x^2 - x - 3 = 0$

Solve the equations in Exercises 10 through 18 by factoring after first "completing a square."

10. $x^2 + 2x - 5 = 0$ **11.** $x^2 + 4x - 6 = 0$ **12.** $t^2 - t - 3 = 0$
13. $y^2 - y = 1$ **14.** $2x^2 + 5x = 1$ **15.** $3x^2 - 4x - 2 = 0$
16. $5x^2 - 7x - 2 = 0$ **17.** $3y^2 + 7y - 2 = 0$ **18.** $3y^2 + y = 3$

Solve the equations in Exercises 19 through 27 by the quadratic formula.

19. $4y^2 - 3y - 3 = 0$ **20.** $x^2 - 5x - 7 = 0$ **21.** $4v^2 + 11v + 4 = 0$
22. $2z^2 - z - 2 = 0$ **23.** $5x^2 + 17x - 3 = 0$ **24.** $5x^2 - 9x + 3 = 0$
25. $11x^2 - 7x + 1 = 0$ **26.** $x^2 - \sqrt{5}x - 1 = 0$ **27.** $0.1x^2 + 0.5x - 1.7 = 0$

By use of the discriminant, determine the number and nature of the roots of each of the following equations without solving the equation:

28. $5x^2 - 7x - 3 = 0$ **29.** $2x^2 + 15x + 27 = 0$ **30.** $x^2 - 3x + 3 = 0$
31. $4x^2 + 5x - 2 = 0$ **32.** $4x^2 - 3x - 3 = 0$ **33.** $x^2 - 8x + 16 = 0$
34. $6x^2 - 13x + 6 = 0$ **35.** $4x^2 - 5x + 2 = 0$ **36.** $9x^2 + 12x + 4 = 0$

Determine the value or values of k for which the following equations will have equal roots:

37. $kx^2 - 4x - 1 = 0$ **38.** $x^2 - 6x + k = 0$
39. $x^2 - 3x + 3 - k = 0$ **40.** $kx^2 + 3x - 2kx + k - 2 = 0$
41. $k^2x^2 + kx + 2x + 1 = 0$ **42.** $4x^2 - (2 + 2k)x + k^2 = 0$

3.5 Equations Containing Radicals

In case of equations containing radicals, as for example,

$$\sqrt{x-1} + \sqrt{3x+1} = 6,$$

the radicals, which by agreement denote *positive* square roots, may be removed by squaring both members of the equation (perhaps more than once). It should be noted, however, that this process is likely to lead to equations that are not equivalent to the original. Hence, the *answers should always be tested by substitution in the original equation.* Before squaring, it is usually best to isolate the most complicated radical. Thus, to solve the equation given above, we subtract $\sqrt{3x+1}$ and 6 from both sides to obtain

$$\sqrt{x-1} - 6 = -\sqrt{3x+1}.$$

Squaring both members yields

$$x - 1 - 12\sqrt{x-1} + 36 = 3x + 1,$$

which upon simplification reduces to

$$-x + 17 = 6\sqrt{x-1}.$$

Squaring once more, we obtain

$$\begin{aligned} x^2 - 34x + 289 &= 36(x-1) \\ x^2 - 34x + 289 &= 36x - 36 \\ x^2 - 70x + 325 &= 0. \end{aligned}$$

On factoring, we have

$$(x-5)(x-65) = 0,$$

so that

$$x = 5 \quad \text{or} \quad x = 65.$$

We now test 5 in the original equation.

$$\begin{aligned} \sqrt{5-1} + \sqrt{15+1} &\stackrel{?}{=} 6 \\ \sqrt{4} + \sqrt{16} &\stackrel{?}{=} 6 \\ 2 + 4 &= 6, \end{aligned}$$

so 5 is a root.

Similarly, we test 65:

$$\begin{aligned} \sqrt{64} + \sqrt{196} &\stackrel{?}{=} 6 \\ 8 + 14 &\neq 6, \end{aligned}$$

so 65 is *not* a root.

In this example, the equations in the derived chain are *not* all equivalent; the original equation and $x^2 - 70x + 325 = 0$ do not have the same solution sets. The operation of squaring both members of an equation gave an equation with more roots than the original. When such an operation is performed, it is necessary to test the roots of the final equation by substitution in the original equation.

It is true that in the sequence of equations given above, the solution set of each is a subset of that of its successor, so that all solutions of the first equation are contained in the solution set of the last equation.

We see by the example that squaring both members of an equation may lead to an equation in which some roots are not roots of the original. To see how this comes about, let us consider an equation

$$f(x) = g(x), \qquad [3.10]$$

where $f(x)$ and $g(x)$ denote expressions in terms of x. If we square both members of this equation, we obtain

$$[f(x)]^2 = [g(x)]^2. \qquad [3.11]$$

Now observe that the new equation has as solutions not only all the roots of the original equation but also those of $f(x) = -g(x)$.

If the two members of an equation are multiplied by an expression containing the variable, the new equation may have roots that are not roots of the original. For example,

$$x + 4 = 5 \qquad [3.12]$$

has only 1 as a root, but

$$(x+4)(x-3) = 5(x-3) \qquad [3.13]$$

has 1 and *also* 3 as a root.

On the other hand, if the two members of an equation are divided by an expression containing x, the solution set of the new equation may fail to contain some of the roots of the original. For example, [3.12], which can be obtained from [3.13] by division by $x - 3$, does not have 3 as a root.

EXERCISES

Solve the equations in Exercises 1 through 14.

1. $x + 4\sqrt{x} = 21$
2. $x - 4\sqrt{x+1} + 4 = 0$
3. $3x - \sqrt{2x+2} = 1$
4. $2\sqrt{2x-1} = 3\sqrt{x-1}$
5. $\sqrt{5x+1} - 1 = \sqrt{3x}$
6. $\sqrt{4x+1} - 2x + 1 = 0$
7. $\sqrt{2x+1} + \sqrt{x} = 1$
8. $\sqrt{x^2+5} = 2x - 1$
9. $\sqrt{4x+1} + \sqrt{x+2} = 5$
10. $\sqrt{8x+1} - \sqrt{x+1} = 3$
11. $\sqrt{x-1} - \sqrt{x-4} = 1$
12. $\sqrt{x+5} - \sqrt{x} = \sqrt{x-3}$
13. $\sqrt{2x+5+\sqrt{x+3}} = 3$
14. $\sqrt{2x - \sqrt{x+1}} = 2$
15. If $v = \sqrt{2gh}$, solve for h.
16. Solve for l and also for g: $t = 2\pi\sqrt{l/g}$.

Inequalities ◄ 4

4.1 Order Properties of the Real Numbers

The real numbers possess a property not shared by all fields; namely, they are **ordered.** This means that in the real number system there is a relation denoted by $<$, read "less than," such that the following properties hold for all real numbers.

▶ PROPERTIES OF ORDER

O_1. If $a < b$, then $a + c < b + c$.

O_2. If $a < b$ and $0 < c$, then $ac < bc$.

O_3. If $a < b$ and $b < c$, then $a < c$. **(Transitive law)**

O_4. For any pair of real numbers a and b, exactly *one* of the following is true:

$$a = b, \qquad a < b, \qquad b < a. \qquad \textbf{(Law of trichotomy)}$$

These statements, O_1 to O_4, are to be taken as additional axioms for the real number system.

As a matter of notation, we define $b > a$ (read "b greater than a") to mean $a < b$. Properties O_1 to O_4 can be stated in terms of the relation $>$. For example, O_1 can be written: If $b > a$, then $b + c > a + c$.

Any field with an order relation satisfying Properties O_1 to O_4 is called an **ordered field.** Thus, the real numbers form an ordered field. The rational number system is another example.

In an ordered number field, **positive** numbers are defined as numbers greater than 0 and **negative** numbers as numbers less than 0.

We now prove a few theorems for real numbers, using O_1 to O_4. The results will be familiar to the reader. The interest lies in seeing how these familiar properties of real numbers are proved by use of the axioms. Not all reasons for each step will be stated, only those involving the order axioms. Also, substitution will be performed sometimes without explicit mention. We employ the symbol $\Rightarrow$ to mean "implies."

▶ THEOREM 1. *$a < b$ is equivalent to "$b - a$ is positive."*

PROOF:

$a < b \quad \Rightarrow \quad 0 < b + (-a)$ (O_1, adding $-a$)

$b + (-a) = b - a$ (Definition)

Therefore,

$0 < b - a$ (Substitution)

$b - a$ is positive (Definition)

To prove the converse, we first observe that

$b - a$ is positive means $0 < b - a$ (Definition)

Hence,

$0 < b + (-a)$ (Substitution)

$a < b$ (O_1, adding a)

▶ THEOREM 2. *The sum of two positive numbers is positive.*

PROOF: Let a and b be two positive numbers. Then,

$0 < a$ and $0 < b$ (Definition)

$0 < b \quad \Rightarrow \quad a < a + b$ (O_1, adding a)

$0 < a$ and $a < a + b \quad \Rightarrow \quad 0 < a + b$ (O_3)

Therefore,

$a + b$ is positive (Definition)

▶ THEOREM 3. *The product of two positive numbers is positive.*

PROOF: Suppose

$0 < a$ and $0 < b$

Then

$$0 < a \quad \text{and} \quad 0 < b \quad \Rightarrow \quad 0 \cdot b < ab \qquad (O_2, \text{multiplying by } b)$$

Hence, since $0 \cdot b = 0$,

$$0 < ab, \quad \text{and } ab \text{ is positive} \qquad \text{(Definition)}$$

▶ THEOREM 4. *The product of two negative numbers is positive.*

PROOF: Suppose $a < 0$ and $b < 0$. Then,

$$a + (-a) < 0 + (-a) \qquad (O_1, \text{adding } -a)$$
$$b + (-b) < 0 + (-b) \qquad (O_1, \text{adding } -b)$$

Thus,

$$0 < -a \quad \text{and} \quad 0 < -b \qquad \text{(Substitution)}$$

Hence,

$$0 < (-a)(-b) \qquad \text{(Theorem 3)}$$

But

$$(-a)(-b) = ab \qquad \text{(Theorem 6 of Chapter 2)}$$

Therefore,

$$0 < ab, \quad \text{and } ab \text{ is positive} \qquad \text{(Substitution and definition)}$$

▶ COROLLARY. *If $a \neq 0$, then $a^2 > 0$.*

PROOF: If $a \neq 0$, then by O_4 either $0 < a$ or $a < 0$.

If $0 < a$, then $a^2 > 0$ by Theorem 3; if $a < 0$, then $a^2 > 0$ by Theorem 4.

In particular, since $1 \neq 0$ and $1 = 1^2$, 1 is positive. Also, since $1 > 0$, then $1 + (-1) > 0 + (-1)$, and thus $0 > -1$. Hence, -1 is negative.

▶ THEOREM 5. *The product of a positive number by a negative number is negative.*

PROOF: Suppose $a < 0$ and $0 < b$. Then, multiplying each member of $a < 0$ by the positive number b, we have

$$ab < 0.$$

▶ THEOREM 6. *If* $a < b$ and $c < 0$, *then* $ac > bc$.

PROOF:

$$a < b \quad \Rightarrow \quad 0 < b - a \qquad \text{(Theorem 1)}$$

Now,

$$c < 0 \quad \text{and} \quad 0 < b - a \text{ imply}$$
$$c(b - a) < 0 \cdot (b - a) \qquad (O_2, \text{ multiplying by } b - a)$$
$$c(b - a) < 0.$$

Hence,

$$cb - ca < 0, \quad cb < ca, \quad ac > bc \qquad (O_1, \text{ definition})$$

▶ THEOREM 7. *If* $a \neq 0$, *then one of the pair* a *and* $-a$ *is positive and the other negative.*

PROOF: There are two cases by the law of trichotomy.

Case 1 $\quad 0 < a.$

Adding $-a$ to both members, we obtain

$$0 + (-a) < a + (-a),$$
$$-a < 0.$$

Thus, in this case, a is positive and $-a$ is negative.

Case 2 $\quad a < 0.$

Then, adding $-a$ to both members, we have

$$0 < -a.$$

Thus, in this case, a is negative and $-a$ is positive.

EXERCISES

1. Restate O_1 to O_4 in terms of the relation $>$.

Prove Exercises 2 through 15, where the letter symbols denote real numbers.

2. If $a > b$ and $c < 0$, then $ac < bc$.

3. If $a < b$ and $c < d$, then $a + c < b + d$.

4. If $a < b$, then $-a > -b$.

5. If $b < c$, then $a - b > a - c$.

6. If $a > b \geqq 0$ and $c \geqq d \geqq 0$, then $ac \geqq bd$ ($x \geqq y$ means $x > y$ or $x = y$).

7. $a^2 + b^2 \geqq 2ab$ [*Hint:* $(a - b)^2 \geqq 0$.]

8. $a^2 + b^2 + c^2 \geqq ab + ac + bc$. [*Hint:* Use Exercise 7.]

9. If $x > 0$, then $1/x > 0$.
10. If $a < b$ and $c > 0$, then $a/c < b/c$.
11. If $x < y$ and x and y are both positive or both negative, then $1/x > 1/y$.
12. If $x > 0$, then $x + 1/x \geqq 2$.
13. If $x > 0$ and $y > 0$, then $x/y + y/x \geqq 2$.
14. If $x \neq y$, then $x^2 + 2xy < 2x^2 + y^2$.
15. If $x > 0$ and $y > 0$ and $x > y$, then $(x - y)^3 < x^3 - y^3$.
16. The arithmetic mean of two real numbers a and b is defined to be $\dfrac{a+b}{2}$. If a and b are unequal, show that the arithmetic mean lies between them.

4.2 Inequalities

An expression of the form $2x + 3 < 9$ is called an **inequality.** A real number that when substituted for x converts this into a true statement is called a **solution,** and the set of all solutions is called the **solution set** of the inequality. In the example $2x + 3 < 9$, 2 belongs to the solution set while 5 does not. By a procedure which parallels that used with equations, a solution set may be found by deriving a chain of **equivalent inequalities,** that is, a sequence of inequalities, all of which have the same solution set. We have

$$2x + 3 < 9,$$
$$2x < 6,$$
$$x < 3.$$

These three inequalities are equivalent, for the first implies the second by O_1, and the second implies the third by O_2. Conversely, the third implies the second by O_2, and the second implies the first by O_1. Thus, the solution set of the inequality $2x + 3 < 9$ consists of all real numbers less than 3. In terms of the notation introduced in Chapter 1, this set can be denoted by $\{x \mid x \text{ is a real number}, x < 3\}$. The geometric picture of this set is indicated in Fig. 4–1, where the circle indicates that the point representing 3 is to be excluded.

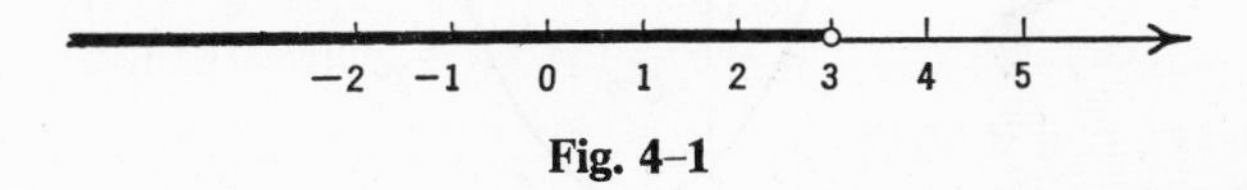

Fig. 4–1

We now give some examples involving quadratic inequalities. The symbol $\Longleftrightarrow$ is used to denote "is equivalent to."

Example 1

Solve the inequality $x^2 - 2x - 8 < 0$.

SOLUTION: $x^2 - 2x - 8 < 0 \iff (x - 4)(x + 2) < 0.$

Hence, one of the pair $x - 4$ and $x + 2$ must be positive and the other negative. There are two cases.

Case 1. If

$$x - 4 < 0 \quad \text{and} \quad x + 2 > 0,$$

then

$$x < 4 \quad \text{and} \quad x > -2.$$

Case 2. If

$$x - 4 > 0 \quad \text{and} \quad x + 2 < 0,$$

then

$$x > 4 \quad \text{and} \quad x < -2.$$

This case is impossible.

The solution set is denoted by $-2 < x < 4$ or in other notation by $\{x \mid x$ is a real number, $-2 < x < 4\}$. The graphical representation of this set is shown in Fig. 4–2.

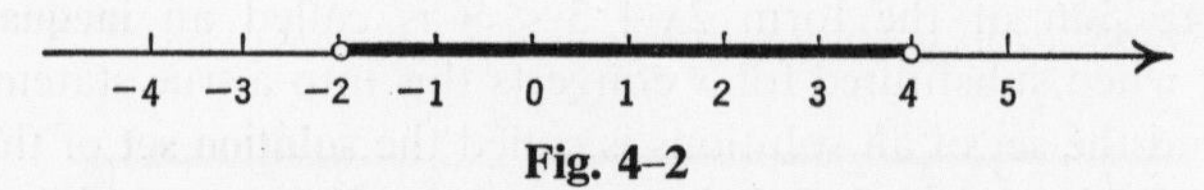

Fig. 4–2

This example can also be solved by plotting a graph of $y = x^2 - 2x - 8$, as shown in Fig. 4–3. We see that for values of x between -2 and 4, $-2 < x < 4$, the graph is below the x-axis, and hence for these values, $x^2 - 2x - 8 < 0$. Thus, we again arrive at the solution set: all x such that $-2 < x < 4$.

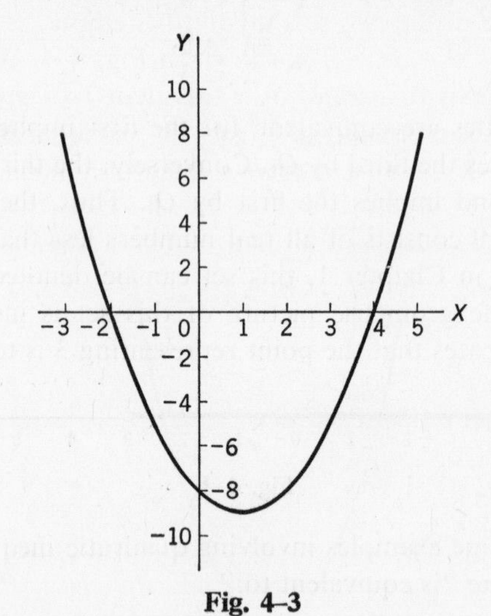

Fig. 4–3

Example 2

Solve the inequality $x^2 - 3x + 2 > 0$.

SOLUTION: $x^2 - 3x + 2 > 0 \iff (x - 2)(x - 1) > 0.$

Hence, both $x - 2$ and $x - 1$ must be positive or both negative.

Case 1. If

$$x - 2 > 0 \quad \text{and} \quad x - 1 > 0,$$

then

$$x > 2 \quad \text{and} \quad x > 1.$$

Hence,

$$x > 2.$$

Case 2. If

$$x - 2 < 0 \quad \text{and} \quad x - 1 < 0,$$

then

$$x < 2 \quad \text{and} \quad x < 1.$$

Hence,

$$x < 1.$$

Thus the solution set is $\{x \mid x \text{ is a real number}, x > 2 \text{ or } x < 1\}$. The graphical representation is shown in Fig. 4–4.

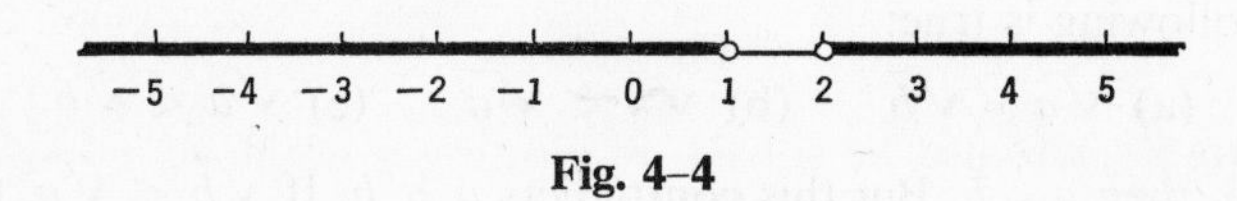

Fig. 4–4

Note that the solution set in this example is the union of two sets, each of which is the intersection of two sets. The same statement holds in the case of Example 1, but one of the two sets involved is empty.

The graph of $y = x^2 - 3x + 2$ is shown in Fig. 4–5. We observe that the graph is above the x-axis for values of x less than 1 or greater than 2. Thus, for these values of x, the inequality $x^2 - 3x + 2 > 0$ is satisfied. This is another illustration of the use of a graph to solve a quadratic inequality.

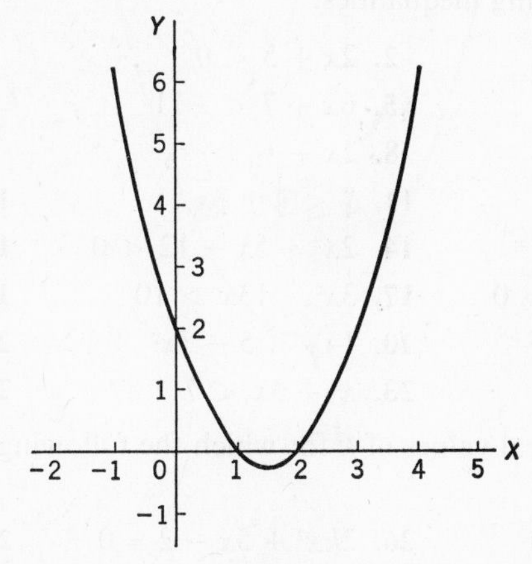

Fig. 4–5

Notice carefully the difference between the description given for the solution set in Example 1 and the description of the solution set in Example 2. In the case of Example 1, each number x in the solution set must satisfy both conditions $x < 4$ and $x > -2$, whereas in the case of Example 2, each member of the solution set satisfies *one or the other* of the conditions $x > 2$, $x < 1$. So, in the first case, we combine the two conditions and write $-2 < x < 4$, whereas in the second case, we must write $x > 2$ *or* $x < 1$.

Example 3

Assuming that every positive real number a has a unique positive square root, denoted by $\sqrt{a}$, show that if a and b are positive numbers, then

$$a < b \iff \sqrt{a} < \sqrt{b}.$$

PROOF: If $\sqrt{a} < \sqrt{b}$, then multiplication of both members by $\sqrt{a}$ yields $a < \sqrt{a}\sqrt{b}$, and multiplication by $\sqrt{b}$ yields $\sqrt{a}\sqrt{b} < b$. Hence, by O_3, $a < b$. Thus, we have shown $\sqrt{a} < \sqrt{b} \Rightarrow a < b$.

Now, conversely, suppose $a < b$. By O_4, the law of trichotomy, *exactly one* of the following is true:

$$\text{(a) } \sqrt{a} = \sqrt{b} \qquad \text{(b) } \sqrt{b} < \sqrt{a} \qquad \text{(c) } \sqrt{a} < \sqrt{b}$$

If $\sqrt{a} = \sqrt{b}$, then $a = b$. But this contradicts $a < b$. If $\sqrt{b} < \sqrt{a}$, then by the first part of this proof, $b < a$. This also contradicts $a < b$. Since neither (a) nor (b) can hold, we must have $\sqrt{a} < \sqrt{b}$. Thus, we have shown $a < b \Rightarrow \sqrt{a} < \sqrt{b}$.

The two parts of the proof establish

$$a < b \iff \sqrt{a} < \sqrt{b}.$$

EXERCISES

Solve the following inequalities:

1. $3x - 6 < 0$ **2.** $2x + 5 < 0$ **3.** $5x - 3 > 8$

4. $4x + 2 > 10$ **5.** $6x + 7 < -11$ **6.** $4x + 2 < 10$

7. $3x - 5/2 < 7$ **8.** $2x + 4/3 > 8/5$ **9.** $\frac{3}{2}x - \frac{2}{3} < \frac{5}{6}$

10. $10x < 7/4 - 2x$ **11.** $\frac{9}{4} < \frac{5}{2} + \frac{2}{3}x$ **12.** $\frac{8}{3} > \frac{3}{5}x - 2$

13. $x^2 - x - 2 < 0$ **14.** $2x^2 + 5x - 12 < 0$ **15.** $2x^2 - x - 6 < 0$

16. $4x^2 + 23x + 15 > 0$ **17.** $3x^2 - 13x > 10$ **18.** $5x^2 + 13x < 6$

19. $-12 - 11x < 2x^2$ **20.** $14x < 5 - 3x^2$ **21.** $-12 - 20x < 3x^2$

22. $2x^2 - 3x > 8$ **23.** $x^2 - 3x < 7$ **24.** $2x > 3x^2 - 16$

Find the set of real values of k for which the following quadratic equations have real roots:

25. $kx^2 - 2x + 3 = 0$ **26.** $2kx^2 + 5x - 2 = 0$ **27.** $2x^2 + 7x - 4k = 0$

28. $3x^2 - 2k + 5 = 0$ **29.** $x^2 + kx - 3 = 0$ **30.** $3x^2 - 4x + 2k = 0$

31. Solve for n: $1/3n < 2$.

32. Solve for n: $1/n^2 < 25$.

33. Show that $1/4n$ can be made less than any preassigned positive number by taking n large enough.

34. Show that $1/n^2$ can be made less than any preassigned positive number by taking n large enough.

4.3 Absolute Values

With each real number a there is associated a nonnegative real number called the **absolute value** of a and denoted by $|a|$. It is defined as follows.

$$\text{If}\quad a = 0,\qquad |a| = 0.$$
$$\text{If}\quad a \neq 0,\qquad |a| = a \quad\text{or}\quad -a \qquad \text{(whichever one is positive).}$$

This definition is unambiguous, for Theorem 7, proved in Section 4.1, states that if $a \neq 0$, then exactly one of the pair a and $-a$ is positive.

An equivalent statement for the definition of absolute value is:

$$|a| = \begin{cases} a, \text{ if } a \geqq 0, \\ -a, \text{ if } a < 0. \end{cases}$$

Illustrations

$$|5| = 5,\quad |-3| = 3.$$

A geometrical interpretation of $|a|$ is the (undirected) distance between the origin and the point that represents a on a coordinate line.

A problem of particular importance in calculus is that of finding the values of a variable for which the absolute value of an expression is less than a given positive number.

Example 1

Solve $|3x - 2| < \frac{1}{2}$.

SOLUTION: We consider two cases, determined by whether or not $3x - 2$ is nonnegative.

Case 1. Suppose $3x - 2 \geqq 0$. Then, since in this case $|3x - 2| = 3x - 2$, the given inequality reads

$$3x - 2 < \tfrac{1}{2},$$

which is easily seen to be equivalent to

$$x < \tfrac{5}{6}.$$

The restriction $3x - 2 \geqq 0$ placed upon x in this case is equivalent to $x \geqq \frac{2}{3}$. Thus, the solutions of the given inequality for Case 1 are given by

$$\tfrac{2}{3} \leqq x < \tfrac{5}{6}.$$

Case 2. Suppose $3x - 2 < 0$. In this case, $|3x - 2| = -(3x - 2)$; so, the given inequality reads $-(3x - 2) < \frac{1}{2}$, which is equivalent to $x > \frac{1}{2}$. Since the restriction $3x - 2 < 0$ placed upon x in this case is equivalent to $x < \frac{2}{3}$, the solutions of the given inequality for Case 2 are given by

$$\tfrac{1}{2} < x < \tfrac{2}{3}.$$

The solution set for the given inequality is the union of the solution sets in Cases 1 and 2, namely, the set of all x such that

$$\tfrac{1}{2} < x < \tfrac{5}{6}.$$

This set can be denoted by $\{x \mid x \text{ is a real number}, \tfrac{1}{2} < x < \tfrac{5}{6}\}$.

▶ THEOREM 8. *If k is a positive number, then*

$$|y| < k \iff -k < y < k.$$

PROOF: By definition, $|y|$ is the nonnegative member of the pair y and $-y$. Thus, $|y| < k$ is equivalent to "the nonnegative member of the pair y and $-y$ is less than k." But, since any negative number is less than any nonnegative number, $|y| < k$ is equivalent to "$y < k$ *and* $-y < k$." But

$$-y < k \iff -k < y.$$

Hence, we conclude that

$$|y| < k \iff -k < y < k.$$

Geometrically, Theorem 8 means that $|y| < k$ if and only if the point representing y on a coordinate line lies within a distance k from the origin.

Once Theorem 8 has been proved, it can, of course, be used to solve such problems as Example 1. We now use it to prove the following theorem.

▶ THEOREM 9. *If $k > 0$, then $|x - a| < k \iff a - k < x < a + k$.*

PROOF:

$$|x - a| < k \iff -k < x - a < k \qquad \text{(Theorem 8)}$$
$$-k < x - a < k \iff a - k < x < a + k \qquad (O_1)$$

Therefore,

$$|x - a| < k \iff a - k < x < a + k.$$

See Fig. 4–6 for the geometrical picture. The points representing the solutions of $|x - a| < k$ all lie within a distance k from the point representing a.

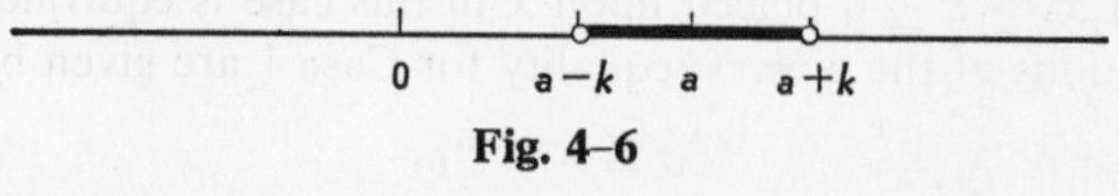

0 a−k a a+k

Fig. 4–6

Example 2

Solve $|x^2 - 10| < 6$.

SOLUTION:

$$|x^2 - 10| < 6 \iff -6 < x^2 - 10 < 6 \qquad \text{(Theorem 8)}$$
$$-6 < x^2 - 10 < 6 \iff 4 < x^2 < 16 \qquad (O_1)$$

$$4 < x^2 < 16 \iff \left\{\begin{matrix} 2 < x < 4 \text{ if } x > 0 \\ \text{or} \\ 2 < (-x) < 4 \text{ if} \\ -x > 0 \end{matrix}\right\}, \qquad \text{(Example 3, Section 4.2)}$$

positive square roots being taken in each case.

Now,

$$2 < -x < 4 \iff -2 > x > -4 \qquad \text{(Theorem 6)}$$

Therefore,

$$|x^2 - 10| < 6 \iff 2 < x < 4 \text{ or } -4 < x < -2.$$

Thus, the solution set is

$$\{x \mid x \text{ is a real number, } 2 < x < 4, \text{ or } -4 < x < -2\}.$$

EXERCISES

1. Plot a graph of the function $y = |x|$, x a real number.

2. Plot the set of points whose coordinates (x, y) are determined by $|x| + |y| = 1$. (This graph will surprise you.)

Solve the inequalities in Exercises 3 through 18.

3. $|x - 3| < 2$ **4.** $|x - 1| < 0.01$ **5.** $|2x - 5| < 1$

6. $|4x - 6| < 3$ **7.** $|3x + 5| < 2$ **8.** $|2x + 3| < \frac{1}{4}$

9. $|x^2 - 5| < 4$ **10.** $|x^2 - 17| < 8$ **11.** $|x^2 - 3| < 1$

12. $|x^2 - 7| < 2$ **13.** $|x^2 - 8| < 5$ **14.** $|x^2 - 8x + 6| < 6$

15. $|2x - 3| < x + 1$ **16.** $|x - 2| \geqq 4x + 1$

17. $|3x + 5| < |2x - 1|$ ★**18.** $|5x + 2| < |3x - 4|$

★**19.** Where are all points with coordinates (x, y) located if:

(a) $x \geqq 0, y > 0$
(b) $x = 5, y < 0$
(c) $x < -2, y \geqq 0$
(d) $x > 3, y > 1$

20. If k is any positive number, find the values of x such that

$$|x^2 - 25| < k.$$

21. If k is any positive number less than 1, find the values of x such that

$$\left|\frac{1}{x} - 1\right| < k.$$

22. By considering the various possibilities for signs prove:

$$|ab| = |a||b|.$$

23. By considering various cases prove:

$$|a+b| \leqq |a| + |b|.$$

24. Prove: $-|a| \leqq a \leqq |a|.$

25. Prove: $\left|\frac{a}{b}\right| = \frac{|a|}{|b|}.$

26. Prove: $|a - b| \leqq |a| + |b|.$

27. Prove: $\sqrt{x^2} = |x|.$

28. If k is a fixed positive number, show that $|x^2 - 9| < k$ is satisfied by all values of x sufficiently close to 3.

29. Prove: $\{y \mid |y| > k, k \text{ a positive number}\} = \{y \mid y > k \text{ or } y < -k\}.$

4.4 The Completeness Property

The addition and multiplication properties of the real number system given in Chapter 2 together with the order properties O_1, O_2, O_3, O_4 given in this chapter constitute a foundation for the algebraic structure of this system. However, as has been observed before, there are other systems, such as the system of rational numbers, that enjoy these same properties; hence, something more must be added to obtain a *defining* set of properties of the real number system. One additional property will suffice. This additional property, called the **completeness property,** is not used in algebra, but is very important in calculus. In order to formulate the property, we must first state some definitions.

An *upper bound* for a subset S of an ordered set M is an element B of M such that $x \leqq B$ for each element x of S. A *least upper bound* L of S is an upper bound of S such that $L \leqq B$ for each upper bound B of S. The **completeness property** for an ordered set is:

Every nonempty subset of the ordered set that has an upper bound has a least upper bound.

An ordered field that has this property is called **complete.** The real number field does have this property, and thus is a **complete ordered field.** It can be proved that there is *only one* complete ordered field, and hence the defining properties for a complete ordered field constitute a definition of the real number system.

As an example of an ordered field that does not have the completeness property, it can be shown in the rational number field that the set of numbers whose squares are less than 2 has an upper bound but does not have a least upper bound.

Systems of Linear Relations ◄ 5

5.1 Solution Sets

A **solution** of a linear equation in two unknowns with real coefficients, such as $2x - y = 5$, is an ordered pair of real numbers which when substituted for x and y converts the equation into a true statement. For example, the number pair (3, 1) is a solution of $2x - y = 5$. But many other number pairs are also solutions: (5, 5), (−1, −7), (0, −5), ($\frac{7}{2}$, 2), (3.75, 2.5), to name only a few. Indeed, any real number may be substituted for one of the unknowns and a corresponding value found for the remaining one such that the pair of numbers is a solution of the equation. Thus, a single linear equation in two unknowns may have infinitely many solutions. These are referred to as the **solution set;** each solution is said to **satisfy** the equation.

The solution set of a linear equation in two variables † with real coefficients comprises a function, called a **linear function,** which has the real numbers as both domain and range. The rule of correspondence is expressed by the given equation. The graph of this function is also called the graph of the equation. It is proved in analytic geometry that the graph of a linear equation is a straight line; indeed, this fact is the reason for the term *linear*.

Now consider the *pair* of linear equations:

$$3x + 4y = 12, \qquad [5.1]$$
$$3x - 2y = 3. \qquad [5.2]$$

† The terms **variables** and **unknowns** are used interchangeably in connection with equations.

A solution of this system is a pair of numbers that satisfies *both* equations. Thus, the solution set of the system is the *intersection* of the solution sets of the individual equations.

5.2 Solution by Graphs

One method of finding the solution set of a pair of linear equations is that of graphs. The solution set of each equation is represented by the points constituting the graph of that equation. Hence, the solution set of the *pair* of equations is represented by the points common to the two graphs. Since the graphs of linear equations are straight lines, the solution set is represented by the point or points of intersection of these lines. The graph of a straight line is easily obtained by plotting two of its points and drawing a straight line through them.

Thus, to solve the pair of equations [5.1] and [5.2] of Section 5.1, we plot their graphs (see Fig. 5–1) and read the coordinates of the point of intersection

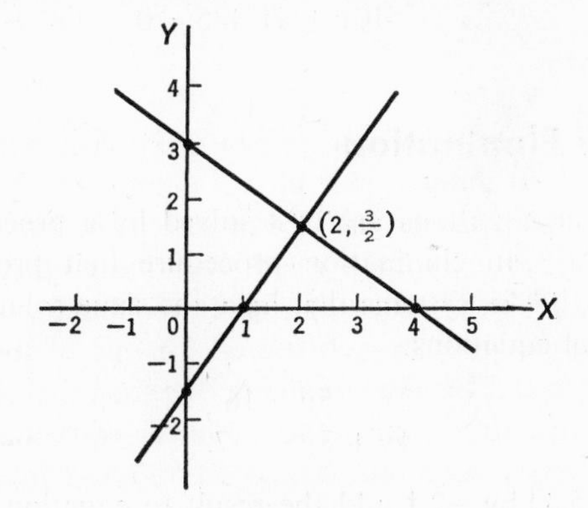

Fig. 5–1

of the two lines. The solution set consists of one member, namely, $(2, 3/2)$, a result that can be checked by substitution in [5.1] and [5.2]. Ordinarily, a solution obtained from graphs will be only approximately correct.

Generally, two lines in a plane will intersect in a single point. Thus, a pair of linear equations usually has a unique solution. If the graphs of the equations are distinct parallel lines, however, the equations have *no* common solution. The solution set in this case is the null set, and the equations are said to be **inconsistent.** If the graphs of the two equations are coincident lines, then every solution of one equation is a solution of the other. In this case, the solution set of the pair contains infinitely many members, and the equations are called **dependent.**

EXERCISES

Solve the following pairs of linear equations by graphs:

1. $x + 2y = -7$
$5x - y = 9$

2. $2x - y = 7$
$4x + y = 8$

3. $2x - 3y - 8 = 0$
$3x + 2y + 6 = 0$

4. $5x + 2y + 9 = 0$
$2x + 6y - 6 = 0$

5. $8x + 4y = 4$
$6x - 2y = -14$

6. $3x + 3y = -2$
$4x - y = 9$

7. $\frac{2}{3}x - \frac{3}{2}y = \frac{5}{6}$
$\frac{1}{4}x + \frac{5}{3}y = \frac{3}{4}$

8. $\frac{x}{2} + \frac{y}{6} = 1$
$\frac{x}{3} - \frac{y}{2} = 2$

9. $\frac{1}{2}x - \frac{2}{3}y = -2$
$\frac{4}{3}x + 4y = \frac{10}{3}$

Plot graphs of the following pairs of equations and state what they indicate about solutions:

10. $3x - 6y - 12 = 0$
$3x - 6y + 5 = 0$

11. $x + 2y = 10$
$3x + 6y = 12$

12. $3y - 2x + 3 = 0$
$8x - 12y = 12$

13. $y = 2 - 3x$
$9x + 3y = 6$

14. $2x + 5y = 10$
$10y + 4x + 5 = 0$

15. $6x - 3y - 9 = 0$
$y = 2x - 6$

5.3 Solution by Elimination

Systems of linear equations are best solved by a process of elimination. We shall demonstrate an elimination procedure that produces a chain of **equivalent systems**—that is, systems that have the same solutions. We illustrate by solving the pair of equations:

I
$$2x - 5y = 16 \quad [5.3]$$
$$4x + 3y = -7. \quad [5.4]$$

Multiply equation [5.3] by -2,† add the result to equation [5.4], and replace equation [5.4] in I by this sum to obtain

II
$$2x - 5y = 16 \quad [5.3]$$
$$13y = -39. \quad [5.5]$$

Multiply equation [5.3] by $\frac{1}{2}$ and equation [5.5] by $\frac{1}{13}$ to obtain

III
$$x - \tfrac{5}{2}y = 8 \quad [5.6]$$
$$y = -3. \quad [5.7]$$

Finally, in III replace equation [5.6] by the sum of equation [5.6] and $\frac{5}{2}$ times equation [5.7], and obtain

† The expression "multiply an equation" means multiply both members of the equation.

$$\text{IV} \qquad \begin{aligned} x &= \tfrac{1}{2} \\ y &= -3. \end{aligned}$$

The systems I, II, III, and IV are equivalent systems. That is, they have exactly the same solution sets. Thus, $(\frac{1}{2}, -3)$ is a solution of system I, and it is the only solution.

To see that the four systems given above are equivalent, observe that each system is obtained from the preceding one by one or more of the operations:

(i) Interchange two equations of the system.
(ii) Replace an equation by a nonzero multiple of itself.
(iii) Replace an equation by the sum of that equation and a multiple of another equation of the system.

It is certainly clear that an operation of type (i) on a system of linear equations does not change the solution set. (This property was actually not used in the example given above.) The equations in a system can be changed to any order by repeated operations of type (i).

To see that operations of types (ii) and (iii) always lead to equivalent systems, let

$$\textbf{(A)} \qquad L_1 = 0, \qquad L_2 = 0$$

be a system of two linear equations, where L_1 and L_2 represent expressions of the form $ax + by + c$.

Let k be a nonzero constant and consider the system

$$\textbf{(B)} \qquad kL_1 = 0, \qquad L_2 = 0,$$

obtained from **(A)** by an operation of type (ii). It is obvious that **(A)** and **(B)** have the same solution set, and thus are equivalent.

Now consider the system

$$\textbf{(C)} \qquad L_1 + kL_2 = 0, \qquad L_2 = 0,$$

obtained from **(A)** by an operation of type (iii). It is clear that any solution of **(A)** is a solution of **(C)**. It is also true that any pair of numbers which substituted for x and y make both $L_1 + kL_2$ and L_2 zero must also make L_1 zero and consequently must be a solution of **(A)**. Thus, **(A)** and **(C)** are equivalent.

The geometric interpretation of this situation is that the three pairs of lines represented by **(A)**, **(B)**, and **(C)** all intersect in the same point. Thus, in the process of solving a system of two equations in two unknowns by obtaining a sequence of equivalent systems, we are at each step replacing a pair of lines by another pair that has the same point of intersection. If the final system has the form $x = x_0$, $y = y_0$, the two corresponding lines are respectively vertical and horizontal. The student should plot the graphs of the four systems I, II, III, and IV, given above, and observe this phenomenon.

System II (and also III) is said to be in **echelon form.** The second equation contains one less unknown than the first. Once a system in echelon form is obtained, a solution is easy to find. This idea will be developed further in the next section, where we study systems of equations with more than two unknowns.

EXERCISES

Solve the following pairs of equations by first obtaining an equivalent system in echelon form.

1. $2x - 4y = -6$, $3x + y = 5$

2. $2x + 5y = 4$, $5x - 2y = -3$

3. $3x - 2y = -15$, $5x + 6y = 3$

4. $3x - 4y + 2 = 0$, $4x + y - 7 = 0$

5. $2x - y + 4 = 0$, $3x + 6y + 1 = 0$

6. $3x - 2y = 8$, $2x + 3y = 1$

7. $4x - y = 5$, $2x + 3y = -2$

8. $3x - 4y = 5$, $2x + 5y = -3$

9. $3x + 10y = 3$, $6x - 5y = 16$

10. $u + 3v = -3$, $2u - 5v = 16$

11. $\dfrac{x-y}{5} + \dfrac{x+y}{2} = 1$, $\dfrac{x+2y}{3} - \dfrac{x-y}{6} = 2$

12. $\dfrac{x}{3} + \dfrac{y}{3} = 1$, $3x - 5y = 2$

13. $mx + ny = p$, $2mx - 3ny = q$

14. $px - qy = r$, $3px - 2qy = 2r$

15. $a_1x + b_1y = c_1$, $a_2x + b_2y = c_2$

16. If the altitude of a certain triangle were increased by 2 in. and the base by 4 in., the area would be increased by 32 sq in. and the new base would be equal to the new altitude. Find the altitude and base of the original triangle.

17. If the length of a certain rectangular plot were decreased by 10 ft and the width increased by 10 ft, the area would be increased by 300 sq ft and the new width would be one-half the original length. Find the dimensions of the plot.

18. A lever of negligible weight is in equilibrium under two weights, one of them 5 ft to the left of the fulcrum, the other 7 ft to the right. If the first weight were increased by 20 lb and moved up to a point 6 ft to the left of the fulcrum, the other would have to be moved to a point 10 ft to the right of the fulcrum in order to maintain equilibrium. Find the value of each of the original weights.

19. An airplane flies 1430 miles in $4\frac{2}{5}$ hr with the help of a tail wind. Flying against the same wind as a head wind, it takes $5\frac{1}{5}$ hr to fly the same distance. Find the speed of the plane in still air and the speed of the wind.

20. An airplane flies 1290 miles with a tail wind in 6 hr. If the wind had been half as great, it would have taken 6 hr and 27 min. Find the speed of the wind.

21. How much copper and how much magnesium should be added to 200 lb of an alloy containing 20 percent copper and 40 percent magnesium to produce an alloy containing 25 percent copper and 50 percent magnesium?

22. How much nickel and how much zinc must be added to 50 lb of an alloy containing 15 percent nickel and 20 percent zinc to produce an alloy containing 25 percent nickel and 30 percent zinc?

23. In a certain two-digit number the sum of the digits is 13. If 27 were subtracted from the number, the digits would be reversed. Find the number.

24. In a two-digit number the sum of the digits is 9 less than the value of the number. If the digit in the tens' place were increased by 2, the resulting number would be 4 greater than twice the original number. Find the original number.

5.4 Systems of Equations in More than Two Variables

The elimination process of Section 5.3 may also be applied to systems containing more than two unknowns. Let us illustrate by solving the following system:

$$\text{V} \qquad \begin{aligned} 3x + 2y + 5z &= 7 \\ 2x - 3y - 2z &= -3 \\ x + 2y + 3z &= 5 \end{aligned}$$

We rewrite the equations in a different order to obtain the equivalent system:

$$\text{VI} \qquad \begin{aligned} x + 2y + 3z &= 5 & [5.8] \\ 3x + 2y + 5z &= 7 & [5.9] \\ 2x - 3y - 2z &= -3 & [5.10] \end{aligned}$$

Now replace [5.9] by the sum of itself and −3[5.8] and replace [5.10] by the sum of itself and −2[5.8] to obtain

$$\text{VII} \qquad \begin{aligned} x + 2y + 3z &= 5 & [5.8] \\ -4y - 4z &= -8 & [5.11] \\ -7y - 8z &= -13 & [5.12] \end{aligned}$$

Multiply [5.11] by $-\frac{1}{4}$ and [5.12] by −1 and get

$$\text{VIII} \qquad \begin{aligned} x + 2y + 3z &= 5 & [5.8] \\ y + z &= 2 & [5.13] \\ 7y + 8z &= 13 & [5.14] \end{aligned}$$

Finally replace [5.14] by the sum of itself and −7 times [5.13] to obtain

$$\text{IX} \qquad \begin{aligned} x + 2y + 3z &= 5 & [5.8] \\ y + z &= 2 & [5.13] \\ z &= -1 & [5.15] \end{aligned}$$

The systems V, VI, VII, VIII, and IX are equivalent because each is obtained from the preceding one by operations of type (i), (ii), or (iii), and these were observed in Section 5.3 to produce equivalent systems. (The argument given there can be extended to systems of any number of equations.) System IX is in echelon form, and we can easily find a solution by substituting -1 for z in [5.13] to obtain $y = 3$, and then substituting 3 for y and -1 for z in [5.8] to obtain $x = 2$. Thus, a solution of IX, and consequently of the equivalent original system V, is $(2, 3, -1)$, and this solution is the only solution of V, since it is obviously the only solution of IX.

The systems of equations studied so far contain the same number of equations as unknowns. As an example of a system in which these two numbers are different, consider:

X
$$x + y - 2z = -1 \qquad [5.16]$$
$$3x + 2y - z = 4 \qquad [5.17]$$

We reduce this system to echelon form by the same elimination process previously employed. Replace [5.17] by the sum of itself and -3[5.16].

XI
$$x + y - 2z = -1 \qquad [5.16]$$
$$-y + 5z = 7 \qquad [5.18]$$

Now XI is in echelon form; each equation contains one less unknown than the preceding one. It is clear that we can assign any value to z, find a corresponding value of y from [5.18], and a value of x corresponding to these two values from [5.16]. We may obtain, for example, $x = 3$, $y = -2$, $z = 1$, and $x = 0$, $y = 3$, $z = 2$. Thus, system XI, and consequently system X, does not have a unique solution, but rather infinitely many solutions. The set of all solutions can be represented as follows, where k is an arbitrary real number:

$$x = -3k + 6, \quad y = 5k - 7, \quad z = k.$$

This result is obtained by assigning to z the unspecified value k and solving first [5.18] for y and then [5.16] for x.

A system of equations does not necessarily have a solution at all. For example, the system

$$2x + 3y = 4 \qquad [5.19]$$
$$4x + 6y = -1 \qquad [5.20]$$

does not have a solution. A system in echelon form equivalent to this system, found by replacing [5.20] by the sum of itself and -2[5.19], is

$$2x + 3y = 4$$
$$0 = -9$$

which shows immediately that the original system has no solution.

One type of linear equation system that always has a solution is the one in which the constant terms are all zero. Equations with constant term zero are called **homogeneous.** A system of homogeneous linear equations always has as a solution the set of zeros for the unknowns. This solution is referred to as the **trivial solution.** For a given system of homogeneous equations, an important question is whether the system has a **nontrivial** solution. One method of obtaining an answer to this question is to derive an equivalent system in echelon form. If the last equation in the echelon form system contains more than one unknown, then the system has a nontrivial solution.

The practical importance of systems of linear equations is suggested by the fact that most problems have to be reduced to the solving of such a system before a modern high-speed computer can be used in making the calculations. Sometimes the number of equations in the system may be several hundred.

EXERCISES

Solve the systems of equations in Exercises 1 through 18 by first obtaining equivalent systems in echelon form.

1. $3x - 2y + 3z = 8$
$2x + y - z = 1$
$4x - 3y + 2z = 4$

2. $5x + 3y - 2z = 5$
$3x - 4y + 3z = 13$
$x + 6y - 4z = -8$

3. $x + 5y - z = -7$
$3x + 4y - 2z = 2$
$2x - 3y + 5z = 19$

4. $2x - 3y + 5z = 18$
$3x + 2y - 2z = -2$
$4x - y - 3z = 8$

5. $2x - 4y + 6z = 18$
$3x + 7y + 2z = 9$
$5x - 8y + 3z = 4$

6. $4x - 3y + 5z = -8$
$2x + 4y - 6z = 20$
$3x - 5y + 2z = -3$

7. $x + 2y - 4z = -3$
$3x + y + 2z = 8$
$2x - 3y - 6z = 9$

8. $2x - 6y = 1$
$3y + 5z = -3$
$3x - 7z = 9$

9. $x + 4y + 3z = 0$
$2x - 2y - 5z = -2$
$5x + 6y - 10z = 2$

10. $2x + 3y - 5z = -6$
$5x + 2y + 4z = 18$
$3x - y + 3z = 9$

11. $x - 2y + 3z = 4$
$7x - 4y + 5z = -3$
$2x + y - 2z = 1$

12. $3x - 2y + 2z = 8$
$2x + 3y - 6z = 0$
$4x + 6y - 9z = 1$

13. $x + 3y - 2z = -6$
$3x + 2y + 4z = 1$

14. $2x + 5y + 3z = 10$
$6x - 3y - 4z = -14$

15. $3x + 4y + z = 0$
$x + 8y - 3z = 0$

16. $2x - 3y + z = 0$
$x + 2y - 3z = 0$
$3x - 2y + 4z = 0$

17.
$$\begin{aligned} x + 2y - 7z &= 0 \\ 2x - y + 6z &= 0 \\ 4x + 3y - 8z &= 0 \end{aligned}$$

18.
$$\begin{aligned} x + 2y - z + 2w &= 6 \\ x + 3y + z - 4w &= 0 \\ x - 2y - z + 9w &= 5 \end{aligned}$$

19. A weight of 45 lb is attached to a lever of negligible weight at a point 4 ft to the right of a fulcrum. This weight is balanced by two weights, one 5 ft to the left of the fulcrum and the other $7\frac{1}{2}$ ft to the left of the fulcrum. If the two unknown weights were both moved to a point 6 ft to the left of the fulcrum, the lever would remain in equilibrium. Find the values of the unknown weights.

20. In a three-digit number the sum of the digits is 9, and the digit in the hundreds' place is 2 greater than the digit in the units' place. If the digits in the tens' and units' places were interchanged, the value of the number would be increased by 18. Find the number.

21. In a three-digit number the sum of the digits is 7, and the digit in the tens' place is twice as large as the digit in the units' place. If these last mentioned digits were interchanged, the number would be decreased by 18. Find the number.

22. The sum of the digits of a three-digit number is 11. If 495 were subtracted from the number, the order of the digits would be reversed. If 27 were subtracted from the number, the units' digit and the tens' digit would be interchanged. Find the number.

In each of the following exercises determine a, b, and c in the equation $y = ax^2 + bx + c$ so that x and y will have the corresponding values listed.

23. $x = -1, \quad y = -9$
$x = 1, \quad y = -3$
$x = 3, \quad y = 19$

24. $x = -2, \quad y = 28$
$x = 1, \quad y = -2$
$x = 2, \quad y = 0$

25. $x = -3, \quad y = -8$
$x = -2, \quad y = 3$
$x = 2, \quad y = -13$

26. $x = -4, \quad y = -1$
$x = -1, \quad y = 8$
$x = 3, \quad y = -36$

5.5 Inequalities in Two Variables

Consider the inequality

$$4x - 2y + 5 > 0 \tag{5.21}$$

By a **solution** we mean an ordered pair of numbers which substituted for x and y in [5.21] yields a true statement. For example, (2, 3) is a solution because when x and y are replaced by 2 and 3, respectively, [5.21] becomes $7 > 0$, which is a true statement.

The graph of [5.21] consists of all points in a plane whose coordinates are solutions of [5.21]. To learn something about this graph, let us compare [5.21] with the corresponding equation

$$4x - 2y + 5 = 0. \qquad [5.22]$$

If we solve each of [5.21] and [5.22] for y in terms of x, we get, respectively,

$$y < 2x + 5/2 \qquad [5.23]$$
$$y = 2x + 5/2 \qquad [5.24]$$

Inequalities [5.21] and [5.23] are equivalent; that is, they have the same solution set. The equations [5.22] and [5.24] are also equivalent. For a given value of x, the point with coordinates (x, y) is on the graph of [5.24] if and only if the ordinate y is *equal* to $2x + 5/2$. But, for a given value of x, the point with coordinates (x, y) is on the graph of [5.23] if and only if y is *less* than $2x + 5/2$. This means that the graph of the inequality [5.23] consists of all points *below* the graph of [5.24] (see Fig. 5–2); the graph of the latter is, of course, a straight line.

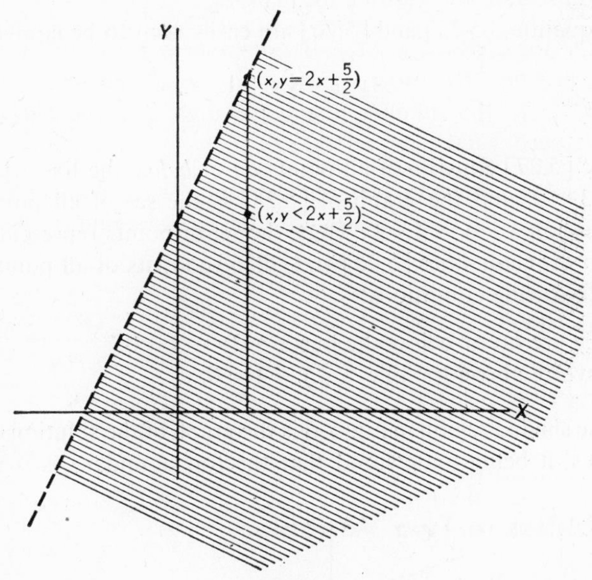

Fig. 5–2

An argument similar to the one given above can be used to establish the fact that for any linear inequality of the form $ax + by + c > 0$ (or $ax + by + c < 0$), the graph consists either of all points in the plane *above* the line whose equation is $ax + by + c = 0$, or all points *below* this line. The graph of $ax + by + c \geqq 0$ (or $ax + by + c \leqq 0$) would include also the points *on* the line $ax + by + c = 0$.

Observe that a linear equation such as [5.22] defines a *function*, since for a given value of x the corresponding value of y is uniquely determined. Recall that a function may be described as a set of ordered pairs in which no first member is associated with two different second members. On the other hand, the inequality [5.21] associates with each value of x many values of y. The inequality determines a set of ordered pairs in which the same first member may be associated with many different second members. The word **relation** is used to refer to any set of ordered pairs. Thus, the concept of a relation is a generalization of the concept of a function; or to put it another way, a function is a special kind of relation.

Consider the pair of inequalities:

$$x + 3y - 3 \leqq 0 \qquad [5.25]$$
$$x - y - 1 < 0 \qquad [5.26]$$

By a solution of this system we mean a pair of numbers that is a solution of both inequalities. Thus, the solution set of the system consists of the intersection of the solution sets of the separate inequalities.

The inequalities [5.25] and [5.26] are easily seen to be equivalent to

$$y \leqq -\tfrac{1}{3}x + 1 \qquad [5.27]$$
$$y > x - 1 \qquad [5.28]$$

The graph of [5.27] consists of all points *on* or *below* the line whose equation is $x + 3y - 3 = 0$, and the graph of [5.28] is the set of all points *above* the line with equation $x - y - 1 = 0$. Thus, the set of points representing solutions of the system of inequalities [5.25] and [5.26] consists of all points that satisfy both of the following conditions:

(i) They are on or below the line $x + 3y - 3 = 0$.
(ii) They are above the line $x - y - 1 = 0$.

Thus, the shaded region in Fig. 5–3 is the graph of the solution set of the pair of inequalities, it being understood that the top boundary is included in the graph.

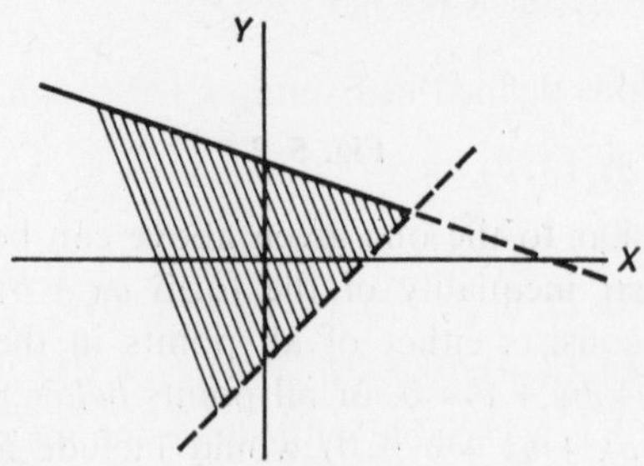

Fig. 5–3

In setting up many problems in the social sciences, particularly economics, the conditions imposed can be stated in terms of inequalities in several variables, and the solutions of the problem are the solutions of a system of such inequalities. As a simple example, let us suppose that a farmer plans to buy x pigs costing \$20 each and y sheep costing \$25 each, and the maximum sum he can spend on both is \$100. What are the possible purchases? The conditions of the problem can be formulated as follows:

$$\begin{aligned} 20x + 25y &\leqq 100 \\ x &\geqq 0 \\ y &\geqq 0 \end{aligned}$$

where x and y are integers.

The graph of the possible solutions of this problem are the points with integral coordinates in or on the triangle formed by the three lines $20x + 25y = 100$, $x = 0$, and $y = 0$, as shown in Fig. 5–4.

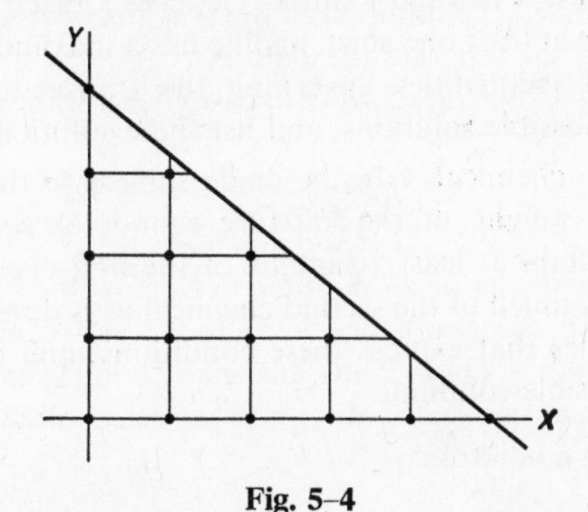

Fig. 5–4

This type of analysis is involved in an important practical application of mathematics called **linear programing.**

EXERCISES

Which of the relations defined in Exercises 1 through 6 are functions?

1. (1, 3), (2, −5), (−1, 3), (3, 7), (4, 6)

2. (3, −2), (−1, 5), (2, 8), (3, 4), (1, 7), (2, 9)

3. (2, 5), (3, 4), (1, 2), (0, 2), (−3, −1), (1, 6), (−2, 0)

4. (5, −2), (−2, 6), (3, 6), (2, 4), (0, −3), (1, 6), (−1, 2)

5. y is less than x and x is a variable with scope the set of real numbers.

6. y is an exact divisor of x and x is a variable with scope the set of integers.

Draw pictures that represent the graphs of solutions of the systems of inequalities in Exercises 7 through 18.

7. $x > 0$
$y > 2$

8. $x > 0$
$y \leqq 2$

9. $x \geqq 0$
$x - y \geqq 0$

10. $x - y \leqq 0$
$x + y \geqq 0$

11. $x \leqq 0$
$y \geqq 0$
$x - y + 1 \geqq 0$

12. $x \geqq 0$
$y \leqq 0$
$2x - 3y < 6$

13. $x - 2y < 4$
$x - 2y > -4$

14. $3x - y + 2 \geqq 0$
$x + 2y - 6 \leqq 0$
$y \geqq 3$

15. $x - y - 1 \leqq 0$
$2x + y + 1 \geqq 0$
$x - 2y + 3 \geqq 0$

16. $x - 2y + 2 \geqq 0$
$2x + y \geqq 3$
$3x - 2y \leqq 6$

17. $x - 2y \geqq 10$
$y \leqq 4$
$y \geqq 1$
$x \geqq 1$

18. $3x + y \leqq 7$
$3x + y \geqq 3$
$x - 2y + 6 \geqq 0$
$x - 2y \leqq 1$

19. A boy is to purchase x ties and y shirts. Ties cost \$2 each and shirts \$5 each. He must purchase at least one shirt, and he has a maximum of \$20 to spend. Write the set of inequalities governing the transaction, draw a graph representing all possible solutions, and list these solutions.

20. A mixture of two chemicals is to be made subject to the following conditions: The total weight of the mixture cannot exceed 100 grams. The mixture must contain at least 10 grams of the first chemical, and it must contain at least as much of the second chemical as it does of the first. Write a set of inequalities that express these conditions, and draw a graph that represents all possible solutions.

Matrices and Determinants ◄ 6

6.1 Matrix of a System of Equations

A **matrix** is a rectangular array of numbers. Examples are

$$\begin{pmatrix} 2 & 3 & -1 \\ 4 & 0 & 5 \end{pmatrix}, \quad \begin{pmatrix} 3 & 1 \\ 2 & 4 \end{pmatrix}, \quad (1 \quad 4 \quad -6), \quad \begin{pmatrix} 5 \\ 8 \end{pmatrix}.$$

The numbers occurring are called the **elements** of the matrix, and they are arranged into horizontal **rows** and vertical **columns.** The first matrix listed above has two rows and three columns; the second is a square matrix with two rows and two columns. The third is called a **row matrix,** since it has only one row, and the last is called a **column matrix,** since it has only one column. In this book the elements of the matrices considered will always be real numbers.

Matrices have many applications in mathematics. We shall study especially their relation to systems of linear equations.

In solving a system of linear equations, one may replace the system by a matrix whose elements are the coefficients and constants occurring in the equations, and work with the matrix instead of the equations themselves. For example, the system of equations

$$\begin{aligned} 2x - 6y &= 3 \\ x + 2y &= 4 \end{aligned} \qquad [6.1]$$

can be represented by the matrix

$$\begin{pmatrix} 2 & -6 & 3 \\ 1 & 2 & 4 \end{pmatrix}. \qquad [6.2]$$

The elements in the first two columns are the coefficients of x and y, respectively, in the two equations, and the elements in the third column are the constant terms in these equations.

Recall from Section 5.3 that a system of equations can be reduced to an equivalent system in echelon form by performing the following types of operations:

(i) Interchange two equations of the system.
(ii) Replace an equation by a nonzero multiple of itself.
(iii) Replace an equation by the sum of that equation and a multiple of another equation of the system.

These operations may be carried out by performing the following operations on the matrix corresponding to the system of equations:

(i) Interchange two rows of the matrix.
(ii) Multiply the elements in a row of the matrix by a nonzero constant.
(iii) Add to the elements of a row of the matrix a constant multiple of the corresponding elements of another row.

Operations of types (i), (ii), and (iii) on a matrix are known as **elementary row operations.**

We carry out a sequence of these operations on the matrix [6.2]:

$$\begin{pmatrix} 2 & -6 & 3 \\ 1 & 2 & 4 \end{pmatrix}.$$

First interchange the two rows to obtain

$$\begin{pmatrix} 1 & 2 & 4 \\ 2 & -6 & 3 \end{pmatrix}.$$

The purpose of this is to get 1 in the upper left-hand corner. Next multiply the elements of the first row by -2 and add the results to the corresponding elements of the second row to obtain

$$\begin{pmatrix} 1 & 2 & 4 \\ 0 & -10 & -5 \end{pmatrix}.$$

Finally multiply the elements of the second row by $-1/10$ to obtain

$$\begin{pmatrix} 1 & 2 & 4 \\ 0 & 1 & 1/2 \end{pmatrix}. \qquad [6.3]$$

The last matrix is the matrix of the system of linear equations:

$$\begin{aligned} x + 2y &= 4 \\ y &= 1/2 \end{aligned} \qquad [6.4]$$

Both the system of equations [6.4] and the corresponding matrix [6.3] are said to be in **echelon form.** The solution of the system [6.4] is easily obtained by substituting ½ for y in the first equation. The solution is $x = 3$, $y = ½$, and since [6.4] is equivalent to [6.1], $x = 3$, $y = ½$ is also a solution of the latter.

The student should write out the steps, as in the example in Section 5.3, in changing the system [6.1] to the equivalent system [6.4], and thus convince himself that such a change can always be effected by working with the corresponding matrices.

EXERCISES

In each of the following exercises write the matrix corresponding to the system of equations, perform elementary row operations on the matrix to change it to echelon form, write and solve the system of equations corresponding to the echelon form matrix, and thus obtain a solution of the original system of equations.

1. $x + 2y = -3$, $2x + 3y = 8$

2. $x + y = 2$, $3x + 2y = 3$

3. $2x + 4y = -8$, $3x + 2y = 0$

4. $3x - 6y = 3$, $2x + 3y = 9$

5. $2x - 2y = 11$, $4x + 5y = -5$

6. $3x + 3y = -10$, $5x + 6y = -16$

7. $3x - 2y = 6$, $5x + 3y = -2$

8. $4x + 3y = -5$, $3x - 2y = 3$

9. $2x - 3y = -1$, $4x - 6y = 3$

10. $3x + 2y = 5$, $9x + 6y = -2$

11. $x + 2y + z = 2$, $2x - 3y - 2z = 2$, $3x + 4y + 2z = 11$

12. $x - 3y + 4z = 9$, $4x - 2y - 3z = 7$, $2x + 5y + 2z = 1$

13. $2x + 4y - 6z = 12$, $3x - 2y - 5z = 18$, $4x + 5y - 2z = 7$

14. $2x - 3y + 2z = -2$, $x + 2y + 3z = 0$, $3x - 2y + 4z = -1$

15. $3x - 3y - 4z = -2$, $x + 4y + 2z = 6$

16. $2x + 4y - 8z = 6$, $3x - 5y + 2z = 1$

6.2 Addition and Multiplication of Matrices

Two matrices are called **equal** if and only if they are of the same order (that is, have the same number of rows and the same number of columns) and elements appearing in corresponding positions are identical.

It is convenient to represent the elements of a matrix by letters with double subscripts, such as a_{23}, where the *first* subscript denotes the *row* and the *second* denotes the *column* in which the element lies. Thus, the following represents an arbitrary 2×3 matrix (that is, a matrix with two rows and three columns).

$$\begin{pmatrix} a_{11} & a_{12} & a_{13} \\ a_{21} & a_{22} & a_{23} \end{pmatrix}$$

Addition of two matrices of the same order is defined by specifying that the sum is the matrix obtained by adding corresponding elements. Thus,

$$\begin{pmatrix} a_{11} & a_{12} & a_{13} \\ a_{21} & a_{22} & a_{23} \end{pmatrix} + \begin{pmatrix} b_{11} & b_{12} & b_{13} \\ b_{21} & b_{22} & b_{23} \end{pmatrix} = \begin{pmatrix} a_{11}+b_{11} & a_{12}+b_{12} & a_{13}+b_{13} \\ a_{21}+b_{21} & a_{22}+b_{22} & a_{23}+b_{23} \end{pmatrix}$$

The sum of two matrices exists if and only if they are of the same order.

The definition of *multiplication* of matrices is not what one would normally expect. We illustrate it by the following example:

$$\begin{pmatrix} a_{11} & a_{12} \\ a_{21} & a_{22} \end{pmatrix} \begin{pmatrix} b_{11} & b_{12} & b_{13} \\ b_{21} & b_{22} & b_{23} \end{pmatrix} = \begin{pmatrix} a_{11}b_{11}+a_{12}b_{21} & a_{11}b_{12}+a_{12}b_{22} & a_{11}b_{13}+a_{12}b_{23} \\ a_{21}b_{11}+a_{22}b_{21} & a_{21}b_{12}+a_{22}b_{22} & a_{21}b_{13}+a_{22}b_{23} \end{pmatrix}$$

To obtain from this illustration the rule for multiplying matrices, observe, for example, that the element $a_{11}b_{12} + a_{12}b_{22}$ in *first row* and *second column* of the product is obtained by taking the sum of the products of the elements $a_{11}\quad a_{12}$ of the *first row* of the left factor by the corresponding elements of the *second column* $\begin{matrix} b_{12} \\ b_{22} \end{matrix}$ of the right factor.

In general, to find the element in the ith row and jth column of the product AB of two matrices A and B, multiply the elements in the ith row of A by the corresponding elements in the jth column of B and add the results. This operation can be performed only if the number of columns of matrix A is equal to the number of rows of matrix B. The product BA may not exist, even though AB does. Two square matrices of the same order can always be multiplied.

Multiplication of matrices is defined in this rather strange manner because this definition gives to matrices the properties that make them so useful. We shall see one instance of this in the next section, where we express a system of linear equations in matrix form.

In the system of *square* matrices of a given order, the operations of addition and multiplication can always be performed. When the designations "second-order," "third-order," etc., are used, it is understood that the matrix referred to is square.

Consider the following two products:

$$\begin{pmatrix} 3 & 1 \\ 2 & -4 \end{pmatrix} \begin{pmatrix} 2 & -3 \\ 1 & 1 \end{pmatrix} = \begin{pmatrix} 7 & -8 \\ 0 & -10 \end{pmatrix}$$

$$\begin{pmatrix} 2 & -3 \\ 1 & 1 \end{pmatrix} \begin{pmatrix} 3 & 1 \\ 2 & -4 \end{pmatrix} = \begin{pmatrix} 0 & 14 \\ 5 & -3 \end{pmatrix}$$

This example shows that interchanging the order of the two factors in a product may change the product. That is, multiplication of matrices is *not* a commutative operation. Perhaps this is the first time the reader has encountered a mathematical system in which multiplication is *not* commutative.

It can be shown that multiplication of matrices is associative, that addition of matrices obeys both the associative and commutative laws, and that the right and left distributive laws hold. Thus, the system of *square* matrices of a *given order* is closed under addition and multiplication, and these operations conform to most, but not all, of the laws governing addition and multiplication of real numbers. The system of square matrices is an example of a type of algebraic system known as a **ring.** A ring resembles a field in many ways, but may not have all the properties of a field.

EXERCISES

Add the matrices in Exercises 1 through 6.

1. $\begin{pmatrix} 2 & -1 \\ 3 & 5 \end{pmatrix} + \begin{pmatrix} 3 & 4 \\ -2 & 1 \end{pmatrix}$

2. $\begin{pmatrix} -1 & 2 \\ 4 & 6 \end{pmatrix} + \begin{pmatrix} 0 & 1 \\ -3 & 2 \end{pmatrix}$

3. $\begin{pmatrix} 2 & -1 & 3 \\ 4 & 2 & -5 \end{pmatrix} + \begin{pmatrix} 3 & 2 & -4 \\ 1 & -5 & 6 \end{pmatrix}$

4. $\begin{pmatrix} 5 & 4 & 2 \\ -2 & -3 & 6 \end{pmatrix} + \begin{pmatrix} -2 & 1 & -3 \\ 4 & 3 & 2 \end{pmatrix}$

5. $\begin{pmatrix} -2 & 1 & 3 \\ 4 & 5 & -1 \\ -3 & 2 & 6 \end{pmatrix} + \begin{pmatrix} 3 & 5 & -1 \\ 2 & -3 & 4 \\ 0 & -3 & 2 \end{pmatrix}$

6. $\begin{pmatrix} 1 & -2 & 3 \\ 5 & -6 & -1 \\ 4 & 3 & 2 \end{pmatrix} + \begin{pmatrix} 7 & 6 & 4 \\ -2 & 4 & 8 \\ -3 & 2 & -5 \end{pmatrix}$

Multiply the matrices in Exercises 7 through 18.

7. $\begin{pmatrix} -1 & 2 \\ -3 & 4 \end{pmatrix} \begin{pmatrix} 2 & 1 \\ 3 & -2 \end{pmatrix}$

8. $\begin{pmatrix} 2 & 0 \\ -1 & 3 \end{pmatrix} \begin{pmatrix} 3 & -2 \\ 4 & 1 \end{pmatrix}$

9. $\begin{pmatrix} 3 & 6 \\ 1 & 2 \end{pmatrix} \begin{pmatrix} 2 & -4 \\ -1 & 2 \end{pmatrix}$

10. $\begin{pmatrix} -2 & 0 \\ 1 & 3 \end{pmatrix} \begin{pmatrix} 4 & -3 \\ 2 & 1 \end{pmatrix}$

11. $\begin{pmatrix} 1 & 2 & -1 \\ -2 & 0 & 3 \\ 4 & -3 & 2 \end{pmatrix} \begin{pmatrix} -2 & -1 & 0 \\ 3 & 1 & 2 \\ -3 & 2 & 4 \end{pmatrix}$

12. $\begin{pmatrix} 2 & -1 & 3 \\ -3 & 2 & 0 \\ 5 & 1 & -1 \end{pmatrix} \begin{pmatrix} -3 & 2 & -1 \\ 0 & 5 & 2 \\ 1 & -2 & 1 \end{pmatrix}$

13. $\begin{pmatrix} 1 & 3 \\ 2 & 1 \end{pmatrix} \begin{pmatrix} 4 \\ -1 \end{pmatrix}$

14. $\begin{pmatrix} 2 & 5 \\ 4 & -3 \end{pmatrix} \begin{pmatrix} 5 \\ -3 \end{pmatrix}$

15. $\begin{pmatrix} 3 & -2 & 1 \\ 2 & 5 & -4 \end{pmatrix} \begin{pmatrix} 1 & -2 \\ 3 & 4 \\ 2 & -3 \end{pmatrix}$

16. $\begin{pmatrix} 1 & 4 & 2 \\ 5 & -2 & 3 \end{pmatrix} \begin{pmatrix} 2 & -4 \\ 1 & -3 \\ 4 & 0 \end{pmatrix}$

17. $\begin{pmatrix} 3 & -2 & 1 \end{pmatrix} \begin{pmatrix} 1 & 0 & 2 \\ 3 & -2 & 4 \\ 2 & 1 & 0 \end{pmatrix}$

18. $\begin{pmatrix} 2 & 3 & -1 \end{pmatrix} \begin{pmatrix} 2 & -3 & 0 \\ 1 & 4 & 3 \\ -2 & 1 & -2 \end{pmatrix}$

19. Show that $\begin{pmatrix} -1 & 2 \\ 3 & 4 \end{pmatrix} \begin{pmatrix} 2 & -3 \\ 5 & 1 \end{pmatrix} \neq \begin{pmatrix} 2 & -3 \\ 5 & 1 \end{pmatrix} \begin{pmatrix} -1 & 2 \\ 3 & 4 \end{pmatrix}$

20. Show that $\begin{pmatrix} 4 & 1 \\ -2 & 0 \end{pmatrix} \begin{pmatrix} -3 & 1 \\ 0 & 5 \end{pmatrix} \neq \begin{pmatrix} -3 & 1 \\ 0 & 5 \end{pmatrix} \begin{pmatrix} 4 & 1 \\ -2 & 0 \end{pmatrix}$

21. Prove the associative law for addition of second-order matrices.
22. Prove the commutative law for addition of second-order matrices.
23. Prove the left distributive law for second-order matrices.
24. Prove that multiplication of second-order matrices is associative.
25. What second-order matrix Z has the property that $M + Z = M$ for all second-order matrices M?
26. Try to find a second-order matrix E such that $E \cdot M = M \cdot E = M$ for all matrices M of the second order. Such a matrix is called a *unit* matrix.
27. Let Z be the matrix referred to in Exercise 25. Try to find two matrices A and B, each different from Z, such that $A \cdot B = Z$. Contrast this with a similar situation with numbers.
28. Consider all second-order matrices with real numbers as elements. Which of the properties A_1 to A_5, M_1 to M_5, D, stated in Chapter 2 for the system of real numbers, hold for this system of matrices?
29. Can you find a subset of the set of matrices of Exercise 28 for which all properties A_1 to A_5, M_1 to M_5, and D hold?

6.3 Matrix Equations and Inverses of Matrices

Consider the system of equations

$$\begin{aligned} a_{11}x_1 + a_{12}x_2 &= b_1 \\ a_{21}x_1 + a_{22}x_2 &= b_2 \end{aligned} \qquad [6.5]$$

which represents all pairs of linear equations in two unknowns. We shall show that this system can be represented by a single equation in terms of matrices as follows:

$$\begin{pmatrix} a_{11} & a_{12} \\ a_{21} & a_{22} \end{pmatrix} \begin{pmatrix} x_1 \\ x_2 \end{pmatrix} = \begin{pmatrix} b_1 \\ b_2 \end{pmatrix} \qquad [6.6]$$

If the indicated multiplication of the two matrices on the left is performed, we obtain an equation in terms of column matrices:

$$\begin{pmatrix} a_{11}x_1 + a_{12}x_2 \\ a_{21}x_1 + a_{22}x_2 \end{pmatrix} = \begin{pmatrix} b_1 \\ b_2 \end{pmatrix} \qquad [6.7]$$

Since equality of matrices means that elements in corresponding positions are identical, we see that [6.5] and [6.7], and consequently also [6.6], are equivalent statements.

We can abbreviate [6.6] by letting A stand for the matrix of coefficients $\begin{pmatrix} a_{11} & a_{12} \\ a_{21} & a_{22} \end{pmatrix}$, X stand for the column matrix of unknowns $\begin{pmatrix} x_1 \\ x_2 \end{pmatrix}$, and B stand for the column matrix of constant terms $\begin{pmatrix} b_1 \\ b_2 \end{pmatrix}$. Then [6.6] can be written symbolically as

$$AX = B. \qquad [6.8]$$

The question arises as to whether the system of equations [6.5] can be solved by matrix operations on [6.6]. Suppose we could find a matrix by which we could multiply the members of [6.6], on the left, and obtain an equation of the form

$$\begin{pmatrix} x_1 \\ x_2 \end{pmatrix} = \begin{pmatrix} c_1 \\ c_2 \end{pmatrix}.$$

Then $x_1 = c_1$ and $x_2 = c_2$ would be a solution of [6.5].

To illustrate, consider the system of equations

$$\begin{aligned} 2x_1 + x_2 &= 3 \\ 5x_1 + 3x_2 &= 7 \end{aligned} \qquad [6.9]$$

The corresponding matrix equation is

$$\begin{pmatrix} 2 & 1 \\ 5 & 3 \end{pmatrix} \begin{pmatrix} x_1 \\ x_2 \end{pmatrix} = \begin{pmatrix} 3 \\ 7 \end{pmatrix} \qquad [6.10]$$

Now multiply both members of [6.10] on the left by the matrix $\begin{pmatrix} 3 & -1 \\ -5 & 2 \end{pmatrix}$. (Where this matrix comes from will be explained later.) Using the fact that multiplication of matrices is associative, we obtain

$$\left\{\begin{pmatrix} 3 & -1 \\ -5 & 2 \end{pmatrix} \begin{pmatrix} 2 & 1 \\ 5 & 3 \end{pmatrix}\right\} \begin{pmatrix} x_1 \\ x_2 \end{pmatrix} = \begin{pmatrix} 3 & -1 \\ -5 & 2 \end{pmatrix} \begin{pmatrix} 3 \\ 7 \end{pmatrix}$$

Carrying out the indicated matrix multiplication, we have

$$\begin{pmatrix} 1 & 0 \\ 0 & 1 \end{pmatrix} \begin{pmatrix} x_1 \\ x_2 \end{pmatrix} = \begin{pmatrix} 2 \\ -1 \end{pmatrix}$$

$$\begin{pmatrix} x_1 \\ x_2 \end{pmatrix} = \begin{pmatrix} 2 \\ -1 \end{pmatrix}.$$

So, $x_1 = 2$, $x_2 = -1$ is a solution of [6.9].

An analysis of the work done above shows that a crucial point is the existence of the matrix $\begin{pmatrix} 3 & -1 \\ -5 & 2 \end{pmatrix}$, which has the property that when we multiply the matrix $\begin{pmatrix} 2 & 1 \\ 5 & 3 \end{pmatrix}$ by it, the matrix $\begin{pmatrix} 1 & 0 \\ 0 & 1 \end{pmatrix}$ is obtained. The latter, called the

unit matrix, is a multiplicative identity for any 2×2 square matrix. When the product of two matrices A and B, taken in either order AB or BA, is the unit matrix, each of the pair is called the **inverse** of the other. Thus, the matrix $\begin{pmatrix} 3 & -1 \\ -5 & 2 \end{pmatrix}$ is the inverse of $\begin{pmatrix} 2 & 1 \\ 5 & 3 \end{pmatrix}$, and conversely. It can be proved that if A and B are square matrices and AB is the unit matrix, then BA is the unit matrix also.

Hence, this method of solving systems of linear equations depends upon finding inverses of matrices. There has been no hint as to how the matrix $\begin{pmatrix} 3 & -1 \\ -5 & 2 \end{pmatrix}$, which turned out to be the inverse of $\begin{pmatrix} 2 & 1 \\ 5 & 3 \end{pmatrix}$, was obtained. One can set about obtaining the inverse of the general second-order square matrix $A = \begin{pmatrix} a_{11} & a_{12} \\ a_{21} & a_{22} \end{pmatrix}$ by letting $\begin{pmatrix} x_{11} & x_{12} \\ x_{21} & x_{22} \end{pmatrix}$ denote the unknown inverse and considering the equation

$$\begin{pmatrix} x_{11} & x_{12} \\ x_{21} & x_{22} \end{pmatrix} \begin{pmatrix} a_{11} & a_{12} \\ a_{21} & a_{22} \end{pmatrix} = \begin{pmatrix} 1 & 0 \\ 0 & 1 \end{pmatrix}$$

Carrying out the indicated multiplication and equating elements in corresponding positions in the matrices constituting the left and right members of the equation, we are led to four equations in the four unknowns x_{11}, x_{12}, x_{21}, x_{22}. These equations can be solved, and the result is the matrix

$$\begin{pmatrix} \dfrac{a_{22}}{a_{11}a_{22} - a_{21}a_{12}} & \dfrac{-a_{12}}{a_{11}a_{22} - a_{21}a_{12}} \\[2ex] \dfrac{-a_{21}}{a_{11}a_{22} - a_{21}a_{12}} & \dfrac{a_{11}}{a_{11}a_{22} - a_{21}a_{12}} \end{pmatrix} \qquad [6.11]$$

if $a_{11}a_{22} - a_{21}a_{12} \neq 0$. We denote this matrix by A^{-1}. It is easy to check that $A^{-1}A = AA^{-1} =$ unit matrix.

We can write A^{-1} as

$$A^{-1} = \begin{pmatrix} \dfrac{a_{22}}{|A|} & \dfrac{-a_{12}}{|A|} \\[2ex] \dfrac{-a_{21}}{|A|} & \dfrac{a_{11}}{|A|} \end{pmatrix} \quad \text{where } |A| = a_{11}a_{22} - a_{21}a_{12}. \qquad [6.12]$$

Thus, [6.11] can be used as a formula for obtaining the inverse of any 2×2 matrix, providing the number $a_{11}a_{22} - a_{21}a_{12}$ is *not* zero.

Larger systems of equations in which we have the same number of unknowns as equations may be treated in the same manner as in our discussion of two equations in two unknowns. For example, the system of equations

$$\begin{aligned} a_{11}x_1 + a_{12}x_2 + a_{13}x_3 &= b_1 \\ a_{21}x_1 + a_{22}x_2 + a_{23}x_3 &= b_2 \\ a_{31}x_1 + a_{32}x_2 + a_{33}x_3 &= b_3 \end{aligned}$$

may be represented by the matrix equation

$$AX = B,$$

where

$$A = \begin{pmatrix} a_{11} & a_{12} & a_{13} \\ a_{21} & a_{22} & a_{23} \\ a_{31} & a_{32} & a_{33} \end{pmatrix}, \qquad X = \begin{pmatrix} x_1 \\ x_2 \\ x_3 \end{pmatrix}, \qquad B = \begin{pmatrix} b_1 \\ b_2 \\ b_3 \end{pmatrix}$$

Then the problem is to find the inverse of the matrix A, which in this case is a 3×3 matrix. This is considerably more difficult than in the 2×2 case, and we cannot go into it in this book.

The more equations and unknowns we have in a system of linear equations, and consequently the larger the matrix of coefficients, the more difficult is the task of finding inverses. Indeed, the process of computing inverses of matrices is a subject of active current research. The advent of high-speed electronic computers has heightened interest in this problem for two reasons. For one thing, the existence of these machines makes possible methods of computing inverses that would not be feasible otherwise. Also, many problems solvable by the use of computers must be reduced to a problem of solving systems of linear equations before the machine can handle them. In practice, the systems of equations may consist of many equations in many unknowns, more than a hundred equations in the same number of unknowns, for example.

Thus, the study of systems of linear equations and the role of matrices in their solution is an important subject in mathematics and its applications.

EXERCISES

Express each of the systems of linear equations in Exercises 1 through 8 as a single matrix equation.

1. $\begin{aligned} 2x_1 + 4x_2 &= 5 \\ x_1 - 5x_2 &= -3 \end{aligned}$

2. $\begin{aligned} 3x_1 - 2x_2 &= -1 \\ 2x_1 + x_2 &= 5 \end{aligned}$

3. $\begin{aligned} 3x - 2y &= 7 \\ 2x + 4y &= -2 \end{aligned}$

4. $\begin{aligned} 5x + 3y &= 2 \\ 2x - 4y &= 6 \end{aligned}$

5. $\begin{aligned} 3x_1 - 2x_2 + x_3 &= -1 \\ 2x_1 + x_2 - 3x_3 &= 2 \\ 4x_1 - 2x_2 + x_3 &= -3 \end{aligned}$

6. $\begin{aligned} x_1 + 2x_2 + x_3 &= 0 \\ 3x_1 - 5x_2 + 6x_3 &= -1 \\ 5x_1 + 7x_2 - 3x_3 &= 7 \end{aligned}$

7. $\begin{aligned} 6x - 4y + 3z &= 5 \\ 3x + 8y - 2z &= 4 \\ 7x - 4y + 5z &= 9 \end{aligned}$

8. $\begin{aligned} 5x + 7y - 3z &= -5 \\ 2x - 6y - 9z &= 8 \\ 6x + 2y - z &= -3 \end{aligned}$

Compute the inverse of each of the matrices in Exercises 9 through 16.

9. $\begin{pmatrix} 2 & 1 \\ 3 & 2 \end{pmatrix}$

10. $\begin{pmatrix} 3 & 2 \\ 2 & 1 \end{pmatrix}$

11. $\begin{pmatrix} 3 & 5 \\ 2 & 4 \end{pmatrix}$ **12.** $\begin{pmatrix} 3 & 3 \\ 2 & 3 \end{pmatrix}$

13. $\begin{pmatrix} 1 & -1 \\ 2 & 3 \end{pmatrix}$ **14.** $\begin{pmatrix} 2 & 1 \\ -3 & 1 \end{pmatrix}$

15. $\begin{pmatrix} 5 & -2 \\ 3 & 0 \end{pmatrix}$ **16.** $\begin{pmatrix} 4 & 5 \\ -2 & -1 \end{pmatrix}$

Write each of the systems of equations in Exercises 17 through 22 in matrix form, multiply by the inverse of the coefficient matrix, and obtain a solution of the original system.

17. $\begin{aligned} 5x_1 + 2x_2 &= 4 \\ 7x_1 + 3x_2 &= 5 \end{aligned}$ **18.** $\begin{aligned} 4x_1 + x_2 &= -1 \\ 7x_1 + 2x_2 &= -1 \end{aligned}$

19. $\begin{aligned} 3x + 5y &= -5 \\ 2x + 4y &= -2 \end{aligned}$ **20.** $\begin{aligned} 5x + 2y &= 3 \\ 3x + 2y &= 5 \end{aligned}$

21. $\begin{aligned} 4x - 3y &= 3 \\ 3x - 5y &= 7 \end{aligned}$ **22.** $\begin{aligned} 2x - y &= -2 \\ 3x + 4y &= 3 \end{aligned}$

23. Verify that $\begin{pmatrix} 3 & 2 & 6 \\ 1 & 1 & 2 \\ 2 & 2 & 5 \end{pmatrix}$ is the inverse of $\begin{pmatrix} 1 & 2 & -2 \\ -1 & 3 & 0 \\ 0 & -2 & 1 \end{pmatrix}$.

24. Carry out the steps indicated in the text to derive the inverse of $\begin{pmatrix} a_{11} & a_{12} \\ a_{21} & a_{22} \end{pmatrix}$ as given in [6.11].

25. Verify that the matrix given in [6.11] really is the inverse of $\begin{pmatrix} a_{11} & a_{12} \\ a_{21} & a_{22} \end{pmatrix}$, by carrying out the two required multiplications.

6.4 Determinants of Second-Order Matrices

A square matrix has associated with it a number called the **determinant** of the matrix. The determinant of the second-order matrix $\begin{pmatrix} a_{11} & a_{12} \\ a_{21} & a_{22} \end{pmatrix}$ is defined to be the number $a_{11}a_{22} - a_{21}a_{12}$. (We encountered this number in the preceding section in connection with inverses of matrices.) The determinant of a matrix is denoted by bordering the array of numbers by vertical lines. Thus,

$$\begin{vmatrix} a_{11} & a_{12} \\ a_{21} & a_{22} \end{vmatrix} = a_{11}a_{22} - a_{21}a_{12}, \qquad \begin{vmatrix} 3 & 5 \\ 2 & 4 \end{vmatrix} = 3 \cdot 4 - 2 \cdot 5 = 2$$

The determinant of a second-order matrix can be easily remembered by reference to the diagram:

$$\begin{vmatrix} a_{11} & a_{12} \\ a_{21} & a_{22} \end{vmatrix} = a_{11}a_{22} - a_{21}a_{12} \qquad [6.13]$$

where the first term in the determinant is the product of the elements indicated by the downward sloping arrow and the second term is the negative of the product of the elements indicated by the upward sloping arrow.

The determinant of a matrix should not be confused with the matrix itself. The former is a single number, whereas the latter is an array of numbers. Many different matrices may have the same determinant. For example,

$$\begin{vmatrix} 5 & 3 \\ 2 & 4 \end{vmatrix} = 14 \quad \text{and} \quad \begin{vmatrix} 2 & 4 \\ -1 & 5 \end{vmatrix} = 14$$

The pair of linear equations

$$\begin{aligned} a_{11}x + a_{12}y &= b_1 \\ a_{21}x + a_{22}y &= b_2 \end{aligned} \qquad [6.14]$$

can be solved by the method of Section 5.3 if $a_{11}a_{22} - a_{21}a_{12} \neq 0$, and the solution is given by

$$x = \frac{b_1a_{22} - b_2a_{12}}{a_{11}a_{22} - a_{21}a_{12}} \qquad y = \frac{a_{11}b_2 - a_{21}b_1}{a_{11}a_{22} - a_{21}a_{12}}.$$

Notice that this result can be expressed in terms of determinants as follows:

$$x = \frac{\begin{vmatrix} b_1 & a_{12} \\ b_2 & a_{22} \end{vmatrix}}{\begin{vmatrix} a_{11} & a_{12} \\ a_{21} & a_{22} \end{vmatrix}} \qquad y = \frac{\begin{vmatrix} a_{11} & b_1 \\ a_{21} & b_2 \end{vmatrix}}{\begin{vmatrix} a_{11} & a_{12} \\ a_{21} & a_{22} \end{vmatrix}} \qquad [6.15]$$

Notice that in each case *the denominator is the determinant of the matrix whose elements are the coefficients of the unknowns, and the determinant in each numerator is obtained from that in the denominator by replacing the coefficients of the unknown for which we are solving by the constant terms of the equations.* This rule applies only if the equations are in form [6.14] with the unknowns on the left and the constants on the right.

Example

Solve by determinants

$$\begin{aligned} 3x + 4y - 4 &= 0 \\ 2x + 5y + 7 &= 0 \end{aligned}$$

SOLUTION: Rewrite the equations as

$$\begin{aligned} 3x + 4y &= 4 \\ 2x + 5y &= -7 \end{aligned}$$

Then

$$x = \frac{\begin{vmatrix} 4 & 4 \\ -7 & 5 \end{vmatrix}}{\begin{vmatrix} 3 & 4 \\ 2 & 5 \end{vmatrix}} = \frac{20 + 28}{15 - 8} = \frac{48}{7}$$

$$y = \frac{\begin{vmatrix} 3 & 4 \\ 2 & -7 \end{vmatrix}}{\begin{vmatrix} 3 & 4 \\ 2 & 5 \end{vmatrix}} = \frac{-21-8}{7} = -\frac{29}{7}$$

As usual, these results may be checked by substitution.

EXERCISES

Solve the following pairs of equations by determinants:

1. $3x - 2y = 1$, $2x + y = 10$

2. $2x + 3y = -5$, $x + 6y = 2$

3. $3x + 2y = 4$, $4x - 3y = 11$

4. $2x - 5y = 2$, $4x + 3y = -7$

5. $x + 5y = 7$, $4x + 3y = -6$

6. $5x - 2y = 3$, $2x + 3y = 5$

7. $4m - 3n = 6$, $3m + 2n = -7$

8. $3u - 2v = 4$, $2u + 3v = -3$

9. $3x + 2y - 4 = 0$, $2x + 5y + 3 = 0$

10. $7x - 2y + 5 = 0$, $8x + 3y - 8 = 0$

11. $5x + 3y + 1 = 0$, $2x - 4y - 5 = 0$

12. $4x - 3y + 2 = 0$, $3x - 2y - 6 = 0$

13. $\frac{x}{2} + \frac{y}{3} = \frac{5}{6}$, $\frac{x}{4} - \frac{y}{2} = \frac{3}{2}$

14. $\frac{x}{2} - \frac{y}{3} - \frac{5}{6} = 0$, $\frac{x}{4} + \frac{y}{6} + \frac{2}{3} = 0$

15. $\frac{x+y}{3} = \frac{2x-5}{2}$, $\frac{x-2y}{4} = \frac{y+5}{3}$

16. $2(x - y) = 5(y + 2)$, $3x - 2y = \frac{1}{2}(x - 3)$

17. $2x - 5y = \frac{2}{3}(y + 5)$, $\frac{2}{5}x - 2y = \frac{1}{2}(x - 5)$

18. $\frac{3}{x} + \frac{5}{y} = 3$, $\frac{2}{x} - \frac{4}{y} = -5$

19. $\frac{5}{x} - \frac{2}{y} = -4$, $\frac{2}{x} - \frac{6}{y} = 3$

Hint: First solve for $1/x$ and $1/y$.

20. $mx + ny = s$, $px + qy = t$

21. $y = m_1x + b_1$, $y = m_2x + b_2$

22. Solve equations [6.14] of Section 6.4 by elimination, to obtain the results listed in [6.15].

6.5 Determinants of Third-Order Matrices

For ease of writing, we change our notation here and represent the general third-order matrix as follows:

$$M = \begin{pmatrix} a_1 & b_1 & c_1 \\ a_2 & b_2 & c_2 \\ a_3 & b_3 & c_3 \end{pmatrix} \qquad [6.16]$$

Notice that the single subscript indicates the row in which the element occurs, and the letter indicates the column.

The **determinant** of the matrix [6.16] is defined by

$$\begin{vmatrix} a_1 & b_1 & c_1 \\ a_2 & b_2 & c_2 \\ a_3 & b_3 & c_3 \end{vmatrix} = a_1b_2c_3 + a_2b_3c_1 + a_3b_1c_2 - a_1b_3c_2 - a_2b_1c_3 - a_3b_2c_1 \quad [6.17]$$

Observe that in each term of the determinant, each *row* of the matrix is represented exactly once, since each of the numbers 1, 2, and 3 occurs as a subscript; each *column* of the matrix is represented exactly once, since each of the letters a, b, and c occurs. Indeed, the determinant of the matrix M consists of the result of combining by addition and subtraction all terms that can be obtained by forming the products of three elements of M, each product containing as a factor an element from each row and an element from each column. The rule governing which terms should be added and which subtracted is too complicated to be given at this point. A method of computing determinants of third-order matrices will be given in the next section, and thus it is not necessary to memorize [6.17].

The reader should reexamine the definition of the determinant of a second-order matrix in the light of the remarks in the preceding paragraph. With obvious alterations, these remarks apply to the determinant of a square matrix of any order.

6.6 Minors and Cofactors

If in matrix M given in [6.16] of Section 6.5 we suppress the row and the column in which a_1 lies and form the determinant of the second-order matrix of the elements remaining, we get $\begin{vmatrix} b_2 & c_2 \\ b_3 & c_3 \end{vmatrix}$. This determinant is called the **minor** of a_1. Similarly, $\begin{vmatrix} b_1 & c_1 \\ b_3 & c_3 \end{vmatrix}$ is the minor or a_2, $\begin{vmatrix} a_1 & c_1 \\ a_3 & c_3 \end{vmatrix}$ is the minor of b_2, etc.

Now consider the checkerboard pattern

$$\begin{pmatrix} + & - & + \\ - & + & - \\ + & - & + \end{pmatrix}$$

This pattern associates with each element of a third-order matrix a plus sign or a minus sign according to its position in the array. Thus, associated with the element a_1 of M is a plus sign, with the element a_2 a minus sign, etc. Elements with which our checkerboard pattern associates a *plus* sign are said to occupy even positions, or to be **even-position** elements, while those with which the checkerboard pattern associates a *minus* sign are called **odd-position** elements. An alternative definition of even and odd position is as follows: If the sum of the row and the column numbers in which an element lies is *even*, the element is called an *even-position* element; if the sum of the row and column numbers in which an element lies is *odd*, the element is called an *odd-position* element. The reader should convince himself that the two definitions of even and odd position are equivalent.

Now we are prepared to define a cofactor. *The **cofactor** of an element of a matrix is the minor of that element or the negative of the minor, according as the element is an even-position element or an odd-position element.* The cofactor of a_1 in the matrix M is $\begin{vmatrix} b_2 & c_2 \\ b_3 & c_3 \end{vmatrix}$, the cofactor of a_2 is $-\begin{vmatrix} b_1 & c_1 \\ b_3 & c_3 \end{vmatrix}$, etc.

As a further illustration consider the matrix

$$\begin{pmatrix} 2 & 1 & -3 \\ 4 & 5 & 3 \\ -7 & -2 & 6 \end{pmatrix}$$

The cofactor of the element 2 is $\begin{vmatrix} 5 & 3 \\ -2 & 6 \end{vmatrix}$, the cofactor of the element 4 is $-\begin{vmatrix} 1 & -3 \\ -2 & 6 \end{vmatrix}$, the cofactor of the element -7 is $\begin{vmatrix} 1 & -3 \\ 5 & 3 \end{vmatrix}$, etc.

As a matter of notation, in referring to the matrix M we shall denote the cofactor of a_1 by A_1, of a_2 by A_2, of b_1 by B_1, etc.

6.7 Some Properties of Third-Order Matrices

The following theorem can be used to compute the determinant of a third-order matrix. The theorem is true for all square matrices, but we shall indicate the proof only for those of order 3.

▶ THEOREM 1. *If each element of a row (or column) of a square matrix is multiplied by its own cofactor, the sum of the resulting products is equal to the determinant of the matrix.*

In the notation adopted for cofactors, this theorem says with regard to the matrix M that

$$\begin{aligned} a_1A_1 + b_1B_1 + c_1C_1 &= a_2A_2 + b_2B_2 + c_2C_2 \\ &= a_3A_3 + b_3B_3 + c_3C_3 \\ &= a_1A_1 + a_2A_2 + a_3A_3 \\ &= b_1B_1 + b_2B_2 + b_3B_3 \\ &= c_1C_1 + c_2C_2 + c_3C_3 \\ &= \text{the determinant of } M \end{aligned}$$

Let us compute $a_1A_1 + b_1B_1 + c_1C_1$. By definition,

$$A_1 = \begin{vmatrix} b_2 & c_2 \\ b_3 & c_3 \end{vmatrix} = b_2c_3 - b_3c_2 \qquad B_1 = -\begin{vmatrix} a_2 & c_2 \\ a_3 & c_3 \end{vmatrix} = -(a_2c_3 - a_3c_2)$$

$$C_1 = \begin{vmatrix} a_2 & b_2 \\ a_3 & b_3 \end{vmatrix} = a_2b_3 - a_3b_2$$

Substituting these values of A_1, B_1, and C_1, we obtain

$$\begin{aligned} a_1A_1 + b_1B_1 + c_1C_1 &= a_1(b_2c_3 - b_3c_2) - b_1(a_2c_3 - a_3c_2) + c_1(a_2b_3 - a_3b_2) \\ &= a_1b_2c_3 - a_1b_3c_2 - a_2b_1c_3 + a_3b_1c_2 + a_2b_3c_1 - a_3b_2c_1 \end{aligned}$$

Comparing this last result with [6.17], we see that it is indeed the determinant of the matrix M.

This verifies the theorem for the elements of the first row. The complete proof consists of a similar verification for all rows and columns.

Let us use this theorem to compute the determinant of the matrix

$$\begin{pmatrix} 2 & 1 & -3 \\ 4 & 5 & 3 \\ -3 & -2 & 6 \end{pmatrix}.$$

Using the elements of the third column and multiplying each by its own cofactor, we have

$$\begin{aligned} \begin{vmatrix} 2 & 1 & -3 \\ 4 & 5 & 3 \\ -3 & -2 & 6 \end{vmatrix} &= (-3)\begin{vmatrix} 4 & 5 \\ -3 & -2 \end{vmatrix} + 3(-1)\begin{vmatrix} 2 & 1 \\ -3 & -2 \end{vmatrix} + 6\begin{vmatrix} 2 & 1 \\ 4 & 5 \end{vmatrix} \\ &= -3(-8 + 15) - 3(-4 + 3) + 6(10 - 4) \\ &= -21 + 3 + 36 = 18 \end{aligned}$$

Another important property of matrices is stated in the following theorem.

▶ THEOREM 2. *Consider two rows (or two columns) of a square matrix. If each element in one row (or column) is multiplied by the cofactor of the corresponding element of the other row (or column), the sum of the resulting products is zero.*

In the notation introduced in Section 6.6, the theorem says that for the matrix M the following relations are true:

$$a_1A_2 + b_1B_2 + c_1C_2 = 0 \text{ (and five more relations like this one)}$$
$$a_1B_1 + a_2B_2 + a_3B_3 = 0 \text{ (and five more relations like this one)}$$

A proof of this theorem for third-order matrices consists of verifying by actual computation that the twelve relations covered by the theorem are true. We shall do one as a sample. Consider the sum of the products of the elements of the *second* column by the cofactors of the corresponding elements of the *third* column. We have

$$b_1C_1 + b_2C_2 + b_3C_3 = b_1\begin{vmatrix} a_2 & b_2 \\ a_3 & b_3 \end{vmatrix} + b_2(-1)\begin{vmatrix} a_1 & b_1 \\ a_3 & b_3 \end{vmatrix} + b_3\begin{vmatrix} a_1 & b_1 \\ a_2 & b_2 \end{vmatrix}$$

$$= b_1(a_2b_3 - a_3b_2) - b_2(a_1b_3 - a_3b_1) + b_3(a_1b_2 - a_2b_1)$$

$$= a_2b_1b_3 - a_3b_1b_2 - a_1b_2b_3 + a_3b_1b_2 + a_1b_2b_3 - a_2b_1b_3 = 0$$

Although our indicated proof is limited to third-order matrices, Theorem 2, as in the case of Theorem 1, is true for square matrices of any order. There are ways of dealing with the general case that are better than the primitive ones used here, but these more sophisticated methods require more space to develop than we can afford.

As a numerical illustration, consider the matrix

$$\begin{pmatrix} 3 & 2 & -4 \\ 1 & -2 & -3 \\ -2 & 7 & 5 \end{pmatrix}$$

Form the sum of the products of the elements of the third row by the cofactors of the corresponding elements of the first row. We get

$$-2\begin{vmatrix} -2 & -3 \\ 7 & 5 \end{vmatrix} + 7(-1)\begin{vmatrix} 1 & -3 \\ -2 & 5 \end{vmatrix} + 5\begin{vmatrix} 1 & -2 \\ -2 & 7 \end{vmatrix}$$

$$= -2(-10 + 21) - 7(5 - 6) + 5(7 - 4)$$

$$= -22 + 7 + 15 = 0$$

EXERCISES

1. For the matrix $\begin{pmatrix} 1 & 2 & -3 \\ 3 & -2 & 5 \\ -4 & -5 & 4 \end{pmatrix}$:

(a) Find the minors of the elements of the first column.
(b) Find the cofactors of the elements of the first column.
(c) Find the cofactors of the elements of the second row.
(d) Find the cofactors of the elements of the third row.

2. For the matrix $\begin{pmatrix} 2 & -1 & 1 \\ -3 & 3 & -2 \\ -5 & 4 & -4 \end{pmatrix}$:

(a) List the *even-position* elements of the matrix and the *odd-position* elements of the matrix.
(b) Find the minors of the elements of the second column.
(c) Find the cofactors of the elements of the second column.
(d) Find the cofactors of the elements of the first row.

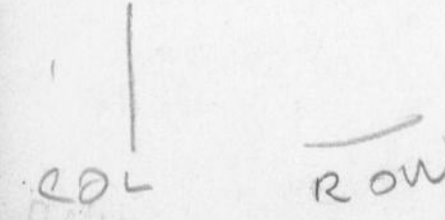

3. Verify Theorem 1 for the elements of the second row of a third-order matrix.

4. Verify Theorem 1 for the elements of the first column of a third-order matrix.

5. Verify Theorem 2 for the elements of the first column and the cofactors of the elements of the second column of a third-order matrix.

6. Verify Theorem 2 for the elements of the third row and the cofactors of the elements of the first row of a third-order matrix.

7. Find the determinant of the matrix

$$\begin{pmatrix} 2 & 4 & -1 \\ 3 & -3 & -5 \\ -2 & 1 & -4 \end{pmatrix}$$

by Theorem 1, using the elements of the first row; also using the elements of the third column.

8. Apply Theorem 1 to find the determinant of the matrix

$$\begin{pmatrix} 1 & 5 & 2 \\ -2 & 1 & 4 \\ -4 & 3 & 6 \end{pmatrix}$$

using the elements of the third row; also using the elements of the second column.

9. Find the value of each of the following determinants:

$$\begin{vmatrix} -2 & 1 & 3 \\ 3 & -1 & 2 \\ 4 & -2 & 3 \end{vmatrix}, \quad \begin{vmatrix} 4 & -2 & 1 \\ 0 & 3 & -5 \\ -3 & 1 & 2 \end{vmatrix}, \quad \begin{vmatrix} 3 & -1 & 0 \\ -2 & 4 & 7 \\ 5 & 2 & -3 \end{vmatrix}$$

10. Find the value of each of the following determinants:

$$\begin{vmatrix} 5 & 0 & 2 \\ 3 & -2 & 4 \\ -1 & 6 & 3 \end{vmatrix}, \quad \begin{vmatrix} 4 & 3 & -2 \\ 5 & -1 & 6 \\ -7 & 2 & -3 \end{vmatrix}, \quad \begin{vmatrix} -1 & 6 & 4 \\ -5 & 7 & 1 \\ 2 & 3 & 5 \end{vmatrix}$$

11. For the matrix $\begin{pmatrix} -5 & 3 & -2 \\ 2 & 4 & -1 \\ 1 & 5 & 2 \end{pmatrix}$:

(a) Verify by computation that the sum of the products of the elements of the second column by the cofactors of the corresponding elements of the first column is zero.

(b) Verify by computation that the sum of the products of the elements of the second row by the cofactors of the corresponding elements of the third row is zero.

12. For the matrix $\begin{pmatrix} 6 & 2 & 1 \\ -3 & -5 & 2 \\ 7 & -3 & 2 \end{pmatrix}$:

(a) Verify by computation that the sum of the products of the elements of the third column by the cofactors of the corresponding elements of the second column is zero.

(b) Verify by computation that the sum of the products of the elements of the first row by the cofactors of the corresponding elements of the third row is zero.

13. Show that the determinant $\begin{vmatrix} 0 & a & b \\ -a & 0 & c \\ -b & -c & 0 \end{vmatrix}$ is zero.

14. Show that the determinant $\begin{vmatrix} 1 & 1 & 1 \\ x & b & a \\ x^2 & b^2 & a^2 \end{vmatrix}$ is $(a-b)(x-a)(x-b)$.

15. The matrix $\begin{pmatrix} 1/3 & 2/3 & 2/3 \\ 2/3 & 1/3 & -2/3 \\ -2/3 & 2/3 & -1/3 \end{pmatrix}$ has a property known as *orthogonality*. Verify that each element is equal to its own cofactor.

16. The square array embodied in the matrix $\begin{pmatrix} 8 & 1 & 6 \\ 3 & 5 & 7 \\ 4 & 9 & 2 \end{pmatrix}$ is an example of a *magic square*. Show that the sum of the cofactors of the elements of any row is equal to the sum of the cofactors of the elements of any other row.

6.8 Applications to Systems of Linear Equations

Consider the set of equations

$$\begin{aligned} 3x + 2y + 5z &= 7 \\ 2x - 3y - 2z &= -3 \\ x + 2y + 3z &= 5 \end{aligned} \qquad [6.18]$$

This system of equations was solved in Section 5.4 by obtaining an equivalent echelon form system. This method is the most satisfactory one for solving particular numerical examples. However, we now demonstrate another method of solution based on Theorem 2 of Section 6.7, which has considerable theoretical interest. The process utilizes cofactors from the matrix

$$\begin{pmatrix} 3 & 2 & 5 \\ 2 & -3 & -2 \\ 1 & 2 & 3 \end{pmatrix}$$

whose elements are the coefficients of the unknowns in the system of equation [6.18]. We compute the cofactors of the elements in the first column (these elements are the coefficients of x in the three equations). These cofactors are -5, 4, and 11. In the system [6.18], we multiply the first equation by -5, the second equation by 4, and the third equation by 11, and add the three new equations. A remarkable thing happens; both y and z disappear. The demonstration follows:

$$\begin{array}{r|l} -5 & 3x + 2y + 5z = 7 \\ 4 & 2x - 3y - 2z = -3 \\ 11 & x + 2y + 3z = 5 \end{array}$$

$$(-15 + 8 + 11)x + (-10 - 12 + 22)y + (-25 - 8 + 33)z = -35 - 12 + 55$$

$$4x + 0 \cdot y + 0 \cdot z = 8, \qquad x = 2$$

Let us see why this process works as it does. Observe that the coefficient of y in the final equation is the sum of the three products formed by multiplying each element in the *second column* of the matrix of coefficients by the cofactor of the corresponding elements in the *first column.* Thus, by Theorem 2, this number is necessarily *zero.* Likewise, the coefficient of z is the sum of the three products formed by multiplying each element in the *third column* by the cofactor of the corresponding element in the *first column*, and hence, also by Theorem 2, the result is zero.

It is also worthy of note that the coefficient of x, the unknown remaining, is the sum of the products obtained by multiplying each element in the first column by its *own cofactor*, and hence, by Theorem 1, the result (4 in this case) is the determinant of the matrix.

Similarly, if the cofactors of the elements in the second column are used as multipliers in the manner just illustrated, in the resulting equation the coefficients of both x and z are zero, and we get $y = 3$. Likewise, use of the cofactors of the elements in the third column results in the elimination of both x and y, and we obtain $z = -1$.

Thus, if the system [6.18] has a solution, it must be $x = 2$, $y = 3$, $z = -1$. It was checked in Section 5.4 that this triple of numbers actually is a solution.

The simultaneous elimination process described in this section, when applied to a set of equations, shows that if the original equations have a common solution, then this solution is also a solution of the new equations derived from the original set. If the new equations have the form $x = k_1$, $y = k_2$, $z = k_3$, where k_1, k_2, and k_3 are numbers, then the fact is established that *if* the original set has a solution, then (k_1, k_2, k_3) is that solution. To show, conversely, that (k_1, k_2, k_3) *is* a solution of the original system, one can substitute these numbers directly in the original equations or else make an argument regarding equivalent systems similar to that of Section 5.3. That is, one can prove that each of the original equations can be obtained by adding multiples of the new equations, which would complete the proof that the two systems are equivalent.

EXERCISES

Solve the following sets of equations by simultaneous elimination of two unknowns:

1. $x + y + z = 2$
   $2x + 3y + 2z = 3$
   $3x + 2y - z = 3$

2. $3x - y - 3z = -10$
   $5x - 2y - 2z = -11$
   $x - y - z = -4$

3. $x + 2y - z = 1$
   $-x + 2y + 2z = 2$
   $2x - 3y - 3z = -3$

4. $x + 2y + 3z = -2$
   $2x + 3y + z = 5$
   $4x + 3y + 5z = 1$

5. $5x + 2y - z = 3$
   $x - 3y + 2z = -4$
   $2x - 4y + 5z = -1$

6. $3x - 2y + z = -1$
   $x + 3y - 2z = -2$
   $2x - y + 3z = 4$

7. $x - y + 2z = -3$
   $2x + 5y - 3z = -2$
   $2x + 2y + z = -5$

8. $2x - 3y + 4z = -2$
   $x + 2y - 3z = 3$
   $3x - 4y + 2z = 7$

9. $3x - 7y + 8z = 4$
   $2x + 5y - z = 5$
   $5x - 2y + 3z = -4$

10. $7x + 2y - 5z = 4$
    $3x - 3y + 5z = 7$
    $4x + 5y - 2z = 11$

11. $7u - 3v + 7w = -2$
    $5u - 6v - 3w = 3$
    $4u - 5v - 4w = 10$

12. $3u - 2v + 5w = 7$
    $2u + 5v - 7w = -3$
    $u - 5v + 6w = 5$

6.9 Cramer's Rule

We now apply the method of Section 6.8 to obtain a rule for getting the solution of a system of linear equations. This rule is chiefly important for its theoretical applications. Consider the set of linear equations

$$\begin{aligned} a_1x + b_1y + c_1z &= d_1 \\ a_2x + b_2y + c_2z &= d_2 \\ a_3x + b_3y + c_3z &= d_3 \end{aligned} \qquad [6.19]$$

The matrix of the coefficients is

$$M = \begin{pmatrix} a_1 & b_1 & c_1 \\ a_2 & b_2 & c_2 \\ a_3 & b_3 & c_3 \end{pmatrix}$$

As agreed upon previously, we denote the cofactor of a_1 by A_1, of a_2 by A_2, and so forth.

Now multiply the first equation by A_1, the second by A_2, the third by A_3, and add the three new equations.

$$\begin{array}{r} a_1A_1x + b_1A_1y + c_1A_1z = d_1A_1 \\ a_2A_2x + b_2A_2y + c_2A_2z = d_2A_2 \\ a_3A_3x + b_3A_3y + c_3A_3z = d_3A_3 \\ \hline \end{array}$$

$$(a_1A_1 + a_2A_2 + a_3A_3)x + (b_1A_1 + b_2A_2 + b_3A_3)y + (c_1A_1 + c_2A_2 + c_3A_3)z = d_1A_1 + d_2A_2 + d_3A_3$$

By Theorem 1 the coefficient of x is the determinant of M, which we shall denote by $|M|$, and by Theorem 2 the coefficients of both y and z are zero. Thus, we have

$$|M| \cdot x = d_1A_1 + d_2A_2 + d_3A_3 \qquad [6.20]$$

Now if in the matrix M the elements in the first column were replaced by the constant terms d_1, d_2, and d_3, we should obtain the matrix

$$\begin{pmatrix} d_1 & b_1 & c_1 \\ d_2 & b_2 & c_2 \\ d_3 & b_3 & c_3 \end{pmatrix} \qquad [6.21]$$

It can be seen by inspection that the cofactors of the elements in the first column of [6.21] are exactly the same as the cofactors of the elements of the first column of M, namely, A_1, A_2, and A_3. Thus, by Theorem 1, the right member of [6.20] is the determinant of the matrix [6.21].

Hence, if $|M| \neq 0$, we may solve [6.20] for x and get

$$x = \frac{\begin{vmatrix} d_1 & b_1 & c_1 \\ d_2 & b_2 & c_2 \\ d_3 & b_3 & c_3 \end{vmatrix}}{|M|} \qquad [6.22]$$

Eliminating x and z from [6.19] by using the cofactors of the elements of the second column of M as multipliers, we obtain

$$y = \frac{\begin{vmatrix} a_1 & d_1 & c_1 \\ a_2 & d_2 & c_2 \\ a_3 & d_3 & c_3 \end{vmatrix}}{|M|} \qquad [6.23]$$

Use of the cofactors of the elements of the third column of M as multipliers eliminates x and y from [6.19] and yields

$$z = \frac{\begin{vmatrix} a_1 & b_1 & d_1 \\ a_2 & b_2 & d_2 \\ a_3 & b_3 & d_3 \end{vmatrix}}{|M|} \qquad [6.24]$$

Direct substitution in [6.19] of the values for x, y, and z given by [6.22], [6.23], and [6.24] would verify that these values constitute a solution of [6.19]. Thus, [6.22], [6.23], and [6.24] may be regarded as formulas for the *unique* solution of a set of three linear equations in three unknowns, provided the determinant of the coefficient matrix is not zero.

The formulas may be remembered in exactly the same manner as was suggested for the case of two equations in two unknowns. We repeat that statement here. For the value of each unknown, *the denominator is the determinant of the matrix of coefficients, while the numerator is obtained from this determinant on replacing by the constant terms the coefficients of the unknown.* The fact embodied in this statement is called **Cramer's rule** after the Swiss mathematician Gabriel Cramer.

As the student might by now suspect from the two instances studied, Cramer's rule applies to a system of any number of linear equations in the same number of unknowns, provided the determinant of the coefficient matrix is not zero. Systems of more than three equations give rise to matrices of higher order than the third. The definitions of minors and cofactors given in Section 6.6 for third-order matrices generalize to square matrices of any order. Also, as noted previously, Theorems 1 and 2 of Section 6.7 hold for square matrices of any order. The derivation of Cramer's rule for the general system of linear equations with the same number of unknowns as equations follows the same pattern as exhibited in this section for three equations in three unknowns.

In point of fact, Cramer's rule is of more theoretical importance than of practical value as a method of solving specific systems of equations. If the number of equations in the system is at all large, evaluating the determinants is a formidable task. Even for systems of few equations, some form of elimination is generally easier than using Cramer's rule.

In the case of many practical problems, the answer depends upon the solution of systems of linear equations containing many equations in many unknowns—systems containing more than a hundred equations may arise. High-speed electronic computers have made feasible the solution of such large systems.

In cases of systems in which the determinant of the coefficient matrix is zero, or of systems in which the number of unknowns is different from the number of equations, Cramer's rule does not apply.

EXERCISES

Apply Cramer's rule to obtain solutions of the sets of linear equations in Exercises 1 through 16.

1.
$$\begin{aligned} x - y + z &= 5 \\ 2x + 3y - 4z &= -2 \\ 3x - 2y + 7z &= 1 \end{aligned}$$

2.
$$\begin{aligned} 3x + 2y + z &= 4 \\ 2x - 3y - z &= -4 \\ 4x - y + 3z &= 2 \end{aligned}$$

3.
$$\begin{aligned} 4x - 3y + 5z &= 1 \\ 2x + 5y + 2z &= -5 \\ 3x - 7y + 4z &= 2 \end{aligned}$$

4.
$$\begin{aligned} 2x + 5y - 6z &= -3 \\ 3x - 2y + 4z &= -5 \\ 5x - 4y + z &= 7 \end{aligned}$$

5. $3x - 2y + 7z + 4 = 0$
   $2x + 5y - 3z - 3 = 0$
   $4x + 3y - 6z + 5 = 0$

6. $x + 6y - 2z - 4 = 0$
   $3x - 2y + 5z + 5 = 0$
   $4x - 3y + z - 3 = 0$

7. $x - 2y - 3z = 3$
   $x + y - 2z = 7$
   $2x - 3y - 2z = 0$

8. $x + y + 2z = 10$
   $5x + 3y - z = 1$
   $3x - y - 3z = -3$

9. $3x + 2y - 4 = 0$
   $x - 3z + 7 = 0$
   $2y + z - 1 = 0$

10. $2x + 3z = 0$
   $x + 5y - 2 = 0$
   $y + 3z + 4 = 0$

11. $3x_1 - 7x_2 + 5x_3 = 3$
   $4x_1 + 3x_2 - x_3 = -5$
   $6x_1 - 4x_2 + 5x_3 = -7$

12. $5x_1 + 3x_2 - 4x_3 = -6$
   $7x_1 - 5x_2 + 8x_3 = 10$
   $4x_1 - 7x_2 + 9x_3 = -4$

13. $4r - 7s + 2t = 4$
   $3r + 6s - 7t = 5$
   $2r + 4s - 2t = -3$

14. $3r + 6s - 5t = -1$
   $r - 2s + 4t = 4$
   $5r + 6s - 7t = -5$

15. $ax + by + cz = k$
   $bx + ay + dz = k$
   $cx + dy + az = k$

16. $l_1x + m_1y + n_1z = X$
   $l_2x + m_2y + n_2z = Y$
   $l_3x + m_3y + n_3z = Z$

17. Solve by Cramer's rule exercises in Section 6.8 as selected by the instructor.

18. Derive [6.23] in detail.

19. Derive [6.24] in detail.

6.10 Other Properties of Determinants of Matrices

Matrices have many applications other than in the solution of systems of linear equations. Since we have been concerned mainly with their connection with linear equations, many of the properties of matrices considered here have involved their determinants. In this section we study additional properties of matrices which also relate to their determinants.

The properties of matrices stated in this section are possessed by square matrices of any order, although we indicate proofs only for the third-order case. It is understood that all the matrices considered in this section are square.

▶ PROPERTY 1. *If the rows and columns of a matrix be interchanged, the value of the determinant of the matrix is unaltered.*

PROOF: To prove this property, compute the values of

$$\begin{vmatrix} a_1 & b_1 & c_1 \\ a_2 & b_2 & c_2 \\ a_3 & b_3 & c_3 \end{vmatrix} \quad \text{and} \quad \begin{vmatrix} a_1 & a_2 & a_3 \\ b_1 & b_2 & b_3 \\ c_1 & c_2 & c_3 \end{vmatrix}$$

and observe that they are the same.

▶ PROPERTY 2. *The sign of the determinant of a matrix is changed by interchanging two rows or two columns of the matrix.*

PROOF: First observe that this statement is certainly true for second-order matrices, for

$$\begin{vmatrix} a_2 & b_2 \\ a_1 & b_1 \end{vmatrix} = a_2b_1 - a_1b_2 = -\begin{vmatrix} a_1 & b_1 \\ a_2 & b_2 \end{vmatrix}$$

$$\begin{vmatrix} b_1 & a_1 \\ b_2 & a_2 \end{vmatrix} = a_2b_1 - a_1b_2 = -\begin{vmatrix} a_1 & b_1 \\ a_2 & b_2 \end{vmatrix}$$

Now consider a third-order matrix in which two rows or two columns have been interchanged. Use the elements of the row or column not affected by the interchange, to compute the determinant of the matrix. The cofactors of the elements of this row or column, being determinants of second-order matrices, will be exactly the negatives of their values before the interchange. Hence, the value of the determinant of the third-order matrix after the interchange will be exactly the negative of its original value.

▶ PROPERTY 3. *If a matrix has two of its rows or two of its columns identical, the value of the determinant of the matrix is zero.*

PROOF: By Property 2, interchanging the two identical rows or columns of the matrix would change the sign of the determinant. But if two rows or columns are identical, interchanging them would not affect the determinant at all. The only number whose sign can be changed without changing the number is zero.

▶ PROPERTY 4. *If a matrix has a row or column consisting entirely of zeros, the determinant of the matrix is zero.*

PROOF: Use of the elements of the row or column consisting entirely of zeros to compute the determinant of the matrix shows immediately that the determinant is zero.

▶ PROPERTY 5. *Multiplying each element of a row (or column) of a matrix by the same number multiplies the determinant of the matrix by that number.*

PROOF: Suppose the elements of a row or column of a matrix have been multiplied by a number k. Using this row or column to find the value of the determinant of the matrix, we see that each term in the value of the determinant of the new matrix is k times the corresponding term in the determinant of the original. Hence the determinant of the new matrix is k times the determinant of the original.

▶ PROPERTY 6. *If to the elements of any row (or column) of a matrix are added constant multiples of the corresponding elements of another row (or column), the value of the determinant of the matrix is unchanged.*

PROOF: We indicate the proof by showing that the following is a true statement:

$$\begin{vmatrix} a_1 & b_1 & c_1 \\ a_2 & b_2 & c_2 \\ a_3 & b_3 & c_3 \end{vmatrix} = \begin{vmatrix} a_1 + kb_1 & b_1 & c_1 \\ a_2 + kb_2 & b_2 & c_2 \\ a_3 + kb_3 & b_3 & c_3 \end{vmatrix}$$

The left member is the determinant of the matrix M and the right member is the determinant of the matrix obtained from M by multiplying the elements in the second column by k and adding the results to the corresponding elements in the first column. To show that the determinant of the new matrix has the same value as that of the original, we compute the determinant of the new matrix, using the elements of the first column, and obtain

$$\begin{aligned} (a_1 + kb_1)A_1 + (a_2 + kb_2)A_2 + (a_3 + kb_3)A_3 &= \\ a_1A_1 + a_2A_2 + a_3A_3 + k(b_1A_1 + b_2A_2 + b_3A_3) &= \\ |M| + k \cdot 0 = |M| \end{aligned}$$

by Theorems 1 and 2.

It is clear from this sample that the method of proof would be applicable whatever combination of rows (or columns) were involved.

Property 6 is useful for changing a matrix without changing the value of its determinant. The following example illustrates this use.

Example 1

Use Property 6 to aid in computing the determinant of the matrix

$$\begin{pmatrix} 3 & -1 & 3 \\ -7 & 5 & 7 \\ 4 & -3 & 2 \end{pmatrix}$$

SOLUTION: We perform the following operations in order:

1. Multiply elements of second column by 2 and add to corresponding elements of first column (in order to obtain 1 in the upper left-hand corner).
2. Multiply elements of first row by -3 and add to corresponding elements of second row.
3. Multiply elements of first row by 2 and add to corresponding elements of third row.

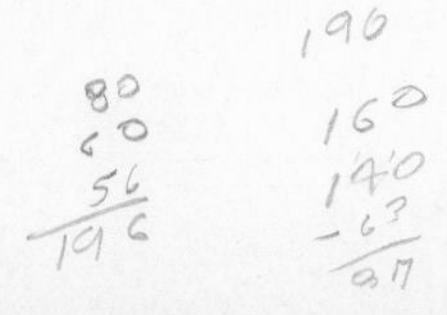

Since these operations do not change the value of the determinant, we have

$$\begin{vmatrix} 3 & -1 & 3 \\ -7 & 5 & 7 \\ 4 & -3 & 2 \end{vmatrix} = \begin{vmatrix} 1 & -1 & 3 \\ 3 & 5 & 7 \\ -2 & -3 & 2 \end{vmatrix} = \begin{vmatrix} 1 & -1 & 3 \\ 0 & 8 & -2 \\ -2 & -3 & 2 \end{vmatrix} = \begin{vmatrix} 1 & -1 & 3 \\ 0 & 8 & -2 \\ 0 & -5 & 8 \end{vmatrix}$$

It is very easy to find the value of the last determinant by using the first column. It is

$$1 \cdot \begin{vmatrix} 8 & -2 \\ -5 & 8 \end{vmatrix} = 64 - 10 = 54$$

An example of an application of Properties 5 and 6 follows.

Example 2

Show without expanding that $a - b$ is a factor of the determinant

$$\begin{vmatrix} 1 & a & bc \\ 1 & b & ac \\ 1 & c & ab \end{vmatrix}$$

SOLUTION: By Property 6 we may multiply the elements of the second row by -1 and add to the corresponding elements of the first row to obtain

$$\begin{vmatrix} 0 & a-b & c(b-a) \\ 1 & b & ac \\ 1 & c & ab \end{vmatrix}$$

Now, by Property 5, we may "factor out" $a - b$ from the first row and obtain

$$(a-b)\begin{vmatrix} 0 & 1 & -c \\ 1 & b & ac \\ 1 & c & ab \end{vmatrix}$$

EXERCISES

Illustrate Properties 1, 2, 5, and 6 in the case of each of the matrices in Exercises 1 through 6.

1. $\begin{pmatrix} 2 & 3 & 4 \\ 5 & 6 & -2 \\ -1 & -3 & -4 \end{pmatrix}$ **2.** $\begin{pmatrix} 1 & -2 & 5 \\ 4 & -3 & 7 \\ -2 & 5 & 3 \end{pmatrix}$ **3.** $\begin{pmatrix} 2 & -3 & 4 \\ -1 & 6 & 7 \\ -4 & 1 & 3 \end{pmatrix}$

4. $\begin{pmatrix} 3 & -2 & 4 \\ 5 & 7 & -5 \\ 2 & -4 & 3 \end{pmatrix}$ **5.** $\begin{pmatrix} 1 & 2 & 5 \\ 3 & -4 & 6 \\ -2 & -5 & -3 \end{pmatrix}$ **6.** $\begin{pmatrix} 5 & -2 & -4 \\ -3 & -1 & 2 \\ 5 & 7 & 6 \end{pmatrix}$

Without expanding, state why each of the determinants in Exercises 7 through 10 is zero.

7. $\begin{vmatrix} 1 & 0 & 6 \\ 3 & 0 & -2 \\ -5 & 0 & 8 \end{vmatrix}$ 8. $\begin{vmatrix} 1 & 3 & -5 \\ 2 & 1 & 8 \\ 1 & 3 & -5 \end{vmatrix}$

9. $\begin{vmatrix} 2 & 4 & 5 \\ -3 & -6 & 4 \\ 1 & 2 & -3 \end{vmatrix}$ 10. $\begin{vmatrix} 4 & -3 & 9 \\ 10 & -5 & -6 \\ 0 & 0 & 0 \end{vmatrix}$

Apply Property 6 to make zero any two of the elements of some row or column of each of the matrices in Exercises 11 through 14. Then find the value of the determinant by the elements of this row or column.

11. $\begin{pmatrix} 9 & -6 & 2 \\ 3 & -2 & -1 \\ 5 & 7 & 3 \end{pmatrix}$ 12. $\begin{pmatrix} -2 & 1 & 4 \\ -3 & -2 & 6 \\ 5 & 3 & -8 \end{pmatrix}$

13. $\begin{pmatrix} 6 & -3 & 5 \\ -3 & 2 & 9 \\ 5 & -2 & -7 \end{pmatrix}$ 14. $\begin{pmatrix} 8 & -5 & 1 \\ 4 & -3 & -1 \\ 3 & 7 & 6 \end{pmatrix}$

Show without expanding that $a - b$, $a - c$, and $b - c$ are factors of each of the following determinants:

15. $\begin{vmatrix} 1 & a & a^2 \\ 1 & b & b^2 \\ 1 & c & c^2 \end{vmatrix}$ 16. $\begin{vmatrix} 1 & 1 & 1 \\ a & b & c \\ a^3 & b^3 & c^3 \end{vmatrix}$ 17. $\begin{vmatrix} 1 & 1 & 1 \\ a^2 & b^2 & c^2 \\ a^3 & b^3 & c^3 \end{vmatrix}$

18. Show without expanding that $x + y + z$ is a factor of

$$\begin{vmatrix} x & y & z \\ z & x & y \\ y & z & x \end{vmatrix}$$

Without expanding the determinants, prove each of the relations in Exercises 19, 20, and 21.

19. $\begin{vmatrix} 1 & b & (a+c) \\ 1 & a & (b+c) \\ 1 & c & (a+b) \end{vmatrix} = 0$ 20. $\begin{vmatrix} a_1 & a_3 & a_2 \\ kb_1 & kb_3 & kb_2 \\ c_1 & c_3 & c_2 \end{vmatrix} = -k \begin{vmatrix} a_1 & b_1 & c_1 \\ a_2 & b_2 & c_2 \\ a_3 & b_3 & c_3 \end{vmatrix}$

21. $\begin{vmatrix} x_1 & (y_1 + sx_1) & (z_1 - ty_1) \\ x_2 & (y_2 + sx_2) & (z_2 - ty_2) \\ x_3 & (y_3 + sx_3) & (z_3 - ty_3) \end{vmatrix} = \begin{vmatrix} x_1 & x_2 & x_3 \\ y_1 & y_2 & y_3 \\ z_1 & z_2 & z_3 \end{vmatrix}$

6.11 Matrices of Higher Order

While attention has been limited mainly to square matrices of the second and third orders, most of the development in this chapter is immediately generalizable to square matrices of any order. Minors and cofactors are defined as before (they would be determinants of matrices of an order lower by one than the original matrix). Theorems 1 and 2 of Section 6.7 and Properties 1 to 6 of Section 6.10 hold for square matrices of order n, where n is any positive integer. We shall assume without proof the truth of this statement.

In finding the value of a determinant of a matrix of higher order, it is particularly helpful to use Property 6 of Section 6.10 to get several zeros in a row or column before applying Theorem 1.

Example

Find the value of

$$\begin{vmatrix} 2 & -2 & 4 & -2 \\ -3 & 3 & -2 & 5 \\ 4 & 2 & 4 & 3 \\ 3 & -4 & 2 & -2 \end{vmatrix}$$

SOLUTION: We first apply Property 5 of Section 6.10 to "factor out" 2 from the elements of the first row in order to get 1 as an element in this row. We have

$$\begin{vmatrix} 2 & -2 & 4 & -2 \\ -3 & 3 & -2 & 5 \\ 4 & 2 & 4 & 3 \\ 3 & -4 & 2 & -2 \end{vmatrix} = 2 \begin{vmatrix} 1 & -1 & 2 & -1 \\ -3 & 3 & -2 & 5 \\ 4 & 2 & 4 & 3 \\ 3 & -4 & 2 & -2 \end{vmatrix}$$

In order to get three zeros in the first row on the right, we multiply the elements of the first column by 1, −2, and 1 in turn and add to the corresponding elements of the second, third, and fourth columns, respectively. The result is

$$2 \begin{vmatrix} 1 & 0 & 0 & 0 \\ -3 & 0 & 4 & 2 \\ 4 & 6 & -4 & 7 \\ 3 & -1 & -4 & 1 \end{vmatrix}$$

Expanding by the elements of the first row, since all elements except one in this row are zero, we have

$$2 \begin{vmatrix} 0 & 4 & 2 \\ 6 & -4 & 7 \\ -1 & -4 & 1 \end{vmatrix} = 2\left\{0 \begin{vmatrix} -4 & 7 \\ -4 & 1 \end{vmatrix} - 4 \begin{vmatrix} 6 & 7 \\ -1 & 1 \end{vmatrix} + 2 \begin{vmatrix} 6 & -4 \\ -1 & -4 \end{vmatrix}\right\}$$
$$= 2\{0 - 52 - 56\} = -216$$

As previously remarked, Cramer's rule applies in the case of any system of linear equations in which the number of unknowns is the same as the number of equations, provided the determinant of the coefficient matrix is not zero. However, in case this number is large, it is not practical to use Cramer's rule because of the difficulty of computing the values of the determinants involved.

EXERCISES

Find the value of each of the following determinants after first applying appropriate properties to make several elements zero in some row or some column.

1. $\begin{vmatrix} 1 & 2 & -3 \\ 2 & -5 & -4 \\ 3 & -1 & 2 \end{vmatrix}$

2. $\begin{vmatrix} 2 & 3 & 1 \\ -3 & -4 & 2 \\ -2 & 2 & -3 \end{vmatrix}$

3. $\begin{vmatrix} 2 & 1 & 3 & 2 \\ -3 & -2 & 2 & 5 \\ 4 & 3 & -1 & 2 \\ -2 & 4 & -4 & 3 \end{vmatrix}$

4. $\begin{vmatrix} -4 & 2 & 3 & -2 \\ 5 & -4 & 1 & 3 \\ 2 & -5 & 2 & 0 \\ 3 & 0 & -3 & 2 \end{vmatrix}$

5. $\begin{vmatrix} 3 & 0 & 2 & 0 \\ 4 & -2 & 3 & -2 \\ 2 & 5 & -4 & 0 \\ -4 & 3 & -3 & -5 \end{vmatrix}$

6. $\begin{vmatrix} 0 & -2 & -3 & 2 \\ 2 & 3 & 4 & -3 \\ 3 & 5 & 0 & -2 \\ -4 & 2 & -3 & 4 \end{vmatrix}$

7. $\begin{vmatrix} -4 & 2 & 3 & -5 \\ 2 & 0 & -2 & 4 \\ 3 & -4 & 5 & 2 \\ 2 & -3 & 0 & 4 \end{vmatrix}$

8. $\begin{vmatrix} 5 & 2 & 3 & -4 \\ -2 & 4 & 2 & 3 \\ 4 & 2 & -3 & -7 \\ 3 & 4 & 6 & -3 \end{vmatrix}$

9. Without expanding, prove

$$\begin{vmatrix} x_1 + y_1 & x_2 + y_2 & x_3 + y_3 \\ y_1 + z_1 & y_2 + z_2 & y_3 + z_3 \\ z_1 + x_1 & z_2 + x_2 & z_3 + x_3 \end{vmatrix} = 2 \begin{vmatrix} x_1 & y_1 & z_1 \\ x_2 & y_2 & z_2 \\ x_3 & y_3 & z_3 \end{vmatrix}$$

10. Show without expanding that a and b are roots of the quadratic equation

$$\begin{vmatrix} 1 & x & x^2 \\ 1 & a & a^2 \\ 1 & b & b^2 \end{vmatrix} = 0$$

Solve each of the following systems of equations by Cramer's rule.

11. $2x - 3y + z - w = -6$
$x + 2y - z = 8$
$3y + z + 3w = 0$
$3x - y + w = 0$

12. $x + z - 2w = 3$
$y + 2z - w = 2$
$2x + 3y - 2z = -1$
$x - y - 4w = 0$

13. $3x + 2y - 4w = 0$
$y - 2z + w = -1$
$2x + 3y = 1$
$x + 4z - 2w = 2$

14. $3x + 4y + z - 2w = 0$
$x + 2y - w = -3$
$2x - 3z + 2w = 2$
$3x + 2y - z = 0$

Mathematical Induction, the Binomial Theorem, and Sequences ◄ 7

7.1 Mathematical Induction

Mathematical induction is a method of proof. In explaining what it is, we want to emphasize at the outset that it is *not* the kind of "proof by induction" used in experimental sciences, whereby a general conclusion is reached by observing many specific cases. Mathematical induction is a particular kind of mathematical reasoning, and conclusions established by it are as valid as any in mathematics. The method is especially valuable in proving that certain formulas or statements in algebra are true for all positive integers. The method can best be explained by an example.

Example 1

Prove that the following formula for the sum of the first n positive odd integers is true for all positive integral values of n.

$$1 + 3 + 5 + \cdots + (2n - 1) = n^2. \qquad [7.1]$$

PROOF: The truth of formula [7.1] may be tested for particular values of n by direct substitution. For example, substituting 1 for n in both members of [7.1], we get

$$1 = 1^2,$$

which is clearly a true statement. Similarly, substituting 2 for n, we get

$$1 + 3 = 2^2,$$

which again is a true statement. We could continue in this manner, substituting for n successively the numbers 3, 4, 5, etc. But we could never prove by this process that the formula is true for *all* positive integers. For no matter how many values we might substitute for n, there would still remain some positive integers untried. Thus, it is impossible to prove formula [7.1] by direct verification for each positive integer.

What we do is to proceed as follows: Let k denote any value of n for which formula [7.1] is true. Thus, if k be substituted for n, the result, given below, is a true equation.

$$1 + 3 + 5 + \cdots + (2k - 1) = k^2. \qquad [7.2]$$

Now we wish to prove that if formula [7.1] is true for $n = k$, then it is also true for $n = k + 1$. In other words, starting with [7.2] as a hypothesis, we wish to show that the truth of

$$1 + 3 + 5 + \cdots + (2k + 1) = (k + 1)^2 \qquad [7.3]$$

follows, [7.3] being what [7.1] becomes when $n = k + 1$. When we have done this, we shall have shown that if [7.1] is true for any positive integral value of n, then it is also true for the next greater integral value.

To carry on with the proof, we observe that the left member of [7.3] differs from the left member of [7.2] only in having the additional term $(2k + 1)$. Hence we add $(2k + 1)$ to both sides of [7.2] and obtain

$$1 + 3 + 5 + \cdots + (2k - 1) + (2k + 1) = k^2 + (2k + 1),$$

which may be written

$$1 + 3 + 5 + \cdots + (2k - 1) + (2k + 1) = (k + 1)^2.$$

Thus [7.3] is shown to be true if [7.2] is true. That is, if formula [7.1] is true for any positive integer k, it is also true for the next greater integer $k + 1$. But we have verified that formula [7.1] is true for the integer 1. Hence, it is true for the next greater integer 2. But since it is true for 2, it is true for the next greater integer 3. Since it is true for 3, it is true for 4, etc. If one assumes that any positive integer n can be reached by starting with 1 and adding 1 sufficiently many times, it is clear that formula [7.1] is true for every positive integral value of n.

We see from this example that a proof by mathematical induction consists of two parts:

I. *A verification that the formula or theorem is true for the integer* 1.
II. *A demonstration that if the formula or theorem is true for any positive integer* k, *then it is true also for the next greater integer*, $k + 1$.

Proof by mathematical induction has been compared to the proof that it is possible to climb to every rung of a ladder by proving that

(a) the *first* rung can be reached;

(b) if *any* rung is reached, then the *next higher* rung can be reached.

A rigorous justification of the validity of proof by mathematical induction rests upon the following property of the positive integers, called the **principle of mathematical induction.**

If S is a set of positive integers that has the two properties

(i) *S contains* 1,

(ii) *S contains* $k+1$ *whenever it contains the positive integer* k,

then S contains all positive integers.

To see the application of this property, suppose that I and II have been carried out for a proposition. Then the set S of positive integers for which the proposition is true has properties (i) and (ii) and hence must contain all positive integers.

The property of the set of positive integers cited above can be shown to be equivalent to the following property, in the sense that either can replace the other in a defining set of axioms for the system of integers.

Every nonempty subset of the set of positive integers contains a least member.

Example 2

Prove that the following formula for the sum of the squares of the first n positive integers is true for all positive integral values of n.

$$1^2 + 2^2 + 3^2 + \cdots + n^2 = \tfrac{1}{6}n(n+1)(2n+1). \qquad [7.4]$$

PROOF: I. We verify that [7.4] is true for $n = 1$ by substituting 1 for n to get

$$1^2 = \tfrac{1}{6}(1)(2)(3),$$

which is clearly true.

II. We now assume that [7.4] is true for $n = k$. That is, we assume the truth of

$$1^2 + 2^2 + 3^2 + \cdots + k^2 = \tfrac{1}{6}k(k+1)(2k+1), \qquad [7.5]$$

and seek to show that this assumption leads to the conclusion that [7.4] is true also for $n = k+1$. To this end we add $(k+1)^2$ to both sides of [7.5]. This gives us

$$1^2 + 2^2 + 3^2 + \cdots + k^2 + (k+1)^2 = \tfrac{1}{6}k(k+1)(2k+1) + (k+1)^2. \qquad [7.6]$$

Now observe that the left member of [7.6] is what [7.4] becomes when n is equal to $k+1$. (To achieve just this result was the reason $(k+1)^2$ was added to both sides of [7.5].) Now we must show that the right member of [7.6] is what the right member of [7.4] becomes if n is replaced by $k+1$. Bringing the right member of [7.6] to a common denominator, factoring, and changing the form slightly, we obtain the following:

$$
\begin{aligned}
1^2 + 2^2 + 3^2 + \cdots + k^2 + (k+1)^2 &= \tfrac{1}{6}k(k+1)(2k+1) + \frac{6(k+1)^2}{6} \\
&= \tfrac{1}{6}(k+1)[k(2k+1) + 6(k+1)] \\
&= \tfrac{1}{6}(k+1)[2k^2 + 7k + 6] \\
&= \tfrac{1}{6}(k+1)(k+2)(2k+3) \\
&= \tfrac{1}{6}(k+1)[(k+1)+1][2(k+1)+1]
\end{aligned}
$$

A comparison of this final form with [7.4] shows that we have proved that [7.4] is true for $n = k + 1$ if it is true for $n = k$. Since we had previously verified the truth of [7.4] for $n = 1$, this completes the proof by mathematical induction.

Example 3

If $h > -1$, prove that $(1 + h)^n \geqq 1 + nh$ for all positive integral values of n.

PROOF: If $n = 1$, the inequality becomes $1 + h \geqq 1 + h$, which is certainly true.

Assume that the statement

$$(1 + h)^k \geqq 1 + kh$$

is true. Multiply both members of the inequality by the positive number $1 + h$ and obtain

$$
\begin{aligned}
(1 + h)^{k+1} &\geqq (1 + kh)(1 + h), \\
(1 + h)^{k+1} &\geqq 1 + (k + 1)h + kh^2.
\end{aligned}
$$

Since $1 + (k + 1)h + kh^2 \geqq 1 + (k + 1)h$, we have, by the transitive law,

$$(1 + h)^{k+1} \geqq 1 + (k + 1)h.$$

Thus, our proposition is true for $n = k + 1$ whenever it is true for $n = k$. This completes both parts of the proof by induction.

EXERCISES

Prove by mathematical induction that each of the formulas in Exercises 1 through 16 is true for all positive integral values of n.

1. $1 + 2 + 3 + \cdots + n = \frac{1}{2}n(n + 1)$

2. $2 + 4 + 6 + \cdots + 2n = n(n + 1)$

3. $3 + 6 + 9 + \cdots + 3n = \frac{3}{2}n(n + 1)$

4. $5 + 10 + 15 + \cdots + 5n = \frac{5}{2}n(n + 1)$

5. $1 + 4 + 7 + \cdots + (3n - 2) = \frac{1}{2}n(3n - 1)$

6. $1 + 3 + 3^2 + \cdots + 3^{n-1} = \frac{1}{2}(3^n - 1)$

7. $2^2 + 4^2 + 6^2 + \cdots + (2n)^2 = \frac{2}{3}n(n + 1)(2n + 1)$

8. $1^3 + 2^3 + 3^3 + \cdots + n^3 = \frac{1}{4}n^2(n+1)^2$

9. $1 \cdot 2 + 2 \cdot 3 + 3 \cdot 4 + \cdots + n(n+1) = \frac{1}{3}n(n+1)(n+2)$

10. $1^2 + 3^2 + 5^2 + 7^2 + \cdots + (2n-1)^2 = \frac{1}{3}n(2n+1)(2n-1)$

11. $2 + 2^2 + 2^3 + \cdots + 2^n = 2^{n+1} - 2$

12. $\dfrac{1}{1 \cdot 2} + \dfrac{1}{2 \cdot 3} + \dfrac{1}{3 \cdot 4} + \cdots + \dfrac{1}{n(n+1)} = \dfrac{n}{n+1}$

13. $2^3 + 4^3 + 6^3 + \cdots + (2n)^3 = 2n^2(n+1)^2$

14. $\dfrac{1}{1 \cdot 3} + \dfrac{1}{3 \cdot 5} + \dfrac{1}{5 \cdot 7} + \cdots + \dfrac{1}{(2n-1)(2n+1)} = \dfrac{n}{2n+1}$

15. $a + (a+d) + (a+2d) + \cdots + [a+(n-1)d] = \frac{1}{2}n[2a+(n-1)d]$

16. $a + ar + ar^2 + \cdots + ar^{n-1} = \dfrac{a(1-r^n)}{1-r}$

17. Prove that $a^n - b^n$ is divisible by $a - b$ for all positive integers n.

Hint: In part II of the proof observe that $a^{k+1} - b^{k+1}$ may be written

$$a^{k+1} - ab^k + ab^k - b^{k+1} \qquad \text{or} \qquad a(a^k - b^k) + b^k(a - b).$$

18. Prove that $a^{2n} - b^{2n}$ is divisible by $a + b$.

19. Prove that $a^{2n-1} + b^{2n-1}$ is divisible by $a + b$.

20. Prove that if $0 < a < b$, then $a^n < b^n$ for all positive integers n.

21. Prove that $3n \leqq 3^n$ for all positive integers n.

22. Prove that $2^n \geqq 1 + n$ for all positive integers n.

23. Prove that if n is any positive integer, $n^3 + 2n$ is divisible by 3.

24. Prove that $9^n - 8n - 1$ is divisible by 64 for all positive integers n.

7.2 The Binomial Theorem

The **binomial theorem** furnishes a method shorter than ordinary multiplication for expanding a positive integral power of a binomial, such as $(a+b)^n$. Before stating this famous theorem, let us first exhibit the expansions of the binomial $a + b$ to several specific powers.

$$\begin{aligned}
(a+b)^1 &= a + b \\
(a+b)^2 &= a^2 + 2ab + b^2 \\
(a+b)^3 &= a^3 + 3a^2b + 3ab^2 + b^3 \\
(a+b)^4 &= a^4 + 4a^3b + 6a^2b^2 + 4ab^3 + b^4 \\
(a+b)^5 &= a^5 + 5a^4b + 10a^3b^2 + 10a^2b^3 + 5ab^4 + b^5
\end{aligned}$$

These expansions can be verified by direct multiplication, and it is suggested that the reader carry out the verification.

Now let us write down certain facts about the expansion of $(a+b)^n$ that we observe to be true for these examples.

1. *The first term of the expansion is a^n, the last term is b^n, and there are $n+1$ terms altogether.*

2. *The symbol a occurs in each term after the first to a power less by 1 than in the preceding term. The symbol b enters to the first power in the second term and occurs in each term thereafter to a power greater by 1 than in the preceding term. Thus, in each term the sum of the exponents of a and b is exactly n.*

3. *The coefficient of the second term is n. From any given term, to get the coefficient of the succeeding term, multiply the coefficient of the given term by the exponent of a in that term and divide by the number of the given term.*

These three rules, which the student should verify to be true for the examples, actually constitute a statement of the binomial theorem for positive integral exponents. The theorem will be proved in Section 7.5. In the meantime we shall get some practice in its use. In the examples given, note the relative ease of expanding by the binomial theorem as compared with direct multiplication.

Example 1

Expand $(x+y)^6$ by the binomial theorem.

SOLUTION: Here we identify x with a, y with b, and 6 with n, and apply the rules stated above.

$$
\begin{aligned}
(x+y)^6 &= x^6 + 6x^5y + \frac{6 \cdot 5}{2} x^4y^2 + \frac{6 \cdot 5 \cdot 4}{2 \cdot 3} x^3y^3 \\
&\quad + \frac{6 \cdot 5 \cdot 4 \cdot 3}{2 \cdot 3 \cdot 4} x^2y^4 + \frac{6 \cdot 5 \cdot 4 \cdot 3 \cdot 2}{2 \cdot 3 \cdot 4 \cdot 5} xy^5 + y^6 \\
&= x^6 + 6x^5y + 15x^4y^2 + 20x^3y^3 + 15x^2y^4 + 6xy^5 + y^6
\end{aligned}
$$

In obtaining the coefficients by rule 3, the arithmetic of multiplying by the exponent of a and dividing by the number of the term should be done mentally in case the numbers involved are small enough to make this feasible. In Example 1, the operations to be performed in obtaining the successive coefficients are indicated in order to make clear the working of rule 3. In actual practice, however, for a simple example, this step would not be written down.

Example 2

Expand $(2x^2 - y)^8$ by the binomial theorem.

SOLUTION: We may write $(2x^2 - y)^8$ as $[2x^2 + (-y)]^8$ and identify $2x^2$ with a, $-y$ with b, and 8 with n. Moreover, it is clear that the signs of the terms in which $-y$ enters to even powers will be positive, and those in which $-y$ enters to odd powers will be negative. Thus, the sign of the first term and alternate terms thereafter will be positive and the others negative. Applying the binomial theorem, we get

18
5
90

$$\begin{aligned}(2x^2 - y)^8 &= (2x^2)^8 - 8(2x^2)^7y + 28(2x^2)^6y^2 - 56(2x^2)^5y^3 + 70(2x^2)^4y^4 \\ &\quad - 56(2x^2)^3y^5 + 28(2x^2)^2y^6 - 8(2x^2)y^7 + y^8 \\ &= 256x^{16} - 1024x^{14}y + 1792x^{12}y^2 - 1792x^{10}y^3 + 1120x^8y^4 \\ &\quad - 448x^6y^5 + 112x^4y^6 - 16x^2y^7 + y^8\end{aligned}$$

Notice that in the first step, $2x^2$ is kept in parentheses and its powers are merely indicated. This is a good practice to follow, as confusion and errors would be likely to result if the arithmetic of raising $2x^2$ to the various powers were carried out in this first step.

7 13 19 25 31

EXERCISES

Expand the following by the binomial theorem and simplify the results:

1. $(x + y)^4$ **2.** $(2x - y)^4$ **3.** $(x^2 + 3y)^4$
4. $(a + x)^5$ **5.** $(x - y)^5$ **6.** $(p - q)^7$
7. $(m + n)^7$ **8.** $(x^2 + y)^4$ **9.** $(a^2 - b)^4$
10. $(x + 2y)^5$ **11.** $(3x - y)^5$ **12.** $(2x - y^2)^5$
13. $(x^3 + 2y)^5$ **14.** $(2x^2 + \frac{1}{2}y)^6$ **15.** $\left(3x^2 - \frac{1}{3x}\right)^6$
16. $\left(2a - \frac{1}{2b}\right)^6$ **17.** $\left(x^3 + \frac{2}{x^2}\right)^6$ **18.** $\left(x^2 + \frac{3}{y^2}\right)^7$
19. $\left(3a^2 - \frac{1}{b}\right)^7$ **20.** $(x^4 + \frac{1}{2}y^2)^7$ **21.** $(2x + \sqrt{x})^7$
22. $\left(x - \frac{1}{\sqrt{x}}\right)^8$ **23.** $\left(a^2 + \frac{1}{2\sqrt{a}}\right)^8$ **24.** $\left(x^2 - \frac{1}{2x}\right)^9$
25. $\left(2x^3 - \frac{1}{2\sqrt{x}}\right)^9$ **26.** $\left(a + \frac{1}{a}\right)^{10}$ **27.** $\left(2a + \frac{1}{2\sqrt{a}}\right)^{10}$

Obtain the first four terms in the expansions of Exercises 28 through 36 and simplify.

28. $(a + b)^{15}$ **29.** $(x - y)^{20}$ **30.** $\left(x - \frac{1}{x}\right)^{12}$
31. $\left(x^2 + \frac{1}{2x}\right)^{16}$ **32.** $(x^3 + \frac{1}{2}y^2)^{14}$ **33.** $\left(a^3 - \frac{1}{3a}\right)^{11}$
34. $(pq - r)^{18}$ **35.** $\left(\sqrt{x} + \frac{1}{2\sqrt{x}}\right)^{16}$ **36.** $\left(\frac{1}{a^2} + 2b\right)^{20}$

7.3 The General Term in the Binomial Expansion

In subsequent work with the binomial theorem we shall find it convenient to employ the symbol ***n*!**, read ***n* factorial.** This symbol $n!$ is defined for positive integral values of n to be the product of all the integers from 1 to n inclusive.

Thus, $3! = 1 \cdot 2 \cdot 3 = 6$, $4! = 1 \cdot 2 \cdot 3 \cdot 4 = 24$, etc. Also, the symbol $0!$ is defined to have the value 1.

Example 1

Find the value of $\dfrac{8!}{3!4!}$.

SOLUTION: $\dfrac{8!}{3!4!} = \dfrac{1 \cdot 2 \cdot 3 \cdot 4 \cdot 5 \cdot 6 \cdot 7 \cdot 8}{1 \cdot 2 \cdot 3 \cdot 1 \cdot 2 \cdot 3 \cdot 4} = 280.$

Example 2

Prove that $\dfrac{12 \cdot 11 \cdot 10 \cdot 9}{4!} = \dfrac{12!}{4!8!}$.

SOLUTION: Multiplying the numerator and denominator of the left member by 8!, we have

$$\frac{12 \cdot 11 \cdot 10 \cdot 9}{4!} = \frac{12 \cdot 11 \cdot 10 \cdot 9 \cdot 8!}{4!8!} = \frac{12!}{4!8!}.$$

The binomial theorem for positive integral exponents can be stated as the following formula:

$$\begin{aligned}(a+b)^n = a^n + na^{n-1}b + \frac{n(n-1)}{2!}a^{n-2}b^2 + \cdots \\ + \frac{n(n-1)(n-2)\cdots(n-r+2)}{(r-1)!}a^{n-r+1}b^{r-1} \\ + \frac{n(n-1)(n-2)\cdots(n-r+1)}{r!}a^{n-r}b^r + \cdots + b^n. \end{aligned} \quad [7.7]$$

Formula [7.7], which we shall refer to as the **binomial formula,** embodies the same mathematical truth as rules 1 through 3 of Section 7.2. It can be used as a formula to expand a power of a binomial, although the rules are more convenient for this purpose.

The expression

$$\frac{n(n-1)(n-2)\cdots(n-r+2)}{(r-1)!}a^{n-r+1}b^{r-1} \quad [7.8]$$

is the **rth** term in the expansion of $(a+b)^n$.

The expression

$$\frac{n(n-1)(n-2)\cdots(n-r+1)}{r!}a^{n-r}b^r \quad [7.9]$$

is the $(r+1)$st term.

A comparison of the coefficients in the terms given by [7.8] and [7.9] shows that the second can be obtained from the first by rule 3 of Section 7.2.

Either of the expressions [7.8] or [7.9] can be called the **general term.** Each term after the first in the expansion of $(a+b)^n$ can be obtained by assigning to r in either [7.8] or [7.9] the proper value. Thus, in case some particular term in the expansion of a power of a binomial is desired, [7.8] or [7.9] furnishes an easy means of obtaining it. An aid to remembering the formula for the rth term is the following set of rules, in the statement of which $r - 1$ is a sort of *key number*.

1. The exponent of b is $r - 1$.
2. The exponent of a is the difference between n and $r - 1$.
3. The denominator of the coefficient is $(r - 1)!$, and the numerator of the coefficient is the product of $r - 1$ consecutive integers, the largest of which is n.

Example 3

Write the sixth term in the expansion of $\left(x^2 + \frac{y}{2}\right)^{15}$.

SOLUTION: Here the key number $r - 1$ is 5. Hence, the sixth term is

$$\frac{15 \cdot 14 \cdot 13 \cdot 12 \cdot 11}{5!} (x^2)^{10} \left(\frac{y}{2}\right)^5 = \frac{3003}{32} x^{20} y^5.$$

Example 4

Write the term containing b^{21} in the expansion of $(2a - b^3)^{50}$.

SOLUTION: The term containing b^{21}, or $(b^3)^7$, is the eighth, and since $-b^3$ is raised to an odd power, the sign is negative. The key number is 7. Applying our rules, we get

$$-\frac{50 \cdot 49 \cdot 48 \cdot 47 \cdot 46 \cdot 45 \cdot 44}{7!} (2a)^{43} (b^3)^7.$$

Another form for the $(r + 1)$st term is obtained by multiplying both numerator and denominator of [7.9] by $(n - r)!$. The result is

$$\frac{n!}{r!(n - r)!} a^{n-r} b^r. \qquad [7.10]$$

The coefficients in the expansion of $(a + b)^n$ as n is assigned successively the values 0, 1, 2, · · · form the interesting triangular array displayed below.

$$\begin{array}{c}
1 \\
1 \quad 1 \\
1 \quad 2 \quad 1 \\
1 \quad 3 \quad 3 \quad 1 \\
1 \quad 4 \quad 6 \quad 4 \quad 1 \\
1 \quad 5 \quad 10 \quad 10 \quad 5 \quad 1 \\
1 \quad 6 \quad 15 \quad 20 \quad 15 \quad 6 \quad 1 \\
\cdot \quad \cdot \quad \cdot \quad \cdot \quad \cdot \quad \cdot \quad \cdot \quad \cdot
\end{array}$$

This array, which can be extended indefinitely, is called **Pascal's triangle.** Notice that it is bordered by 1's, and that each interior number is the sum of the two closest numbers in the line above.

7.4 The Binomial Theorem for Exponents Other than Positive Integers†

If we start expanding $(a+b)^n$ by the binomial theorem in case n is a real number not a positive integer or zero, we get a series of infinitely many terms. In certain cases, the conditions for which we cannot at this stage state precisely, the first few terms furnish an adequate approximation for the power of the binomial. In the exercises we give, it will be understood that the proper conditions are satisfied.

Example

Use the binomial theorem to approximate the value of $\sqrt[3]{10}$ to two decimal places.

SOLUTION: $\sqrt[3]{10}$ may be written as $(8+2)^{1/3}$. Expanding $(8+2)^{1/3}$ by the binomial theorem, we get

$$(8+2)^{1/3} = (8)^{1/3} + \tfrac{1}{3}(8)^{-2/3}(2) - \frac{\frac{1}{3}\cdot\frac{2}{3}}{2}(8)^{-5/3}(2)^2 + \frac{\frac{1}{3}\cdot\frac{2}{3}\cdot\frac{5}{3}}{2\cdot 3}(8)^{-8/3}(2)^3 + \cdots$$

$$= 2 + \frac{1}{6} - \frac{1}{72} + \frac{5}{2592} + \cdots$$

$$= 2 + 0.1667 - 0.014 + 0.002 + \cdots$$

$$= 2.15$$

7.5 Proof of the Binomial Theorem for Positive Integral Exponents

Using form [7.10] for the $(r+1)$st term and the corresponding form for the rth term, the binomial formula may be written as follows:

$$(a+b)^n = a^n + na^{n-1}b + \cdots + \frac{n!}{(r-1)!(n-r+1)!}a^{n-r+1}b^{r-1} + \frac{n!}{r!(n-r)!}a^{n-r}b^r + \cdots + b^n. \quad [7.11]$$

We shall prove by mathematical induction that this formula is true for all positive integral values of n.

† If the reader is not familiar with fractional and negative exponents, this section and the corresponding exercises at the end of Section 7.5 may be omitted until these types of exponents are studied in Chapter 8.

First observe that when $n = 1$ each side of [7.11] becomes $a + b$. Hence [7.11] is true for $n = 1$.

Next we assume that [7.11] is true for $n = k$ and prove on this assumption that it is true for $n = k + 1$. Thus, we assume the truth of

$$(a + b)^k = a^k + ka^{k-1}b + \cdots + \frac{k!}{(r-1)!(k-r+1)!}a^{k-r+1}b^{r-1} + \frac{k!}{r!(k-r)!}a^{k-r}b^r + \cdots + b^k. \quad [7.12]$$

Now multiply both sides of [7.12] by $a + b$. The left member becomes $(a + b)^{k+1}$. To see what the new right member is, we compute its $(r + 1)$st term. The $(r + 1)$st term of the new right member contains b^r, and consequently is the sum of a times the $(r + 1)$st term and b times the rth term of the right member of [7.12]. This sum is

$$\begin{aligned}\frac{k!}{r!(k-r)!}a^{k-r+1}b^r + \frac{k!}{(r-1)!(k-r+1)!}a^{k-r+1}b^r &= \left[\frac{k!}{r!(k-r)!} + \frac{k!}{(r-1)!(k-r+1)!}\right]a^{k-r+1}b^r \\ &= \frac{k![(k-r+1)+r]}{r!(k-r+1)!}a^{k-r+1}b^r \\ &= \frac{(k+1)!}{r!(k+1-r)!}a^{k+1-r}b^r\end{aligned}$$

This result we recognize as the $(r + 1)$st term in the expansion of $(a + b)^{k+1}$ as given by [7.11]. Thus, since the $(r + 1)$st term represents all terms, [7.11] is shown to be true for $k + 1$ if it is true for k. This completes the proof (by mathematical induction) of the binomial theorem for positive integral exponents.

Another proof of the binomial theorem will be given in Chapter 13.

EXERCISES

In Exercises 1 through 17, write the term indicated in the expansion of the power of the given binomial.

1. Fourth term of $(a + x)^{12}$
2. Fifth term of $(a + b)^{10}$
3. Sixth term of $(x - y)^{14}$
4. Seventh term of $(a - b)^{11}$
5. Twelfth term of $(a + x)^{18}$
6. Eighth term of $(x^2 - y^3)^{20}$
7. Tenth term of $(a^2 - 2b)^{15}$
8. Ninth term of $(a^3 + b^2)^{14}$
9. Eleventh term of $\left(p^2 - \frac{q}{2}\right)^{25}$
10. Sixteenth term of $(2x + y^2)^{40}$
11. Term containing y^7 of $(x + y)^{18}$
12. Term containing b^{10} of $(a - b)^{14}$

13. Term containing x^9 of $(x - y)^{12}$ **14.** Term containing b^8 of $(a - b^2)^{20}$
15. Term containing y^9 of $(x^2 + y^3)^{28}$ **16.** Middle term of $(x^2 - 2y)^{16}$
17. Middle term of $(x^3 - y)^{20}$

Obtain the first four terms in the expansions of the following:

18. $(a + x)^{-2}$ **19.** $(a - b)^{-1}$ **20.** $(a - b)^{1/2}$ **21.** $(x + y)^{2/3}$
22. $(x + 2)^{-1/3}$ **23.** $(a - 3)^{-2/3}$ **24.** $(a^3 + b)^{4/3}$ **25.** $(x^2 - y)^{3/2}$
26. $(a^2 - 2b)^{-1/2}$ **27.** $(a + 2b)^{-3/5}$ **28.** $(8a^3 + b)^{-1/3}$ **29.** $(4x^2 + y)^{-3/2}$

Compute to two decimal places by use of the binomial theorem in Exercises 30 through 41.

30. $(1.01)^8$ **31.** $(1.02)^{12}$ **32.** $(0.99)^7$ **33.** $(.98)^{10}$
34. $\sqrt{103}$ **35.** $\sqrt{23}$ **36.** $\sqrt[3]{62}$ **37.** $10^{2/3}$
38. $(1.03)^{-6}$ **39.** $(1.02)^{-7}$ **40.** $7^{-1/3}$ **41.** $8^{-1/2}$

7.6 Sequences and Progressions

Consider a succession of numbers

$$a_1, a_2, a_3, \cdots, a_n, \cdots \qquad [7.13]$$

arranged in order so that there is a first number, a second number, etc. There may or may not be a last number in the array. The first number, a_1, can be associated with the positive integer 1; the second number, a_2, can be associated with 2; and, in general, a_n can be associated with n if a_n occurs in the nth position. This correspondence is a *function* from a set of positive integers to the set of numbers represented by the a's. The domain of the function is the set of positive integers 1 to m if a_m is the last number occurring in [7.13]; the domain is the set of all positive integers if there is no last member. Such a function is called a **sequence,** and the a's are called the **terms** of the sequence. If a sequence has a last term, it is called a *finite* sequence; otherwise, it is called an *infinite* sequence. Frequently the unqualified word sequence is interpreted to mean infinite sequence.

As examples, consider the following:

$$2, 3, 5, 7, 11, \qquad [7.14]$$

$$2, 4, 6, 8, 10, \cdots \qquad [7.15]$$

In [7.14] we have defined a finite sequence, the terms of which consist of the first five prime integers, and [7.15] indicates an infinite sequence the terms of which are the positive even integers. In the case of [7.14], the correspondence is $1 \to 2$, $2 \to 3$, $3 \to 5$, $4 \to 7$, $5 \to 11$. In example [7.15], the correspondence can be given by the rule $f(n) = 2n$. In the case of sequences, however, notation such as a_n is used for the value of the nth term instead of $f(n)$. Thus, $a_n = 2n$ defines the sequence [7.15]. A sequence whose nth term is a_n is indicated by the symbol $\{a_n\}$.

Another way of defining a sequence is to state a value for the first term and a rule for obtaining the $(n + 1)$st term from the nth term. For example, let

$$a_1 = 1, \qquad a_{n+1} = a_n + \frac{1}{a_n}.$$

We can compute the values of successive terms of the sequence as follows:

$$a_1 = 1, \qquad a_2 = 1 + \frac{1}{1} = 2, \qquad a_3 = 2 + \frac{1}{2} = \frac{5}{2}, \qquad a_4 = \frac{5}{2} + \frac{1}{5/2} = \frac{29}{10}.$$

A particular type of sequence, which may be familiar to the reader, is an **arithmetic progression.** If we denote this sequence by $\{a_n\}$, it can be defined by

$$a_1 = a, \qquad a_{n+1} = a_n + d, \tag{7.16}$$

where a and d are constants. Thus, each term is obtained from the preceding term by adding a constant d, called the **common difference.**

Let us show by induction that

$$a_n = a + (n - 1)d. \tag{7.17}$$

Clearly, this formula is correct for $n = 1$. Assume that it is correct for $n = k$; that is, assume the truth of

$$a_k = a + (k - 1)d.$$

Then,

$$a_{k+1} = a_k + d = a + (k - 1)d + d = a + [(k + 1) - 1]d.$$

Hence, if the formula [7.17] holds for $n = k$, it is also correct for $n = k + 1$. Thus, by the principle of mathematical induction, it is true for all natural numbers n.

We next derive a formula for the sum S_n of n terms of an arithmetic progression:

$$S_n = a + (a + d) + (a + 2d) + \cdots + (a_n - d) + a_n. \tag{7.18}$$

Writing [7.18] with the terms on the right in reverse order, we obtain

$$S_n = a_n + (a_n - d) + (a_n - 2d) + \cdots + (a + d) + a. \tag{7.19}$$

Adding [7.18] and [7.19], we get

$$2S_n = (a + a_n) + (a + a_n) + (a + a_n) + \cdots + (a + a_n) + (a + a_n) = n(a + a_n)$$

$$\boxed{S_n = \frac{n}{2}(a + a_n).} \tag{7.20}$$

If in [7.20] the symbol a_n is replaced by its value from [7.17], we obtain another expression for S_n,

$$S_n = \frac{n}{2}[2a + (n-1)d]. \quad [7.21]$$

Formula [7.21] can be verified by mathematical induction, and the verification is one of the exercises at the end of this section. Here we have another example of the fact that mathematical induction can be used to prove a result, once the result has been discovered by another method.

The terms of an arithmetic progression between two given terms of the progression are called **arithmetic means** between the two given terms. In particular, if a, x, b are three consecutive terms in an arithmetic progression, x is called the **arithmetic mean** of a and b.

Another useful type of sequence is a **geometric progression,** which can be defined by

$$a_1 = a, \qquad a_{n+1} = a_n r. \quad [7.22]$$

Each term is obtained from the preceding term by multiplying it by a constant r, called the **common ratio.** It is easily proved by mathematical induction that

$$a_n = ar^{n-1}. \quad [7.23]$$

If we let

$$S_n = a + ar + \cdots + ar^{n-1}$$

then

$$rS_n = \qquad ar + \cdots + ar^{n-1} + ar^n$$

Hence, by subtraction we obtain

$$rS_n - S_n = ar^n - a$$

$$(r-1)S_n = a(r^n - 1)$$

$$S_n = \frac{a(r^n - 1)}{r - 1} \quad [7.24]$$

Formula [7.24] can be proved by mathematical induction.

In any geometric progression the terms that lie between two given terms are called **geometric means** between the given terms. In particular, the **geometric mean** of two numbers a and b is a number x such that a, x, b are consecutive terms in a geometric progression.

EXERCISES

1. Write the first four terms of the sequence $\{a_n\}$ defined by $a_n = 2n - 1$.
2. Write the first four terms of the sequence $\{a_n\}$ defined by $a_n = n^2$.

3. A sequence $\{a_n\}$ is defined by $a_1 = 2$, $a_{n+1} = (a_n/2)^2 + 1$. Write the first three terms of the sequence.

4. A sequence $\{a_n\}$ is defined by $a_1 = 5$, $a_{n+1} = 2a_n - 3$. Write the first five terms of the sequence.

Show that in each of Exercises 5 through 8 the sequence can be an arithmetic progression; find d, a_n, and S_n for each.

5. $17, 12, 7, 2, -3, \cdots (n = 11)$

6. $2, 3\frac{1}{2}, 5, 6\frac{1}{2}, 8, \cdots (n = 100)$

7. $\frac{1}{6}, \frac{1}{3}, \frac{1}{2}, \frac{2}{3}, \frac{5}{6}, 1, \cdots (n = 30)$

8. $0.3, 0.8, 1.3, 1.8, 2.3, \cdots (n = 10)$

9. Insert six arithmetic means between 2 and 17.

10. Insert ten arithmetic means between 3 and 9.

11. Insert five arithmetic means between 2 and 6.

12. Insert two arithmetic means between a and b.

13. The fourth term of an arithmetic progression is 4 and the seventh term is 2. Find the first three terms.

14. The second term of an arithmetic progression is 1 and the fifth term is -11. Find the sum of ten terms.

15. Find three consecutive terms of an arithmetic progression whose sum is 9 and the sum of whose squares is 35.

16. Find the sum of the first million positive integers.

17. A contract on a construction job specifies a penalty for delay of completion beyond a certain date, as follows: \$200 for the first day, \$250 for the second day, \$300 for the third day, etc., the penalty for each succeeding day being \$50 more than for the preceding day. How much does a delay of 30 days cost the contractor?

18. The sum \$280 is to be used to award four prizes. If each prize after the first is \$20 less than the next most valuable one, find the value of each of the prizes.

19. An exploring party travels 10 miles the first day and on each day thereafter travels 2 miles farther than on the preceding day. How many days does it take to travel 252 miles?

20. At a raffle 200 tickets are marked, 5, 10, 15, 20, etc., and are drawn at random by those entering. If the price of each ticket is the number of cents marked on the ticket, how much money would be taken in if all tickets are sold?

21. If the value of the articles to be raffled in Exercise 20 was \$100, what is the smallest number of tickets that must be sold so as to insure no loss to those conducting the raffle?

22. A farmer wishes to have his horse shod. He offers the blacksmith \$1.25 per shoe, or 1 cent for the first nail, 2 cents for the second, 3 cents for the third, and so on for the 4 shoes. Each shoe requires 8 nails. Which is the better proposition for the blacksmith?

23. Prove formula [7.21] by mathematical induction.

Determine which of the following sequences can be arithmetic or geometric progressions, and continue each progression two more terms.

24. $3, 6, 12, 24, \cdots$

25. $8, 4, 2, 1, \frac{1}{2}, \cdots$

26. $\frac{1}{3}, -\frac{1}{6}, \frac{1}{12}, -\frac{1}{24}, \cdots$

27. $2, 4, 6, 8, 10, \cdots$

28. $1, \frac{3}{5}, \frac{3}{7}, \frac{1}{3}, \frac{3}{11}, \cdots$

29. $1, \frac{2}{3}, \frac{4}{9}, \frac{8}{27}, \cdots$

30. $1, 1.02, (1.02)^2, (1.02)^3, \cdots$

31. $.63, .0063, .000063, \cdots$

Find a_n and S_n in each of the progressions in Exercises 32 through 36.

32. $2, 6, 18, 54, \cdots (n = 8)$

33. $27, -9, 3, -1, \cdots (n = 6)$

34. $64, 48, 36, 27, \cdots (n = 8)$

35. $1, \frac{5}{6}, \frac{2}{3}, \frac{1}{2}, \frac{1}{3}, \cdots (n = 15)$

36. $1, 1.03, (1.03)^2, (1.03)^3, \cdots (n = 8)$

37. Insert three geometric means between 2 and 8.

38. Insert five geometric means between 8 and 27.

39. Find the geometric mean of 3 and 12.

40. Find the geometric mean of a and b.

41. The third term of a geometric progression is $\frac{1}{2}$ and the eighth term is 16. Find the twelfth term.

42. The sixth term of a geometric progression is 6 and the ninth term is 18. Find the seventeenth term.

43. If a, b are the first two terms of a geometric progression, find the next two terms.

44. A chemist has 12 gal of alcohol. He draws out 3 gal and replaces it with water. He draws out 3 gal of the mixture, again replacing it with water. After five such operations, what is the amount of alcohol left in the mixture?

45. The *half-life* of a certain radioactive isotope is 7 years. This means that for any 7-year interval, exactly half of the atoms present in any sample of the isotope at the beginning of the interval will remain in the sample unchanged at the end of the interval. In a sample that contained 6.02×10^{21} atoms on Jan. 1, 1927, how many unchanged atoms will remain on January 1, 1969?

46. Find the number of ancestors of a person during the eight preceding generations if no ancestor appears in more than one line of descent.

47. A vacuum pump at each stroke draws from a container one-fifth of the air present at the beginning of the stroke. What percent of the original air is in the container after six strokes? After ten strokes?

48. Prove that the squares of the terms of a geometric progression form a geometric progression. Is this true also for an arithmetic progression?

49. An equilateral triangle is inscribed in a circle of radius 32 in. In the triangle is inscribed another circle, and in the second circle another triangle, and so on. Find the radius of the fifth circle. Find also the area of the sixth circle.

50. Prove formula [7.23] by mathematical induction.

51. Prove formula [7.24] by mathematical induction.

7.7 Infinite Series and Repeating Decimals

An infinite series is an expression of the form

$$a_1 + a_2 + a_3 + \cdots$$

the dots indicating that the terms continue indefinitely. This is not a sum in the ordinary sense, for only a finite number of numbers can be added. To make some sense out of the preceding expression, consider the following sequence of partial sums:

$$\begin{aligned} S_1 &= a_1 \\ S_2 &= a_1 + a_2 \\ S_3 &= a_1 + a_2 + a_3 \\ &\cdots\cdots\cdots\cdots \\ S_n &= a_1 + a_2 + \cdots + a_n \\ &\cdots\cdots\cdots\cdots \end{aligned}$$

It may happen that for large values of n, the values of S_n cluster close to some fixed number. If for each positive number p there exists a natural number N such that for all values of n greater than N, S_n differs from a fixed number k by less than the preassigned positive number p, we say that S_n has k as a **limit** as n increases without bound. In this case we write $\lim_{n \to \infty} S_n = k$, and say the series has the sum k.

In the case of an infinite geometric progression with $|r| < 1$, the sum of n terms does have a limit as n increases without bound. This can be seen by writing [7.24], the formula given in Section 7.6 for the sum of n terms, as follows:

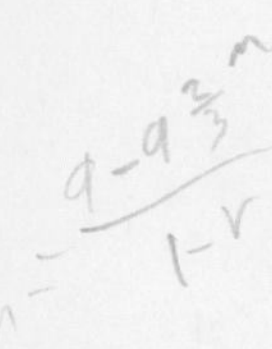

$$S_n = \frac{a - ar^n}{1 - r} = \frac{a}{1 - r} - \frac{a}{1 - r} r^n$$

As n increases, r^n decreases, and by taking n large enough $\frac{a}{1 - r} r^n$ can be made smaller in absolute value than any preassigned positive number. Thus,

$$S = \lim_{n\to\infty} S_n = \frac{a}{1-r}, \qquad [7.25]$$

and we call $\frac{a}{1-r}$ the sum of an infinite geometric progression with first term a and ratio r.

A repeating decimal may be written as an infinite series. For example,

$$x = 0.363636\cdots = 0.36 + 0.0036 + 0.000036 + \cdots$$

By applying formula [7.25] and letting $a = 0.36$ and $r = 0.01$, we have

$$x = \frac{0.36}{1-0.01} = \frac{0.36}{0.99} = \frac{36}{99} = \frac{4}{11}.$$

By this method any repeating decimal may be written as a rational fraction, and thus it is a rational number.

This analysis assumes that a repeating decimal represents the limit of the sum of an infinite geometric progression.

It is obvious that any terminating decimal can be written as a rational fraction; for example, $0.723 = 723/1000$.

Conversely, when we attempt to express a fraction such as $3/8$ or $4/11$ as a decimal, the decimal always either *terminates* or ultimately *repeats in blocks*. Thus,

$$3/8 = 0.375,$$
$$4/11 = 0.363636\cdots$$

It is clear why this should be true, for in the division process by which we express the fraction p/q as a decimal, the remainders can be only the numbers $0, 1, 2, \cdots, q-1$. If at any stage in the division we obtain a remainder 0, the process terminates. Otherwise, after not more than q divisions, one of the remainders $1, 2, \cdots, q-1$ must recur and the decimal begins to repeat.

Hence, we have the important result:

Every terminating or repeating decimal can be expressed as a rational fraction; and, conversely, every rational fraction can be expressed as a terminating or as a repeating decimal.

From this it follows that the irrational numbers such as $\sqrt{2}$ and π are *infinite nonrepeating decimals.*

Example

Express the repeating decimal

$$0.5378378378\cdots$$

as a rational fraction.

SOLUTION: We can write this decimal in the form

$$0.5 + 0.0378 + 0.0000378 + \cdots$$

Hence, our number consists of the decimal 0.5 plus the sum of an infinite geometric progression with first term $a = 0.0378$ and common ratio $r = 0.001$. The sum of the infinite progression is expressible as the fraction

$$S = \frac{0.0378}{1 - 0.001} = \frac{0.0378}{0.999} = \frac{378}{9990} = \frac{7}{185}$$

Hence,

$$0.5378378\cdots = \frac{5}{10} + \frac{7}{185} = \frac{185 + 14}{370} = \frac{199}{370}$$

EXERCISES

Find the sum of each of the following infinite geometric progressions.

1. $9, 6, 4, 8/3, \cdots$

2. $4, 3, 9/4, 27/16, \cdots$

3. $25, -20, 16, -64/5, \cdots$

4. $2, -4/3, 8/9, -16/27, \cdots$

5. $45, 4.5, 0.45, \cdots$

6. $32, 0.32, 0.0032, \cdots$

By actual division express each of the following fractions either as a terminating or as a repeating decimal.

7. $7/25$ **8.** $5/7$ **9.** $3/16$ **10.** $19/21$ **11.** $16/33$

12. $17/37$ **13.** $5/13$ **14.** $3/125$ **15.** $13/41$ **16.** $19/74$

Express each of the repeating decimals in Exercises 17 through 25 as a rational fraction and check your results by division.

17. $0.55555\cdots$ **18.** $0.575757\cdots$ **19.** $0.151515\cdots$

20. $5.727272\cdots$ **21.** $6.342342342\cdots$ **22.** $1.236363636\cdots$

23. $0.5540540540\cdots$ **24.** $0.142857142857\cdots$ **25.** $0.727272\cdots$

26. The bob of a pendulum, when released, describes on the first swing an arc of 20 cm. On each succeeding swing, it travels 0.9 as far as on the preceding swing. How far does the bob move on the sixth swing? Before coming to rest?

27. A rubber ball is dropped from a height of 20 ft. Each time the ball hits the ground, it rebounds to a height half as great as that from which it fell. How far would the ball move before coming to rest? How far would it move up to the time that it strikes the ground for the fifth time?

28. The sum of three consecutive terms of an arithmetic progression is 21. If these numbers are increased by 1, 3, and 10, respectively, the resulting numbers form consecutive terms of a geometric progression. Find the numbers.

Exponents and Logarithms ◄ 8

8.1 Laws of Exponents

Positive integral **exponents** can be defined by the two equations

$$x^1 = x, \qquad [8.1]$$

$$x^{n+1} = x^n \cdot x \qquad [8.2]$$

where x denotes a real number and n is a positive integer. Equation [8.1] defines the exponent 1, and [8.2] defines the exponent $n + 1$ in terms of the exponent n. Thus, for example, the meaning of 4 as an exponent is found by use of [8.1] and the repeated use of [8.2]:

$$x^1 = x, \quad x^2 = x^1 \cdot x = x \cdot x, \quad x^3 = x^2 \cdot x = x \cdot x \cdot x, \quad x^4 = x^3 \cdot x = x \cdot x \cdot x \cdot x$$

We now prove that a definition of the type given here, called a **recursive definition,** really does define the concept of an exponent for all positive integral values of n.

Let S denote the set of positive integers n for which [8.1] and [8.2] define n as an exponent. Clearly, $1 \in S$ because of [8.1]. Assume that $k \in S$. Then [8.2] defines $k + 1$ as an exponent. Thus, if $k \in S$, then so does $k + 1 \in S$. Hence, by the principle of mathematical induction stated in Section 7.1, S consists of all positive integers, and our proof is complete.

Rules of manipulation for expressions involving exponents, the familiar **laws of exponents,** may be stated as follows:

I $\qquad x^m \cdot x^n = x^{m+n}$

II $\qquad (x^m)^n = (x^n)^m = x^{mn}$

III $\quad (xy)^n = x^n y^n$

IV (a) $\quad \dfrac{x^m}{x^n} = x^{m-n} \qquad (\text{for } m > n,\ x \neq 0)$

(b) $\quad \dfrac{x^m}{x^n} = \dfrac{1}{x^{n-m}} \qquad (\text{for } n > m,\ x \neq 0)$

V $\quad \left(\dfrac{x}{y}\right)^n = \dfrac{x^n}{y^n} \qquad (y \neq 0)$

These laws are easy to establish for *positive integral* exponents. We shall prove **I** as a sample and leave the proof of the others as exercises.

Let m denote an arbitrary but fixed positive integer. We shall prove **I** by induction on n. We first show that **I** holds in case $n = 1$. By a direct application of [8.1] and [8.2], we obtain

$$x^m \cdot x^1 = x^m \cdot x = x^{m+1},$$

which states the truth of **I** for the case $n = 1$.

Now we assume that **I** holds when $n = k$, and try to establish on the basis of this assumption that **I** is true for $n = k + 1$.

$$\begin{aligned} x^m \cdot x^{k+1} &= x^m \cdot (x^k \cdot x) && \text{(by [8.2])} \\ &= (x^m \cdot x^k) \cdot x && \text{(by associativity of multiplication)} \end{aligned}$$

But

$$x^m \cdot x^k = x^{m+k} \qquad \text{(by the inductive assumption)}$$

Hence,

$$x^m \cdot x^{k+1} = x^{m+k} \cdot x \qquad \text{(by substitution)}$$

Therefore,

$$x^m \cdot x^{k+1} = x^{m+k+1} \qquad \text{(by [8.2])}$$

The last equation asserts the truth of **I** in case $n = k + 1$. Thus, we have proved that **I** holds for any positive integer m and all positive integers n.

8.2 Zero and Negative Exponents

It is convenient to assign meaning to exponents other than positive integers. In this section we consider zero and negative integers, and in Section 8.5 we shall deal with fractions as exponents. The guiding principle in the formulation of definitions for these new types of exponents is that they should conform to the same laws of exponents (**I** through **V** as stated in the preceding section) that hold for positive integers.

If law **I** is to hold when $m = 0$, we have

$$x^0 \cdot x^n = x^{0+n} = x^n.$$

Hence, if $x \neq 0$, we must have $x^0 = 1$ if law I is to hold. Thus, we are led to make the definition:

$$x^0 = 1 \qquad \text{(for any number } x \neq 0\text{)}. \qquad [8.3]$$

The symbol 0^0 is not defined.

To obtain some hint as to a suitable definition for a negative integral exponent, again consider law I, this time for $m = -n$, n a positive integer, and $x \neq 0$.

$$x^{-n} \cdot x^n = x^{-n+n} = x^0 = 1.$$

Hence, x^{-n} must be the reciprocal of x^n if law I is to hold. This argument motivates the following definition:

$$x^{-n} = \frac{1}{x^n}, \qquad (n \text{ a positive integer and } x \neq 0). \qquad [8.4]$$

With zero and negative exponents defined by [8.3] and [8.4], it can be shown that laws I through V hold for *all integral exponents*, positive, negative, or zero. For example, since

$$(x^m)^{-p} = \frac{1}{(x^m)^p} = \frac{1}{x^{mp}} = x^{-mp},$$

it follows that law II holds when n is a negative integer as well as when n is a positive integer.

Illustrations

1. $3^{-2} = \dfrac{1}{3^2} = \dfrac{1}{9}$

2. $(-\tfrac{1}{2})^{-3} = \dfrac{1}{(-\frac{1}{2})^3} = \dfrac{1}{-\frac{1}{8}} = -8$

3. $(x^2y^{-1})^{-2} = x^{-4}y^2 = \dfrac{y^2}{x^4}$

4. $\dfrac{x^2y^{-2}}{x^{-1}y^{-3}} = x^{2-(-1)}y^{-2-(-3)} = x^3y^1 = x^3y$

5. $\dfrac{x^{-2} - y^{-2}}{x^{-2}y^{-2}} = \dfrac{\dfrac{1}{x^2} - \dfrac{1}{y^2}}{\dfrac{1}{x^2y^2}} = \dfrac{y^2 - x^2}{x^2y^2} \cdot \dfrac{x^2y^2}{1} = y^2 - x^2$

Observe that $x^{-n} = 1/x^n$ implies $x^n = 1/x^{-n}$. Hence, in a fraction, any integral power of a *factor* of numerator or denominator can be changed from numerator to denominator, or vice versa, provided the sign of the exponent is changed.

8.3 Scientific Notation

In much scientific work, especially in astronomy, chemistry, and physics, numbers that are very large or very small are written as the product of a number between 1 and 10 by the proper power of 10. For example, in physics we learn that in a cubic centimeter of gas under ordinary conditions, there are about 27,000,000,000,000,000,000 molecules. The physicist, instead of using this cumbersome notation, would write this large number in the form 2.70×10^{19}, with the decimal point placed after the first nonzero digit. We shall call this the **standard position** of the decimal point. The exponent of the power of 10 then indicates the number of places the decimal point is to be moved to the right or left of the standard position (here to the *right*, since the exponent is *positive*). Hence, to express 2.70×10^{19} in ordinary notation, we move the decimal point 19 places to the right and we then have 27 followed by 18 zeros. Similarly, the physicist gives the mass of the earth as 5.97×10^{27} grams.

In a similar manner, very *small* numbers are expressed conveniently by the use of *negative* powers of 10. Thus, instead of saying that the compressibility of mercury is 0.0000038, we express this number as 3.8×10^{-6}, the *negative* exponent meaning that the decimal point is to be moved to the *left* six places.

This notation has many advantages, one of them being its compactness; another is that it enables one to see at a glance the relative magnitude of two numbers; while still a third advantage is the relative ease with which computations can be carried out in this notation as compared with ordinary notation.

Example 1

The mean distance in miles of the planet Neptune from the sun is roughly 2,790,000,000. Express this number in scientific notation.

SOLUTION: $$2{,}790{,}000{,}000 = 2.79 \times 10^{9}$$

Example 2

The charge of one electron is approximately 4.8×10^{-10} electrostatic units. Express this in ordinary decimal notation.

SOLUTION: The exponent -10 means that we are to begin at the present position of the decimal point, that is, just after the first digit, and move the point 10 places to the left. We would then have to place 9 zeros to the left of the 4. That is,

$$4.8 \times 10^{-10} = 0.000\,000\,000\,48,$$

where the 0 to the left of the decimal point is adjoined merely for emphasis.

Example 3

The coefficient of linear expansion of steel is 1.05×10^{-5} per centigrade degree. If a steel rail is 28 ft long at 0° C, how much longer would it be if the temperature rose to 20° C?

SOLUTION: By the coefficient of linear expansion we mean the number of units that one linear unit of the steel would expand per degree rise in temperature. Hence, to find the expansion of a 28-ft rail as the temperature rises 20 deg, we form the product $1.05 \times 10^{-5} \times 28 \times 20$. This gives the expansion in feet. To express this in inches, we multiply by 12. Hence, the expansion is

$$\begin{aligned} 1.05 \times 10^{-5} \times 28 \times 20 \times 12 &= 1.05 \times 10^{-5} \times 6720 \\ &= 1.05 \times 6.72 \times 10^{-5} \times 10^{3} = 7.1 \times 10^{-2} \\ &= 0.071, \text{ approximately.} \end{aligned}$$

Thus, the answer is 0.071 in.

EXERCISES

Express each of the following in a form free of negative and zero exponents and simplify:

1. $(-18)^0$ **2.** 2^{-3} **3.** $(\frac{1}{2})^{-2}$ **4.** $\dfrac{3^{-2}}{3^{-3}}$

5. $3^{-2}(6)$ **6.** $(\frac{4}{5})^{-1}$ **7.** $(5^{-2})(5^3)$ **8.** $(4^{-1})^{-2}$

9. $\dfrac{ab^{-2}}{b^3}$ **10.** $\dfrac{a^0c}{b^{-2}c^{-1}}$ **11.** $(2x)^{-3}$ **12.** $(3x^{-2})^{-3}$

13. $(ab^{-1}c^{-2})^2$ **14.** $(x^3y^{-2})^{-1}$ **15.** $\dfrac{y^{-5}z^{-6}}{y^{-3}z^{-4}}$ **16.** $\dfrac{a^3b^{-2}}{a^{-3}b^2}$

17. $\left(\dfrac{2a^{-1}b}{a^{-2}b^2}\right)^{-2}$ **18.** $\dfrac{(125x)^{-1}}{5^{-3}}$ **19.** $(3x^2)^{-2}$ **20.** $(2^{-1}a^{-2})^{-2}$

21. $\left(\dfrac{15abc}{d^2}\right)^0$ **22.** $\left(\dfrac{x^2}{2y}\right)^{-4}$ **23.** $\dfrac{3u^2v^{-1}}{(uv)^2}$ **24.** $\dfrac{(81z^2)^{-2}}{3^{-5}}$

25. $\dfrac{a^{-1}+b^{-1}}{a^{-1}-b^{-1}} \times \dfrac{a-b}{a+b}$ **26.** $\left(\dfrac{a^{-1}b^2}{a^2b^{-1}}\right)^{-2} \div \left(\dfrac{a^3b^{-1}}{ab^2}\right)^3$

27. $(ab^{-1}+ba^{-1}) \div (a^2+b^2)$ **28.** $\dfrac{a^{-1}+b^{-1}}{a^{-1}b^{-1}}$

29. $\dfrac{3^{-2}+4^{-2}}{3^{-2}4^{-2}}$ **30.** $\dfrac{5^{-1}+12^{-1}}{5^{-3}+12^{-3}}$

31. $\dfrac{a^{-2}-b^{-2}}{(a-b)^2}$ **32.** $\dfrac{x^{-3}-1}{x^{-2}+x^{-1}+x^0}$

33. $\dfrac{x-x^{-1}}{1-x^{-1}}$ **34.** $[(a-b)^{-1}+(a+b)^{-1}][a^{-2}-b^{-2}]$

35. $\dfrac{by^{-1}+1}{yb^{-1}+1}$ **36.** $\dfrac{z^3-z^{-3}}{z^2+1+z^{-2}}$

37. $\dfrac{(a+b)^{-1}}{a^{-1}b^{-1}}(a^2-b^2)$ **38.** $\left(\dfrac{2a^{-1}+b^{-1}}{2a^{-1}-b^{-1}}\right)(2b-a)$

39. $\dfrac{x-4x^{-1}}{(1-2x^{-1})(x+2)}$ **40.** $\dfrac{(x^{-1}+y^{-1})(x+y)^{-1}}{x^{-1}y^{-1}}$

41. Prove law II for positive integral exponents.

42. Prove law III for positive integral exponents.

43. Prove law IV for positive integral exponents.

44. Prove law V for positive integral exponents.

45. Prove law I for all integral exponents.

46. Prove law II for all integral exponents.

47. Prove law III for all integral exponents.

48. The wavelength of the shortest ultraviolet wave is 7.6×10^{-9} meter. Express this wavelength in centimeters.

49. The velocity of light is about 30,000,000,000 cm per sec. Express this number in scientific notation.

50. Find the product $(2.71 \times 10^5)(3.14 \times 10^{-4})$ and express the result in scientific notation, rounding off the answer to three significant figures.

51. Find the quotient $\dfrac{3.74 \times 10^{11}}{8.31 \times 10^{13}}$ and express the result in scientific notation.

52. Using scientific notation, calculate: $\dfrac{(1{,}200{,}000)^2(0.000\,000\,065)}{\sqrt[3]{8{,}000{,}000{,}000}}$.

53. Using scientific notation calculate: $\dfrac{\sqrt{0.000\,000\,36}(110{,}000)^3}{3{,}000{,}000}$.

54. Astronomers tell us that it takes a ray of light 7 million years to travel from the spiral Galaxy M81 to the earth. Express in miles the distance from the earth to Galaxy M81. (Velocity of light is 186,000 miles per sec; 1 day = 86,400 sec.)

55. The mean distance of Pluto, the outermost planet, from the sun is about 3.84×10^9 miles, while that of Alpha Centauri, one of the nearest fixed stars, is 2.54×10^{13} miles. How many times farther from the sun is Alpha Centauri than Pluto?

56. The number of miles traveled by a ray of light in one year is roughly 5.9×10^{12}. Using the figures of the preceding exercise, find the distance in light years of Alpha Centauri from the sun.

57. Using the data given in Example 1 of Section 8.3 and Exercise 55, find how many times farther from the sun Alpha Centauri is than the planet Neptune.

58. The coefficient of linear expansion (per centigrade degree) of wrought iron is 1.12×10^{-5}, while that of platinum is 8.90×10^{-6}. Determine which is the greater and how many times it is greater than the other.

59. The coefficient of linear expansion of aluminum (per centigrade degree) is 2.3×10^{-5}. Find the expansion in an aluminum rod 10 cm long if the temperature rises 2° C.

60. The coefficient of linear expansion of invar per centigrade degree is 7.0×10^{-7}, while that of brass is 1.85×10^{-5}. Two rods, one of invar, the other of brass, have length 20 cm at 0° C. Find the difference in their lengths at 3° C.

61. The steel rails of a trolley line are 28 ft long and have a coefficient of linear expansion of 5.85×10^{-6} per Fahrenheit degree. If the rails are laid when the temperature is 40° F, how much space should be left between them if their ends are just to touch at 110° F?

62. The diameter of an oxygen molecule is calculated to be 2.97×10^{-8} cm. Find the number of such molecules that can be laid side by side on a distance of 1 in. (1 in. = 2.54 cm.)

63. In a cubic centimeter of gas under ordinary conditions there are about 2.7×10^{19} molecules. Find the number of molecules in 1 cu ft of gas. (1 cu ft = 2.83×10^4 cc.)

64. The diameter of a molecule of water is 3.8×10^{-8} cm. If water molecules could be placed in a line touching one another, how many would be in one mile? (1 mile = 161,000 cm.)

8.4 The Principal Roots of a Number

If n is a positive integer, by an ***n*th root** of a number x we mean a number whose nth power is x. Thus, 3 is a fourth root of 81, for $3^4 = 81$. Similarly, 2 is a fifth root of 32 and 5 is a cube root of 125. In general, if $y^n = x$, y is called an nth root of x.

A number may have more than one nth root. Thus, 3 and -3 are square roots of 9; 2 and -2 are fourth roots of 16. Indeed, it can be proved that every *positive number* has two real *square* roots, two real *fourth* roots, two real *sixth* roots, and in general two real nth roots if n is *even*, one positive and the other negative.

On the other hand, it can be proved that *every real number*, positive, negative, or zero, has one real *cube* root, one real *fifth* root, one real *seventh* root, and in general one real nth root if n is *odd*.

Since an even power of a real number is positive or zero, a negative number cannot have a real number as an nth root if n is *even*. Thus, -4 has no real square root. New numbers, called *imaginary*, were introduced by mathematicians to serve as even roots of negative numbers. These new numbers will be studied in Chapter 11. Throughout the remainder of this chapter, however, when we consider *even* roots of numbers, we shall understand that the numbers whose roots are being considered are *positive* or *zero*.

We have observed that a number may have more than one nth root. This lack of uniqueness led to the introduction of the concept of principal nth root, which is defined as follows: If x is a *positive number*, its **principal *n*th root** is the *positive* real nth root. Thus, 2 is the principal square root of 4. If x is *negative* (in which case we require n to be odd), the **principal *n*th root** of x is the *negative* real nth root. Thus, -2 is the principal cube root of -8. Under these definitions, it follows that *the principal nth root of a number is unique*. We make the important agreement that the symbol $\sqrt[n]{x}$ will denote the *principal* nth root of x. Thus, $\sqrt{16} = 4$, $\sqrt[3]{-27} = -3$. In particular, $\sqrt[n]{0} = 0$.

In the expression $a\sqrt[n]{x}$, the symbol $\sqrt[n]{x}$ is called a **radical.** Here n is called the **index** or **order** of the radical, x is called the **radicand,** and a is called the **coefficient** of the radical.

From the definition of the symbol $\sqrt[n]{x}$, we have

$$(\sqrt[n]{x})^n = x.$$

Hence, if $\sqrt[n]{x} = \sqrt[n]{y}$, it follows, by raising both members to the nth power, that $x = y$. Conversely, if $x = y$, then $\sqrt[n]{x} = \sqrt[n]{y}$, since each member of this last equation represents the *unique* principal nth root of the same number.

8.5 Fractional Exponents

Let us recall the agreement made in Section 8.4 that throughout this chapter *whenever radicals of even orders occur, the radicands will be understood to be nonnegative.* This assumption is necessary for the validity of some of the statements of this section.

Up to the present, the symbol $x^{1/2}$ has no meaning. The meaning of positive integral exponents furnishes no clue, for while x^2 stands for the product obtained by taking x as a factor twice, it would be absurd to speak of taking x as a factor one-half a time. As in the case of zero and negative integral exponents, we want the usual laws of exponents to hold for fractional exponents. To see what meaning must be assigned to $x^{1/2}$ to accomplish this, let us *assume* that law II holds for $m = \frac{1}{2}$ and $n = 2$. We have

$$(x^{1/2})^2 = x^1 = x.$$

Hence, in order for law II to hold in the case $m = \frac{1}{2}$, $x^{1/2}$ must represent a square root of x. Thus, we are led to make the definition

$$x^{1/2} = \sqrt{x}.$$

Similarly, we define

$$x^{1/3} = \sqrt[3]{x}.$$

And, in general, if n *is any positive integer*, we make the definition

$$x^{1/n} = \sqrt[n]{x}. \qquad [8.5]$$

Now let m and n be any two positive integers. If law II is to apply in the case of fractional exponents generally, we must have

$$x^{m/n} = (x^{1/n})^m = (\sqrt[n]{x})^m.$$

Hence, we define

$$x^{m/n} = (\sqrt[n]{x})^m. \qquad [8.6]$$

The expression $(\sqrt[n]{x})^m$ is an nth root of x^m, for raising $(\sqrt[n]{x})^m$ to the nth power, we get

$$[(\sqrt[n]{x})^m]^n = [(\sqrt[n]{x})^n]^m = x^m.$$

Moreover, $(\sqrt[n]{x})^m$ is a *principal* nth root of x^m. To see this, we consider two cases:

(i) x a positive number or zero.
(ii) x a negative number.

In case (i), where x is positive or zero, $(\sqrt[n]{x})^m$ is nonnegative, and hence is the *principal* nth root of the nonnegative number x^m. On the other hand, if x is negative, n is restricted to being an odd integer. In this case, $(\sqrt[n]{x})^m$ is positive if m is even, and negative when m is odd. But also in this case, x^m is positive if m is even and negative when m is odd. Thus, also in case (ii), $(\sqrt[n]{x})^m$ is the principal nth root x^m. Hence, because of the uniqueness of a principal root, we may write

$$(\sqrt[n]{x})^m = \sqrt[n]{x^m}, \qquad [8.7]$$

where, as usual, the symbol $\sqrt[n]{x^m}$ denotes the principal nth root of x^m.

Note: The student should be warned that the two members of [8.7] are not necessarily the same if n is even and x is negative. For example,

$$\sqrt[6]{(-1)^2} = \sqrt[6]{1} = 1.$$

On the other hand, $(\sqrt[6]{(-1)})^2$ is not defined at this stage, there being no *real* number whose sixth power is -1.

If x is a *positive number*, or *zero*, and m, n, and p are *positive integers*, then we can show that

$$x^{m/n} = x^{mp/np}, \qquad [8.8]$$

for each member of [8.8] can be shown to be the principal npth root of x^{mp}. Thus, subject to the conditions stated, the exponent m/n in the expression $x^{m/n}$ may be replaced by the equivalent fraction mp/np.

Finally, just as we defined x^{-n} to be $1/x^n$ when n is an integer, so here we define

$$x^{-(m/n)} = \frac{1}{x^{m/n}}, \qquad [8.9]$$

where m/n is any rational number.

With the definitions of zero, negative, and fractional exponents we have given, it can be shown that laws I to V, which were proved for *positive integral* exponents, hold also for all *rational* exponents, subject always to the conditions that no zero is to be allowed as a divisor and no radical of even order with a negative radicand is to be permitted. A detailed verification of these laws for all cases is too lengthy to be undertaken here.

Illustrations

1. $9^{1/2} = \sqrt{9} = 3$

2. $(-8)^{1/3} = \sqrt[3]{-8} = -2$

3. $(8a^3)^{2/3} = (\sqrt[3]{8a^3})^2 = (2a)^2 = 4a^2$

4. $32^{-2/5} = \dfrac{1}{32^{2/5}} = \dfrac{1}{(\sqrt[5]{32})^2} = \dfrac{1}{2^2} = \dfrac{1}{4}$

5. $(16x^2)^{-1/2} = \dfrac{1}{(16x^2)^{1/2}} = \dfrac{1}{\sqrt{16x^2}} = \dfrac{1}{4x}$

6. $(81)^{6/8} = 81^{3/4} = (\sqrt[4]{81})^3 = 3^3 = 27$

7. $\sqrt{a^2} = |a|$

The question now arises as to whether definitions of *irrational* exponents can be given. Does the symbol $3^{\sqrt{2}}$ have any meaning? The answer to this question is yes, but it is beyond the scope of this book to give a complete treatment of irrational exponents. The facts needed will be given in the sections on logarithms.

EXERCISES

Find the value of each of the following:

1. $\dfrac{2^{-2}}{2^0}$ **2.** $3^2 \cdot 3^{-1}$ **3.** $8^{2/3}$ **4.** $9^{1/2}$

5. $8^{-1/3}$ **6.** $27^{1/3}$ **7.** $25^{-1/2}$ **8.** $4^{-3/2}$

9. $(9/4)^{3/2}$ **10.** $(4/9)^{-1/2}$ **11.** $32^{-3/5}$ **12.** $32^{2/5}$

13. $(25\tfrac{1}{2})^0$ **14.** $(1/8)^{-2/3}$ **15.** $25^{3/2}$ **16.** $16^{1/4}$

17. $(8/27)^{-1/3}$ **18.** $(4/25)^{1/2}$ **19.** $(1000)^0$ **20.** $16^{-3/4}$

21. $125^{-2/3}$ **22.** $64^{5/6}$ **23.** $(2^3 + 1)^{-1/2}$ **24.** $(3^2 + 4^2)^{1/2}$

25. $(5^2 + 12^2)^{-1/2}$ **26.** $(5^2 - 3^2)^{-1/4}$ **27.** $(13^2 - 12^2)^{1/2}$ **28.** $(2^3 - 2^2)^{-1/2}$

Express each of Exercises 29 through 60 in a form free of negative and fractional exponents and simplify.

29. $(a^{-1/3})^3$ **30.** $\left(\dfrac{a^{-4}}{a^{-2}}\right)^{1/2}$ **31.** $\left(\dfrac{4a^3x}{ax^{-1}}\right)^{1/2}$ **32.** $(4x^2y^4)^{1/2}$

33. $\dfrac{2x^{-1}y}{x^2y^{-2}}$ **34.** $(25a^{3/2}b^{-1})^0$ **35.** $\left(\dfrac{8a^3}{b^{-6}}\right)^{2/3}$ **36.** $\left(\dfrac{4x^2}{y^{-2}}\right)^{-1/2}$

37. $(8a^3x^{-6})^{-1/3}$ **38.** $(17x^5)^0\left(\dfrac{x}{y}\right)^{-1}$ **39.** $(16a^2b^4)^{1/2}(2a)^{-3}$

40. $(2^{-3}a^6)^{1/3}$ **41.** $\dfrac{a^{2/3}y^0}{a^{-1/3}x^{-2}}$ **42.** $\dfrac{a^{11/3}}{2^{-1}a^{5/3}}$

43. $\left(\dfrac{x^{1/3}y^{2/3}}{x^{-1/3}y^{1/3}}\right)^3$ **44.** $\dfrac{xy^{-2}+yx^{-2}}{x^{-2}-y^{-2}}$ **45.** $\dfrac{xy^{-1}-yx^{-1}}{x^{-1}+y^{-1}}$

46. $(13^2-12^2)^{1/2}$ **47.** $(2a^{-1/3}b^{2/3}c)^3$ **48.** $(8a^3b^{-3})^{1/3}$

49. $(9x^4)^{3/2}$ **50.** $5(u^2v^{-1})^2$ **51.** $(6^2-3^2)^{1/3}$

52. $(11^2+2^2)^{-2/3}$ **53.** $(7a^{1/2}b^{1/3})^0$ **54.** $3x^{-2}+(2y)^{-1}$

55. $\dfrac{x^{-1}-y^{-1}}{x^{-2}-y^{-2}}$ **56.** $\left(\dfrac{27x^{-3}}{8y^6}\right)^{2/3}$ **57.** $\dfrac{a^{-1}+b^{-1}}{a^{-3}+b^{-3}}$

58. $\left(\dfrac{2x^{1/3}y^{-3/2}}{x^{-2/3}y^{1/2}}\right)^{-2}$ **59.** $\left(\dfrac{8x^{5/2}y^{-4}}{x^{-1/2}y^2}\right)^{-2/3}$ **60.** $\dfrac{y^{-1/2}-x^{-1/2}}{x^{-1/2}y^{-1/2}}$

Multiply the following and express in a form free from negative and fractional exponents, and simplify.

61. $(x^{1/2}+y^{1/2})(x^{1/2}-y^{1/2})$ **62.** $(a^{2/3}-a^{1/3}+1)(a^{1/3}+1)$

63. $(x+y)^{-1}(x^2-y^2)$ **64.** $(x+y)^{1/3}(x-y)^{1/3}(x^2-y^2)^{-2/3}$

65. $(x^{1/2}+2x^{-1/2})^2$ **66.** $(3x^{-1/2}+y^{1/2})(3x^{-1/2}-y^{1/2})$

8.6 The Concept of a System of Logarithms

The notion of a set of **logarithms** derives from exponents. The idea is as follows. Let b denote any positive real number different from 1. Then it can be proved that any positive real number x can be expressed as a power of b. That is, corresponding to a positive real number x, there exists a real number y such that

$$x = b^y.$$

This exponent y is called the **logarithm of x to the base b,** and we write

$$y = \log_b x.$$

Now, a logarithm may not be a rational number, and we have not defined b^y when y is irrational. However, a suitable definition can be given for irrational exponents such that the statements in the preceding paragraph are true and laws I through V hold for all real numbers as exponents. We base the treatment of logarithms on the assumption that this can be done. In calculations, irrational logarithms can be approximated by rational numbers to any desired degree of accuracy.

Thus, a logarithm of a number is an exponent. It is the exponent of the power of the base that is equal to the number. A collection consisting of a set of numbers paired with their logarithms constitutes a system of logarithms.

Logarithms can be used to perform the arithmetical operations of multiplication, division, raising to powers, and extracting roots. They also have theoretical applications involving functions.

8.7 Laws of Logarithms

In computing with logarithms, we need to employ certain rules called **laws of logarithms.** These laws are actually laws of exponents formulated in logarithmic terminology. We give these laws as verbal statements and also as formulas. The symbol b denotes the base of the system of logarithms and M and N denote positive real numbers.

I *The logarithm of the product of two numbers is equal to the sum of the logarithms of the numbers.*

$$\log_b MN = \log_b M + \log_b N.$$

II *The logarithm of a quotient is equal to the logarithm of the dividend minus the logarithm of the divisor.*

$$\log_b \frac{M}{N} = \log_b M - \log_b N.$$

III *The logarithm of a power of a number is equal to the logarithm of the number multiplied by the exponent of the power.*

$$\log_b N^p = p \log_b N.$$

IV *The logarithm of a root of a number is equal to the logarithm of the number divided by the index of the root.*

$$\log_b \sqrt[r]{N} = \frac{1}{r} \log_b N.$$

These laws are all proved in essentially the same way. We give a proof of law II as a sample. Let

$$\log_b M = x \qquad \text{and} \qquad \log_b N = y.$$

Then, by the definition of a logarithm, we have

$$M = b^x \qquad \text{and} \qquad N = b^y.$$

Hence, by division and the application of a law of exponents, we get

$$\frac{M}{N} = \frac{b^x}{b^y} = b^{x-y}.$$

But this equation says that

$$\log_b \frac{M}{N} = x - y.$$

Substituting for x and y, we have

$$\log_b \frac{M}{N} = \log_b M - \log_b N.$$

Illustrations

1. $\log(24.6 \times 6.37) = \log 24.6 + \log 6.37$

2. $\log 3.74^5 = 5 \log 3.74$

3. $\log \dfrac{490.5}{53} = \log 490.5 - \log 53$

4. $\log \sqrt[3]{0.042} = \frac{1}{3} \log 0.042$

8.8 Common Logarithms

The system of logarithms with 10 as a base is called the system of **common logarithms.** Since our Arabic-Hindu positional method of writing numbers assigns a special role to the number 10, it is not surprising that common logarithms are especially suited for purposes of computation. Since we shall be concerned most with common logarithms, when we use the term logarithm hereafter (unless otherwise stated) we shall mean common logarithm, and we shall write $\log N$ for $\log_{10} N$.

The reader should be warned that this convention is not followed in more advanced books in mathematics. Indeed, in calculus the most useful base for a system of logarithms is an irrational number denoted by the letter e (approximate value 2.71828). This system is referred to as the system of **natural logarithms,** and in calculus texts when no base is indicated it is understood to be e.

8.9 Finding the Characteristic

The common logarithm of a number can be expressed as the sum of an integer (positive, negative, or zero) and a nonnegative number less than 1. The integer is called the **characteristic** of the logarithm and the other part is called the **mantissa.** For example, the number 5630 can be written as 5.36×10^3. Hence,

$$\log 5630 = \log 5.63 + \log 10^3 = \log 5.63 + 3 \log 10,$$
$$\log 5630 = \log 5.63 + 3, \quad \text{since } \log 10 = 1.$$

Here 3 is the characteristic of log 5630, and log 5.63, which is a number between 0 and 1, is its mantissa.

The characteristic of the logarithm of a number can be determined by applying the following rule to the number.

Count the number of places the decimal point is removed from standard position (see Section 8.3). *The characteristic is this number or its negative, according as the decimal point is displaced to the right or to the left.*

Illustrations

Characteristic of the logarithm of 657.3 is 2.
Characteristic of the logarithm of 0.006573 is -3.
Characteristic of the logarithm of 6.573 is 0.

To prove the rule given above, recall from Section 8.3 that any positive number N written in decimal notation can be expressed (in scientific notation) as

$$N = M \cdot 10^c,$$

where M is a number with decimal point in standard position. Thus, $1 \leqq M < 10$; and c is the number of places the decimal point in N is removed from standard position, to the right if c is positive and to the left if c is negative. Now

$$\log N = \log M + \log 10^c = \log M + c \log 10,$$
$$\log N = \log M + c, \quad \text{since } \log 10 = 1.$$

Since $1 \leqq M < 10$ and $\log 1 = 0$ and $\log 10 = 1$, $\log M$ is a nonnegative number less than 1.† Thus, $\log M$ is the mantissa of the logarithm of N and c is the characteristic, which proves our rule.

EXERCISES

Express in logarithmic notation each of the relations of Exercises 1 through 9.

1. $100 = 10^2$ **2.** $0.001 = 10^{-3}$ **3.** $5 = 10^{0.699}$
4. $42.8 = 10^{1.6314}$ **5.** $852.4 = 10^{2.9306}$ **6.** $A = 10^x$
7. $P = 10^q$ **8.** $8 = 2^3$ **9.** $25 = 5^2$

Express each of the following relations in exponential notation:

10. $\log 23 = 1.3617$ **11.** $\log 96 = 1.9823$ **12.** $\log 237 = 2.3747$
13. $\log 6.99 = 0.8445$ **14.** $\log 37.5 = 1.5740$ **15.** $\log_2 16 = 4$
16. $\log_3 243 = 5$ **17.** $\log_5 0.04 = -2$ **18.** $\log_4 64 = 3$

19. If 2 is taken as the base for a system of logarithms, give the logarithms of the following numbers:

$$4, \quad 8, \quad 32, \quad 128, \quad \tfrac{1}{2}, \quad \tfrac{1}{4}, \quad \tfrac{1}{16}$$

20. Give the logarithms of the following numbers if 3 is taken as the base of the system:

$$3, \quad 9, \quad 27, \quad 81, \quad \tfrac{1}{9}, \quad \tfrac{1}{27}, \quad \tfrac{1}{81}$$

Apply the laws of logarithms to write each of Exercises 21 through 32 in a different form.

21. $\log (132 \times 46.7)$ **22.** $\log \dfrac{29.3}{37}$ **23.** $\log \dfrac{4.68}{0.054}$

† This conclusion depends upon the assumption in this book that if $x < y$, then $\log x < \log y$.

24. $\log (6.34 \times 82.5)$ 25. $\log (38.4)^3$ 26. $\log (5.2)^7$

27. $\log \sqrt{47.8}$ 28. $\log \sqrt[5]{0.0628}$ 29. $\log (2.4 \times 38 \times 49)$

30. $\log \dfrac{5.8 \times 6.2}{360}$ 31. $\log (68.8\sqrt{429})$ 32. $\log \dfrac{(36.5)^2}{95.6}$

Given $\log 2 = 0.3010$, $\log 3 = 0.4771$, and $\log 5 = 0.6990$, find the values of the following:

33. $\log 4$ 34. $\log 9$ 35. $\log 6$ 36. $\log 15$

37. $\log 2.5$ 38. $\log 1.5$ 39. $\log \sqrt{2}$ 40. $\log \sqrt{5}$

41. $\log 8$ 42. $\log 81$ 43. $\log \sqrt[4]{3}$ 44. $\log \sqrt[3]{5}$

Give the characteristics of the logarithms of the numbers in Exercises 45 through 64.

45. 27.4 46. 4.293 47. 0.0852 48. 8349.6

49. 55,820 50. 0.00062 51. 19.47 52. 0.0041

53. 28,000 54. 4923 55. 0.3261 56. 0.0005

57. 10,643 58. 0.8631 59. 0.000832 60. 69,000.97

61. 2.3485 62. 240,000 63. 36,000 64. 0.000021

65. Would the rule for determining the characteristic work in a system of logarithms with a base different from 10? Explain.

66. Prove law I.

67. Prove law III.

68. Prove law IV.

8.10 Finding the Mantissa

It has been noted that any positive number can be expressed as the product of a number between 1 and 10 by an integral power of 10. Thus, for example,

$$432 = 4.32 \times 10^2.$$

Taking logarithms of both sides, we get

$$\log 432 = \log (4.32 \times 10^2) = \log 4.32 + \log 10^2,$$
$$\log 432 = \log 4.32 + 2.$$

Hence, 2 is the characteristic of log 432, and log 4.32—which is a number between 0 and 1—is the mantissa of log 432.

The example illustrates the following statement: *The mantissa of the logarithm of any number N is equal to the logarithm of the number obtained from N by moving the decimal point to standard position.* From this statement we can make two observations. First, a table of logarithms of numbers between 1 and 10 furnishes mantissas for the logarithms of all numbers. Table III in the back of this book is such a table. Second, the mantissa of the logarithm of any number is independent of the position of the decimal point and is determined entirely by the sequence of significant digits in the number. Thus, the logarithms of 432, 4320, 0.00432, etc., all have the same mantissa.

Tables such as Table III, which contains approximate values for the logarithms of numbers between 1 and 10, are frequently referred to as tables of mantissas. Now, the mantissa part of a logarithm is usually an irrational number that can be only approximated by a decimal fraction to a desired degree of accuracy. For numbers of three significant digits, Table III lists mantissas correct to four decimal places. When greater accuracy is required, tables listing mantissas approximated to more decimal places must be used. Five-place tables are frequently used, and six- and seven-place tables are not unusual.

The following examples illustrate the use of Table III.

Example 1

Find the value of log 432.

SOLUTION: By the rule, the characteristic of log 432 is 2. To obtain the mantissa, we enter Table III and locate the first two digits of the number (43 in this case) in the left-hand column designated at the top by ***n***. Then we go horizontally over to the column designated at the top by the third digit (2 in this case). The entry thus arrived at is 0.6355. The decimal point is omitted in the table, but is understood to belong to the left of the first digit as indicated. Hence, we have

$$\log 432 = 2.6355.$$

Example 2

Find the value of log 0.000785.

SOLUTION: The characteristic is −4. From Table III the mantissa is 0.8949. Therefore, we have

$$\log 0.000785 = 0.8949 - 4,$$

or

$$\log 0.000785 = 6.8949 - 10.$$

Either of the preceding forms may be used in writing logarithms that have negative characteristics.

8.11 Finding a Number Whose Logarithm Is Known

If $\log N = L$, then N is called the **antilogarithm** of L. Thus, if the logarithm of a number N is known, the process of finding N is called **finding an antilogarithm.** This process is exactly the reverse of finding a logarithm and is illustrated by the following examples.

Example 1

If $\log N = 1.9315$, find the value of N.

SOLUTION: The value of N is determined by finding from Table III the number whose logarithm is 0.9315 and then adjusting the decimal point as indicated by the characteristic. This procedure is justified by the observation, made in the preceding section, that all numbers having the same mantissa differ only in the position of the decimal point. We locate 0.9315 in the body of Table III. To read off the corresponding antilogarithm, we go horizontally to the left to the $\boldsymbol{n}$ column to get the first two digits and then obtain the third digit from the top of the column in which the logarithm is located. In this case we find that 8.54 is the number corresponding to 0.9315 as a logarithm. Since the characteristic of $\log N$ is 1, the number N is obtained from 8.54 by moving the decimal point from the standard position one place to the right. Thus

$$N = 85.4.$$

Example 2

If $\log N = 0.6877 - 2$, find N.

SOLUTION: In this case, the mantissa 0.6877 does not occur in Table III, but for three-digit accuracy we select the mantissa in the table closest to 0.6877, namely, 0.6875. The antilogarithm of 0.6875 is 4.87. Since the characteristic of $\log N$ is -2, we move the decimal point two places to the left of the standard position and get

$$N = 0.0487.$$

Later, by a process called **interpolation,** we shall compute such antilogarithms correct to four significant digits.

8.12 Computation by Means of Logarithms

We are now prepared to use logarithms to perform some arithmetical calculations. At present, we shall limit ourselves to exercises involving numbers of no more than three significant digits and obtain answers correct to the same number of digits. In the next section we shall learn how to use Table III for numbers of more than three digits. The processes involved in logarithmic computation are best explained by examples.

Example 1

Use logarithms to find the value of 24.6×7.85.

SOLUTION: Let $x = 24.6 \times 7.85$. Then, applying law I, we can write

$$\log x = \log 24.6 + \log 7.85.$$

We make a skeleton outline for carrying out the operations indicated by this logarithmic equation, leaving spaces for writing in the necessary logarithms and antilogarithm. Then the indicated logarithms are found with the aid of Table III, the operations specified by the logarithmic equation are performed, and finally the antilogarithm is obtained.

The completed work appears as follows:

$$\begin{aligned} \log 24.6 &= 1.3909 \\ \log 7.85 &= 0.8949 \\ \hline \log x &= 2.2858 \\ x &= 193 \end{aligned}$$

Example 2

Use logarithms to compute the value of 896/0.042.

SOLUTION: Let $x = 896/0.042$. Applying law II, we have

$$\log x = \log 896 - \log 0.042.$$

The skeleton outline is made and calculations are carried out as follows:

$$\begin{aligned} \log 896 &= 2.9523 \\ \log 0.042 &= 0.6232 - 2 \\ \hline \log x &= 2.3291 + 2 = 4.3291 \\ x &= 21{,}300 \end{aligned}$$

Example 3

Calculate the value of $(0.634)^3$ by means of logarithms.

SOLUTION: Let $x = (0.634)^3$. Applying law III, we get

$$\log x = 3 \log 0.634.$$

Then we have

$$\begin{aligned} \log 0.634 &= 0.8021 - 1 \\ &3 \\ \hline \log x &= 2.4063 - 3 = 0.4063 - 1 \\ x &= 0.255 \end{aligned}$$

Example 4

Use logarithms to calculate the value of

$$x = \frac{(\sqrt[4]{43.6})(86.3)}{5.84}$$

SOLUTION: The logarithmic equation is

$$\log x = \tfrac{1}{4} \log 43.6 + \log 86.3 - \log 5.84.$$

A skeleton outline is made for the problem and filled in as follows:

$$\begin{aligned} \log 43.6 &= 1.6395 \\ \tfrac{1}{4} \log 43.6 &= 0.4099 \\ \log 86.3 &= 1.9360 \\ \hline \log \text{numerator} &= 2.3459 \\ \log 5.84 &= 0.7664 \\ \hline \log x &= 1.5795 \\ x &= 38.0 \end{aligned} \quad \left.\begin{matrix} \\ \\ \end{matrix}\right\} +$$

EXERCISES

Find the logarithm of each of the following numbers:

1. 24.7 **2.** 639 **3.** 4.76 **4.** 0.0683 **5.** 9650
6. 5.02 **7.** 0.427 **8.** 0.0032 **9.** 15.2 **10.** 3000
11. 0.00062 **12.** 529,000 **13.** 7 **14.** 25.3 **15.** 0.0465

Find the antilogarithm of each of the following:

16. 1.5705 **17.** 2.9248 **18.** 0.7388 **19.** 4.8370
20. 0.3838 – 2 **21.** 9.7589 – 10 **22.** 2.9015 **23.** 0.7709 – 4
24. 0.0625 – 1 **25.** 5.8673 **26.** 8.9821 – 10 **27.** 0.4283 – 5
28. 0.2634 – 3 **29.** 6.4271 **30.** 6.5281 – 10 **31.** 7.8570 – 10

Use logarithms to perform the following indicated computations, obtaining answers correct to three significant digits:

32. $(489)(62.3)$ **33.** $\dfrac{43.2}{29.8}$ **34.** $(8.32)^4$

35. $\sqrt{89.6}$ **36.** $(27.4)^6$ **37.** $(38.5)(758)$

38. $\sqrt[5]{659}$ **39.** $\dfrac{95{,}400}{537}$ **40.** $(0.00528)(856)$

41. $\sqrt{76.3}$ **42.** $(0.0385)^3$ **43.** $\sqrt[3]{7.45}$

44. $\dfrac{319}{1.06}$ **45.** $(56.2)(49.8)$ **46.** $\sqrt[8]{365}$

47. $(4300)(975)$ **48.** $(19.7)^5$ **49.** $\dfrac{87}{0.062}$

50. $\sqrt[7]{8290}$ **51.** $(8.97)^8$ **52.** $(82{,}400)(0.0657)$

53. $\sqrt[9]{6.52}$ **54.** $(3.65)^9$ **55.** $(92.6)^6$

56. $\sqrt[4]{55.7}$ **57.** $\dfrac{(3.68)(46.3)}{62.9}$ **58.** $(48.3)(2.64)^3$

59. $\dfrac{\sqrt{926}}{4.72}$ **60.** $(8.6)\sqrt[3]{42.8}$ **61.** $(0.0623)^4(24)^3$

62. $\dfrac{(4.7)\sqrt{6320}}{52.3}$ **63.** $\dfrac{(32.8)^2}{\sqrt[3]{8950}}$ **64.** $\dfrac{(12.5)^3\sqrt[5]{2.83}}{(5.26)^4}$

8.13 Interpolation

To find the mantissa for a four-digit number using Table III, or to find an antilogarithm to four significant digits, requires the use of a process called **interpolation.** Interpolation is a process of calculating a value between two consecutive values listed in a table. The theory underlying interpolation is based on the assumption that, for small intervals, changes in log N are proportional to the corresponding changes in N. For intervals of the size we need to consider, this assumption leads to results of dependable accuracy. The technique is illustrated in the following examples.

Example 1

Find the value of log 2.673.

SOLUTION: The value of log 2.673 lies between log 2.670 and log 2.680. Further, by our assumption that small changes in a number correspond to proportional changes in the logarithm, log 2.673 occupies approximately the same relative position between log 2.670 and log 2.680 that 2.673 occupies between 2.670 and 2.680. This is used to set up a proportion from which is calculated the correction to be added to log 2.670 to get log 2.673. The work is displayed below:

$$10\left[3\begin{bmatrix}\log 2.670 = 0.4265 \\ \log 2.673 = \quad ? \end{bmatrix} c \atop \log 2.680 = 0.4281\right] 16$$

Writing the indicated changes as a proportion, we have

$$\frac{c}{16} = \frac{3}{10}, \qquad \text{or} \quad c = 16\left(\frac{3}{10}\right) = 4.8.$$

We round off the correction c to the nearest integer (5 in this case) and add it to the last digit of the smaller of the two logarithms listed. This gives us

$$\log 2.673 = 0.4270.$$

Notice in the preceding work that the difference in the logarithms and the differences in the numbers are written as 16, 3, and 10 rather than their actual values 0.0016, 0.003, and 0.010. Since a proportion is formed from these numbers and the unknown c, this procedure is permissible, provided the value obtained for c is rounded off to the nearest integer and this result is added to the last digit of the smaller logarithm.

Example 2

Find the value of log 872.6.

SOLUTION: The mantissa that is equal to log 8.726 is found by interpolating:

$$10\left[\;6\begin{bmatrix}\log 8.720 = 0.9405\\ \log 8.726 = \quad ?\end{bmatrix}c \atop \log 8.730 = 0.9410\right]5$$

$$\frac{c}{5} = \frac{6}{10}, \qquad \text{or} \quad c = 5\left(\frac{6}{10}\right) = 3.$$

Therefore,

$$\log 8.726 = 0.9408 \qquad \text{and} \qquad \log 872.6 = 2.9408.$$

Example 3

If $\log N = 0.3661$, find N correct to four significant digits.

SOLUTION: The mantissa 0.3661 does not occur in Table III, but the two consecutive entries between which 0.3661 lies are 0.3655 and 0.3674. Then the antilogarithm of 0.3661 is between the antilogarithms of these two consecutive entries. The work of computing it by using the proportional-parts method follows:

$$10\left[\;f\begin{bmatrix}\log 2.320 = 0.3655\\ \log N = 0.3661\end{bmatrix}6 \atop \log 2.330 = 0.3674\right]19$$

The proportion is

$$\frac{f}{10} = \frac{6}{19}, \qquad \text{or} \quad f = 10\left(\frac{6}{19}\right) = 3.$$

Hence, by adding the 3 to the last digit of the smaller of the two antilogarithms, we get

$$N = 2.323.$$

In interpolating for antilogarithms, the value f we calculate from the proportion will always represent the fourth digit of the number sought.

Example 4

If $\log N = 2.9580$, find N.

SOLUTION: We ignore the characteristic until we get the antilogarithm of 0.9580, and then use it to locate the decimal point. By locating the entries in Table III between which our logarithm lies, and noting their antilogarithms, we have

$$10\left[\;f\begin{bmatrix}\log 9.070 = 0.9576\\ \log \quad ? \quad = 0.9580\end{bmatrix}4 \atop \log 9.080 = 0.9581\right]5.$$

By proportional parts,

$$\frac{f}{10} = \frac{4}{5}, \qquad \text{or} \quad f = 10\left(\frac{4}{5}\right) = 8.$$

Hence, the antilogarithm of 0.9580 is 9.078. Therefore, since the characteristic of $\log N$ is 2, the decimal point must be moved two places to the right of standard position to get

$$N = 907.8.$$

In the process of interpolating, when the correction before rounding off ends in 5, we shall follow the computer's rule:

Drop the 5 and leave the other digits of the correction unchanged, or drop the 5 and add 1 to the preceding digit, whichever makes the final digit of the logarithm or antilogarithm *even*.

Note: At first the student should write out interpolation exercises in the form illustrated in this section to insure an understanding of the principle involved in interpolation. Later he may wish to do part of the work mentally. To this end, one observes that the method given above for finding the correction c or the fourth digit f amounts to using one or the other of the formulas:

$$c = \frac{f}{10}\,(\text{tabular difference}),$$

$$f = 10\left(\frac{\text{partial difference}}{\text{tabular difference}}\right),$$

where "tabular difference" is the difference between two logarithms in the table, and "partial difference" is the difference between a given logarithm and the logarithm in the table just less than it. These differences may be obtained mentally without writing down the logarithms involved, and in some cases, all arithmetic may be carried out mentally. The reader's skill should determine how much of this arithmetic he attempts to do mentally. Accuracy should not be sacrificed for speed.

In a computation problem involving several operations, it is especially important to maintain an orderly pattern for the work. Making a skeleton outline for the entire solution before looking up any logarithms is a great aid to speed and accuracy. Interpolation calculations may be written at one side of the sheet, apart from the main outline of the problem.

EXERCISES

Find the logarithms of the numbers in Exercises 1 through 15.

1. 3.876	**2.** 7.659	**3.** 22.83	**4.** 52.87	**5.** 874.5
6. 934.2	**7.** 0.07542	**8.** 0.3728	**9.** 28.91	**10.** 178.2
11. 4864	**12.** 0.008951	**13.** 124,400	**14.** 0.06423	**15.** 0.9768

Find the numbers corresponding to the logarithms in Exercises 16 through 33.

16. $\log N = 0.6143$
17. $\log N = 0.9496$
18. $\log N = 1.7342$
19. $\log N = 3.4645$
20. $\log N = 2.3268$
21. $\log N = 0.4459 - 2$
22. $\log N = 9.6591 - 10$
23. $\log N = 4.8672$
24. $\log N = 1.5326$
25. $\log N = 8.7650 - 10$
26. $\log N = 3.2156$
27. $\log N = 9.7393 - 10$
28. $\log N = 4.2163$
29. $\log N = 1.8649$
30. $\log N = 8.7152 - 10$
31. $\log N = 5.6847$
32. $\log N = 1.1812$
33. $\log N = 2.1926$

Use logarithms to perform the indicated computations in Exercises 34 through 57.

34. $(32.63)(459.8)$
35. $(9.862)(12.85)$
36. $(7.615)(0.0434)$
37. $\dfrac{86.37}{3.862}$
38. $\dfrac{965.6}{5.972}$
39. $\dfrac{3824}{27.63}$
40. $(29.78)^2$
41. $(7.875)^3$
42. $(0.6342)^4$
43. $\sqrt{48.83}$
44. $\sqrt[3]{674.9}$
45. $\sqrt[5]{1046}$
46. $\dfrac{284,300}{946.8}$
47. $(0.06235)^5$
48. $\sqrt[7]{562,800}$
49. $(263.8)(0.04279)$
50. $\sqrt[6]{83.67}$
51. $\sqrt[4]{45,830}$
52. $\dfrac{(24.43)(628.5)}{36.82}$
53. $\dfrac{(6.857)(19,820)}{238.4}$
54. $(0.6829)(4.372)^4$
55. $(863.7)(0.5862)^3$
56. $24.85\sqrt[3]{562.3}$
57. $1286\sqrt[6]{7.831}$

8.14 Further Practice in Logarithmic Computation

As was suggested in the preceding section, it is a good practice in logarithmic computations to make an outline for the entire solution at the outset, with interpolation calculations to be written apart at the side of the sheet. In our illustrative examples in this section, in order to save space, we shall not write out the calculations involved in interpolating, but shall merely list the result.

There are two places in logarithmic computation in which usual procedures would produce a logarithm containing a negative decimal. This must be avoided because the table of logarithms consists of positive mantissas. The artifices used to handle the situations are explained in the examples below.

Example 1

Use logarithms to find the value of

$$x = \frac{32.64}{757.2}$$

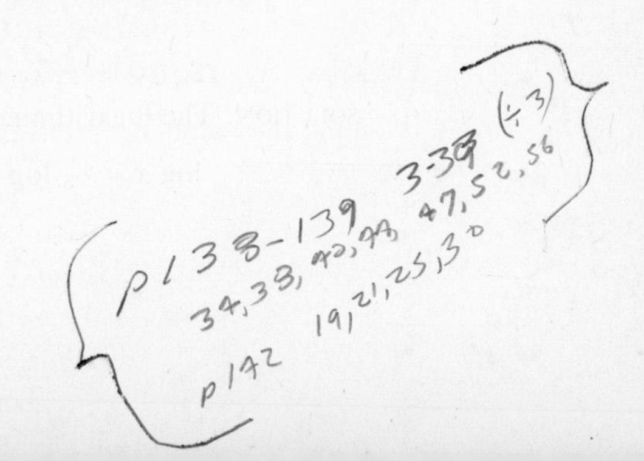

SOLUTION: The logarithmic equation for this problem is

$$\log x = \log 32.64 - \log 757.2.$$

By making the skeleton outline, looking up the necessary logarithms, and performing the required operations, we get the following:

$$\begin{aligned} \log 32.64 &= 1.5137 = 11.5137 - 10 \\ \underline{\log 757.2} &\underline{= 2.8792 = 2.8792} \\ \log x &= 8.6345 - 10 \\ x &= 0.04310 \end{aligned}$$

Notice that in this problem the logarithm of the numerator is smaller than the logarithm of the denominator, and hence subtracting in the original forms would have led to a negative decimal. This was avoided by writing the logarithm of the numerator in the form 11.5137 – 10, which is equivalent to adding and subtracting 10.

Example 2

Use logarithms to find the value of $x = \sqrt{0.365}$.

SOLUTION: The logarithmic equation is

$$\log x = \tfrac{1}{2} \log 0.365.$$

Now

$$\log 0.365 = 0.5623 - 1 = 19.5623 - 20.$$

Therefore,

$$\log x = \tfrac{1}{2} \log 0.365 = 9.7812 - 10.$$

Hence,

$$x = 0.6042.$$

Notice that the negative characteristic, -1, is not exactly divisible by 2. Hence, the logarithm is written as 19.5623 – 20, the negative part of which is exactly divisible by 2. Obviously, the logarithm could also be written in many other ways, such as 3.5623 – 4, etc. The custom of choosing a form such that the negative part of the final logarithm is -10 is due to some circumstances connected with the use of logarithms in trigonometry.

Example 3

Use logarithms to find the value of

$$x = \frac{\sqrt[3]{0.02367}(948.4)}{34.5}.$$

SOLUTION: The logarithmic equation is

$$\log x = \tfrac{1}{3} \log 0.02367 + \log 948.4 - \log 34.5.$$

The outline and numerical work follow:

$$\log 0.02367 = 0.3742 - 2 = 28.3742 - 30.$$

(The characteristic is written in this form to permit dividing by 3 without introducing a negative decimal.)

$$\begin{aligned} \tfrac{1}{3} \log 0.02367 &= 9.4581 - 10 \\ \log 948.4 &= 2.9770 \\ \hline \log \text{numerator} &= 12.4351 - 10 \\ \log 34.5 &= 1.5378 \\ \hline \log x &= 10.8973 - 10 \\ x &= 7.894 \end{aligned}$$

8.15 Other Bases for Systems of Logarithms

Any positive number except 1 can serve as a base for a system of logarithms. Since we write numbers in the decimal system, logarithms to the base 10 are usually best for making numerical calculations. Also, the natural logarithms, which have the irrational number e (approximate value 2.71828) as a base, have been mentioned as being of much importance. The number e is defined by

$$e = \lim_{h \to 0} (1 + h)^{1/h}$$

This number e, like the number π, arises in the most diverse and surprising places, such as biology, physics, and statistics—to name only a few.

There are two equations that hold where b is any base of a system of logarithms:

$$\log_b 1 = 0 \qquad \text{and} \qquad \log_b b = 1.$$

One problem that sometimes arises is that of finding the logarithm of a number to a base b if its logarithm to another base a is known. The equation showing the relation between the two logarithms is obtained as follows.

If we let $\log_a N = x$, then $N = a^x$. Taking logarithms to the base b of both sides of the latter equation, we have

$$\log_b N = x \log_b a.$$

Hence,

$$\log_b N = (\log_b a) \log_a N.$$

The number $\boldsymbol{\log_b a}$ is called the **modulus** of the system of logarithms to the base b with respect to the system of logarithms to the base a.

For example, the relation between natural and common logarithms is given by

$$\log_e N = (\log_e 10) \log_{10} N,$$

or

$$\log_{10} N = (\log_{10} e) \log_e N.$$

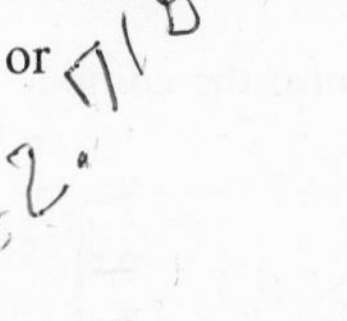

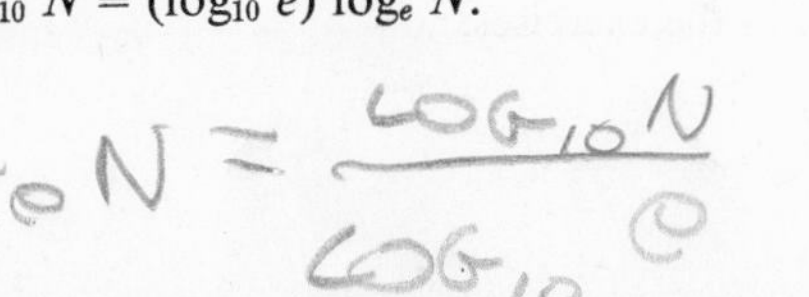

Now $\log_e 10 = 2.303$ † and $\log_{10} e = 0.4343$, so that

$$\log_e N = 2.303 \log_{10} N$$

and

$$\log_{10} N = 0.4343 \log_e N.$$

EXERCISES

Use logarithms to calculate the values in Exercises 1 through 31.

1. $\dfrac{(24.62)(685.3)}{495.6}$ **2.** $978\sqrt[4]{54.83}$ **3.** $\dfrac{(69.45)^3}{387.2}$

4. $\dfrac{0.3724}{9.677}$ **5.** $\dfrac{8847}{(351)^2}$ **6.** $\sqrt[3]{0.8656}$

7. $\sqrt[7]{0.004529}$ **8.** $\dfrac{(2.43)(7.682)}{86{,}920}$ **9.** $(0.047)(1.326)^7$

10. $(12.8)^6(0.03742)^3$ **11.** $\dfrac{(6.487)^2}{(25.32)^3}$ **12.** $\dfrac{(2.463)(82.56)}{(763.2)^2}$

13. $62.3\sqrt[5]{0.006215}$ **14.** $\dfrac{\sqrt[4]{0.09634}}{216.5}$ **15.** $\dfrac{\sqrt[6]{29{,}670}}{(2.58)^3}$

16. $\dfrac{(43.47)\sqrt{62.41}}{8.346}$ **17.** $\dfrac{(56.72)(48.3)}{\sqrt{0.8265}}$ **18.** $\dfrac{(5.289)^3}{\sqrt[3]{0.6375}}$

19. $\dfrac{(8.73)^5(42.7)^3}{983{,}400}$ **20.** $(12.5)^3\sqrt[4]{0.5728}$ **21.** $\dfrac{42.6\sqrt[3]{0.7532}}{(2.78)^6}$

22. $\dfrac{39.39\sqrt[7]{0.00521}}{(62.3)^3}$ **23.** $\dfrac{(2.567)^2\sqrt[8]{6420}}{(8.564)^4}$

24. $\sqrt{(4.3)(67.5)(386.4)(950.1)}$ **25.** $\sqrt{\dfrac{(2.86)(9.53)(12.02)}{75.12}}$

26. $(75.28)^2(0.00473)^{1/3}$ **27.** $\dfrac{(75.62)^{1/5}}{(0.0246)^{1/2}}$

28. $(3.482)^{1.41}$ **29.** $(412.7)^{.717}$

30. $\left[\dfrac{(25.6)^{.42}}{\sqrt[7]{(0.05821)}}\right]^{1/5}$ **31.** $\left[\dfrac{\sqrt[5]{0.06753}}{(8.52)^{0.17}}\right]^3$

32. Use logarithms to calculate the circumference and area of a circle of radius 56.28 in. (Formulas are $C = 2\pi r$ and $A = \pi r^2$.)

33. Find the volume of a sphere of radius 123.5 ft. (Formula: $V = \frac{4}{3}\pi r^3$.)

34. Find the number of seconds required for one complete oscillation of a simple

† This is rounded off to three decimal places in order to minimize the computation required in the exercises.

pendulum of length $l = 5.623$ ft if the acceleration due to gravity g is 32.16. (Formula: $T = 2\pi\sqrt{l/g}$.)

35. Find the area of a triangle whose sides are of lengths 24.16 in., 36.72 in., and 48.54 in., respectively. [Formula: $A = \sqrt{s(s-a)(s-b)(s-c)}$, where a, b, and c are the lengths of the sides and $s = \frac{1}{2}(a+b+c)$.]

36. Find the volume of a right circular cylinder of altitude $h = 7.325$ ft and radius of base $r = 3.526$ ft. (Formula: $V = \pi r^2 h$.)

Use Table III and the formulas of Section 8.15 to calculate the natural logarithms (round off to three decimal places) given in Exercises 37 through 44.

37. $\log_e 3$ **38.** $\log_e 7$ **39.** $\log_e 12$ **40.** $\log_e 25$

41. $\log_e 60$ **42.** $\log_e 100$ **43.** $\log_e 256$ **44.** $\log_e 873$

45. Prove: $(\log_b a) \cdot (\log_a b) = 1$.

8.16 Inverse Functions

To develop an example of the concept of an **inverse function,** let us first consider the function f with domain the set of nonnegative integers and the rule $f(x) = x^2$. The range of f is clearly the set of perfect square integers. Now define a function g with its domain the range of f, that is, the set of perfect square integers, and with its rule given by

$$g(y) = x \quad \text{if and only if} \quad f(x) = y \qquad [8.10]$$

This means that the image of an element y under the function g is found by asking what element the function f maps onto y. Thus, $g(4) = 2$ because $f(2) = 4$; $g(9) = 3$ because $f(3) = 9$, etc. In general, $g(y) = \sqrt{y}$ because $f(\sqrt{y}) = y$. The *range* of g is clearly the set of nonnegative integers, which is the *domain* of f. The function g is called the **inverse** of f, and vice versa.

In general, if g and f are two functions related so that the domain of each is the range of the other and

$$g(y) = x \quad \text{if and only if} \quad f(x) = y,$$

then g and f are called **inverses** of each other.

In order that a function f have an inverse, it is necessary that f be one-to-one. For if, for example,

$$f(a) = y \quad \text{and} \quad f(b) = y \text{ also, with } a \neq b,$$

and we tried to define an inverse function g as above, we would have

$$g(y) = a \quad \text{because} \quad f(a) = y,$$

and

$$g(y) = b \quad \text{because} \quad f(b) = y.$$

Thus, g would not be a function because it does not assign to y a unique number.

Any function f that is one-to-one does have an inverse because in this case rule [8.10] does define a function g whose domain is the range of f and whose range is the domain of f.

The graph of a one-to-one function has the property that a horizontal line meets the graph in no more than one point, and if the graph of a function has this property, then the function is one-to-one and thus has an inverse. The graph of the inverse function is obtainable from that of the original function by interchanging the roles of the x-axis and the y-axis.

In the preceding example of the two functions defined by $f(x) = x^2$ and $g(y) = \sqrt{y}$, let us combine the two functions by the operation of composition as defined in Section 1.8.

$$g(f)(x) = g(f(x)) = g(x^2) = x,$$
$$f(g)(y) = f(g(y)) = f(\sqrt{y}) = y.$$

Thus, both $g(f)$ and $f(g)$ is the identity function, that is, each maps an element onto itself. But the domain (and range) of $g(f)$ is the set of nonnegative integers, whereas the domain (and range) of $f(g)$ is the set of perfect square integers.

In the following sections we shall exhibit two important functions that are inverses of each other, and in trigonometry we shall again encounter some important instances of inverse functions.

If the symbol f is used to denote a function, then the symbol f^{-1} denotes the inverse of the function f.

8.17 Exponential Functions

The function f with the real numbers as domain defined by $f(x) = 2^x$ is an example of an **exponential function.** Its range is the set of positive real numbers. A graph of this function is shown in Fig. 8–1. Observe that the curve continually rises and also gets steeper as it goes to the right. This means that $f(x)$ increases as x increases and at an increasing rate.

Functions involving exponential expressions arise in many different problems, in particular in situations involving growth and decay. A few examples follow.

Example 1

The number N of bacteria in a certain culture at the end of t hours is given by

$$N = 2000e^{0.2t}.$$

Example 2

The quantity Q of radium left after t years from an original amount of 500 mg is given approximately by

$$Q = 500(10)^{-0.0016t}.$$

Example 3

The relation of the velocity V of a nerve impulse to temperature T is given by a formula of the type

$$V = ke^{0.059T}$$

where k is a constant.

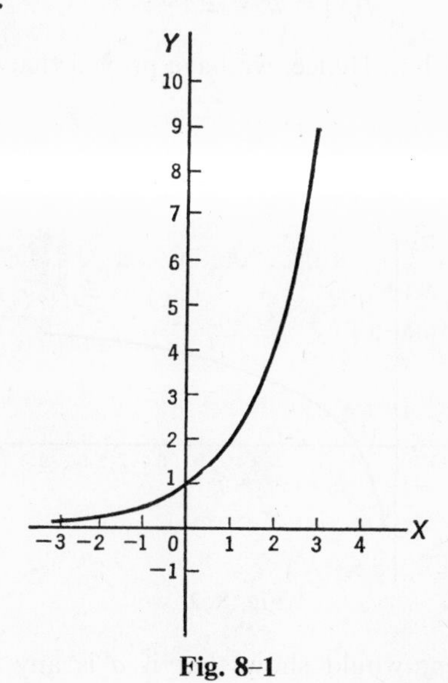

Fig. 8–1

8.18 Logarithmic Functions

The equation $g(x) = \log_2 x$, x positive, defines a function g with the positive real numbers as domain and the set of all real numbers as range. The graph of this function is shown in Fig. 8–2. Note that as it goes to the right, the graph continues to rise but tends to flatten out. This means that $g(x)$ increases with x but at a decreasing rate.

Notice that a table of logarithms, such as Table III in the back of this book, gives a function as a set of ordered pairs of numbers.

Let us study the relation of the function g, given by $g(x) = \log_2 x$, to the function f defined by $f(x) = 2^x$ in the preceding section. It is convenient to use another symbol such as y instead of x for the independent variable in the case of the function g; in this case, its rule is $g(y) = \log_2 y$.

First of all we note that the domain of g is the range of f, and vice versa. Thus, we may suspect that f and g are inverses of each other. Suppose $f(x) = y$, then is $g(y) = x$? Well, if $f(x) = y$, then $y = 2^x$ by the definition of f. Hence,

$$g(y) = \log_2 y = \log_2 2^x = x \log_2 2 = x \cdot 1 = x.$$

Thus, the answer to the question is "yes." Moreover, we can show that if $f(x) \neq y$, then $g(y) \neq x$; or, what is the same thing, if $g(y) = x$, then $f(x) = y$. For if $g(y) = x$, then $x = \log_2 y$ by the definition of g, and thus

$$f(x) = 2^x = 2^{\log_2 y} = y,$$

by definition of a logarithm. Hence, we have proved that

$$g(y) = x \qquad \text{if and only if} \qquad f(x) = y.$$

Thus, g and f are indeed inverses of each other.

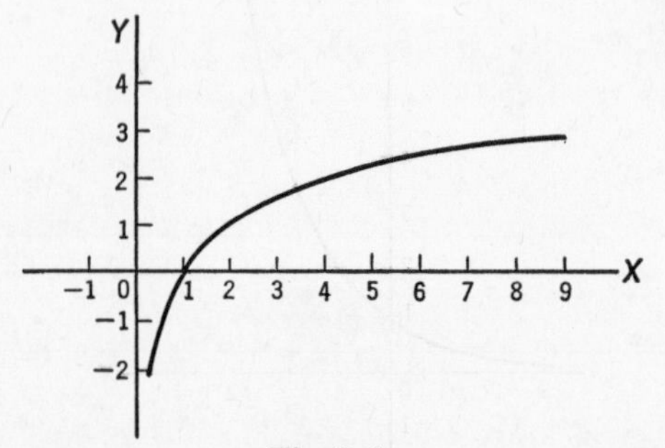

Fig. 8–2

The same argument would show that if a is any positive number, the functions f and g defined by

$$f(x) = a^x \qquad \text{and} \qquad g(x) = \log_a x$$

are inverses of each other.

Observe that the graph of the logarithm function given in Fig. 8–2 can be obtained from the graph of the exponential function given in Fig. 8–1 by rotating the page 90 degrees clockwise and then turning the page over so as to interchange the roles of the two coordinate axes.

8.19 Exponential and Logarithmic Equations

An equation such as $5^{2x-1} = 18$, which has the unknown in the exponent, is called an **exponential** equation. Frequently, such equations can be solved by taking logarithms of both sides of the equation.

Example 1

Solve $5^{2x-1} = 18$ for x.

SOLUTION: Taking common logarithms of both sides, we get

$$\log 5^{2x-1} = \log 18$$
$$(2x - 1) \log 5 = \log 18$$
$$2x - 1 = \frac{\log 18}{\log 5} = \frac{1.2553}{0.6990} = 1.7959$$
$$2x = 2.7959, \quad x = 1.3980$$

Notice that $\log 18/\log 5$ is the *quotient of two logarithms and is quite different from* $\log \frac{18}{5}$.

Example 2

Solve $7^{2x-1} = 3^{x+3}$ for x.

SOLUTION: Taking logarithms of both sides, we get

$$(2x - 1) \log 7 = (x + 3) \log 3$$
$$2x \log 7 - \log 7 = x \log 3 + 3 \log 3$$
$$2x \log 7 - x \log 3 = \log 7 + 3 \log 3$$
$$x(2 \log 7 - \log 3) = \log 7 + 3 \log 3$$
$$x = \frac{\log 7 + 3 \log 3}{2 \log 7 - \log 3} = \frac{0.8451 + 3(0.4771)}{2(0.8451) - 0.4771}$$
$$x = \frac{2.2764}{1.2131} = 1.8765$$

An equation such as $\log x + \log (2x - 1) = 2$, in which we have a logarithm of an expression containing the unknown, is called a **logarithmic** equation. Sometimes such equations can be easily solved by applying properties of logarithms.

Example 3

Solve $\log x + \log (2x - 1) = 2$ for x.

SOLUTION: Applying the first law of logarithms to the equation, we get

$$\log x(2x - 1) = 2.$$

This means that

$$x(2x - 1) = 10^2, \quad \text{or} \quad 2x^2 - x - 100 = 0.$$

The roots of this quadratic are $\frac{1 \pm \sqrt{801}}{4}$. Since negative numbers do not have real logarithms, we list only

$$x = \frac{1 + \sqrt{801}}{4}$$

as a root of the original equation.

EXERCISES

In Exercises 1 through 10, determine whether or not the indicated function f has an inverse function g. If so, give the domain of g and a rule for finding $g(y)$, where y denotes an element in the domain of g.

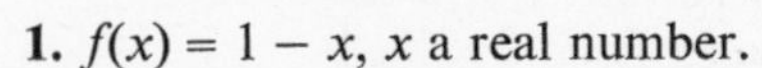

1. $f(x) = 1 - x$, x a real number.
2. $f(x) = x^2$, x a real number.
3. $f(x) = x^3$, x a real number.
4. $f(x) = x^{-1/3}$, x a real number and $x \neq 0$.
5. Define f to be the following ordered pairs:
   (a) $\{(0, 1), (1, -1), (2, 2), (3, -2), (4, 3)\}$
   (b) $\{(1, \pi), (2, \pi^2), (3, 3), (4, \pi), (5, 4)\}$
   (c) {(cats, pigs), (dogs, rabbits), (pencils, cows), (mud, pigs)}.
6. $f(x) = \sqrt{1 - x^2}$, all real x, $0 \leqq x \leqq 1$.
7. $f(x) = \sqrt{1 - x^4}$, all real x, $-1 \leqq x \leqq 1$.
8. Define f on the set of integers as follows:
   (a) $f(n) = \begin{cases} n & \text{if } n \text{ is even integer} \\ 2n & \text{if } n \text{ is odd integer} \end{cases}$
   (b) $f(n) = \begin{cases} n & \text{if } n \text{ is even integer} \\ -n & \text{if } n \text{ is odd integer} \end{cases}$
9. $f(x) = \begin{pmatrix} x & 0 \\ 0 & x^2 \end{pmatrix}$, x is an integer.
10. $f(x) = \begin{pmatrix} x & 0 \\ 0 & -x \end{pmatrix}$, x is an integer.

For the functions in Exercises 11 through 18, the domain in each case is the largest possible set of real numbers.

11. Plot a graph of $y = 10^x$. What is the domain and what is the range of this function?
12. Find the rule, domain, and range of the inverse of the function given in Exercise 11, and plot a graph of this inverse function.
13. Plot a graph of $y = e^x$. What is the domain and what is the range of this function?
14. Find the rule, domain, and range of the inverse of the function given in Exercise 13 and plot a graph of this inverse function.
15. Draw a graph of $y = \log_{10} x$. What is the domain and what is the range of this function?
16. Find the rule, domain, and range of the inverse of the function given in Exercise 15 and plot a graph of this inverse function.

17. Draw a graph of $y = \log_e x$. What is the domain and what is the rule of this function?

18. Find the rule, domain, and range of the inverse of the function given in Exercise 17, and plot a graph of this inverse function.

Solve the exponential and logarithmic equations in Exercises 19 through 40.

19. $2^{x-1} = 32$ **20.** $3^{2x-3} = 27$ **21.** $16^{x+1} = 64^{x-2}$

22. $6^{2x} = 53$ **23.** $11^{3x-1} = 43$ **24.** $15^{2x-1} = 7^{x+1}$

25. $7.5^{x} = 6^{2x}$ **26.** $7^{3x} = 3.9^{x+1}$ **27.** $(1.06)^{x} = 3$

28. $(1.035)^{x} = 2$ **29.** $(1.02)^{-x} = 0.375$ **30.** $(1.04)^{-x} = 0.523$

31. $\dfrac{(1.03)^{x} - 1}{0.03} = 6.248$ **32.** $\dfrac{(1.015)^{x} - 1}{0.015} = 12.834$

33. $\log 4x + \log x = 2$ **34.** $\log 12x^2 - \log 3x = 2$

35. $\log 6x^2 - \log 3x = 0.9031$ **36.** $\log 3x^2 + \log \dfrac{1}{x} = 0.7782$

37. $\log (x^2 - 1) - \log (x + 1) = 3$ **38.** $\log \sqrt{x + 1} = 1 - \frac{1}{2} \log x$

39. $\log (3x - 1) = -2 + \log (2x - 1)$ **40.** $\log (4x - 3) = 2 - \log 20$

The Trigonometric Functions

9.1 Angles

In this chapter and the next we study the subject of **trigonometry.** The word, derived from the Greek, literally means the measure of triangles. While trigonometry is used by surveyors for measuring distances by means of triangles, its most important modern applications are of a quite different character. We shall emphasize those aspects of the subject that are important for these modern uses. As is true in much of mathematics, the concept of a function is central.

First of all, we need a clear understanding of what an angle is.

If a half line or ray, originally in the position OA (see Fig. 9–1), rotates in a plane about the point O until it assumes the position OP, an **angle** AOP is

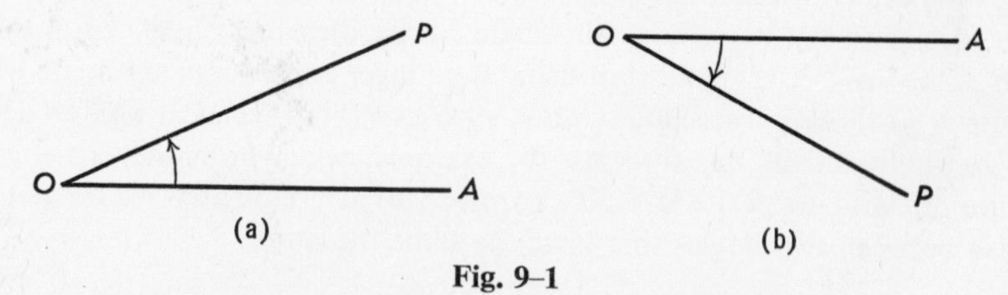

Fig. 9–1

said to be generated. The amount of rotation is the **measure** of the angle. The ray OA is called the **initial side** of the angle, and the ray OP is called the **terminal side.** The point O is called the **vertex.** Angles that are formed by a *counterclockwise* rotation, such as the one shown in Fig. 9–1(a), are said to have *positive* measure or to be *positive*. Angles that are generated by a *clockwise* rotation, like the one in Fig. 9–1(b), are said to have *negative* measure or to be *negative*. Thus, an angle has an *initial side* and a *terminal side* (both of which are rays originating at the same point), and a *measure*. There is no limit on the magnitude of the measure an angle can have, for the rotation can include any number of complete revolutions. Figure 9–2 exhibits angles of various measures, some positive and some negative.

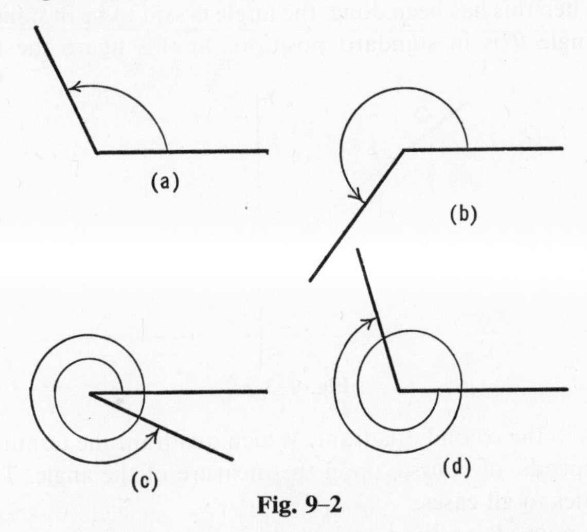

Fig. 9–2

In the measure of angles, as in the measure of anything else, a unit must be adopted. A unit frequently used is the **degree** (°), which is defined as the measure of $\frac{1}{360}$ of a complete revolution. The degree is divided into 60 equal parts called **minutes** (′), and each minute is divided into 60 equal parts called **seconds** (″). The form for expressing the measure of an angle is illustrated by 34° 16′ 42″. Another system of angular measure will be discussed in Section 10.3. An instrument called a **protractor** is used for measuring angles and constructing angles of specified measures.

It is customary to refer to an angle by its measure. Thus, we speak of a "30° angle" or "30°," instead of using the longer expression "an angle whose measure is 30°." Also, the same symbol, such as θ (read *theta*), is used to denote both an angle and its measure; as, for example, when θ denotes an angle of measure 30° and we write $\theta = 30°$. In much of trigonometry we do not distinguish between two angles that have the same measure.

9.2 The Six Trigonometric Functions

We now define six functions, each of which has a set of angles as domain and a set of real numbers as range. That is, in each case, we shall describe a rule that assigns to each angle in the domain of the function a definite real number in its range. The six functions to be defined are called **trigonometric functions,** and their individual names are **sine, cosine, tangent, cotangent, secant,** and **cosecant.**

If an angle of any measure be given, one can always construct a Cartesian coordinate reference frame in such a manner that the origin is at the vertex of the angle and the positive half of the x axis coincides with the initial side of the angle. When this has been done, the angle is said to be in **standard position.** In Fig. 9–3, angle θ is in standard position. In this figure the terminal side

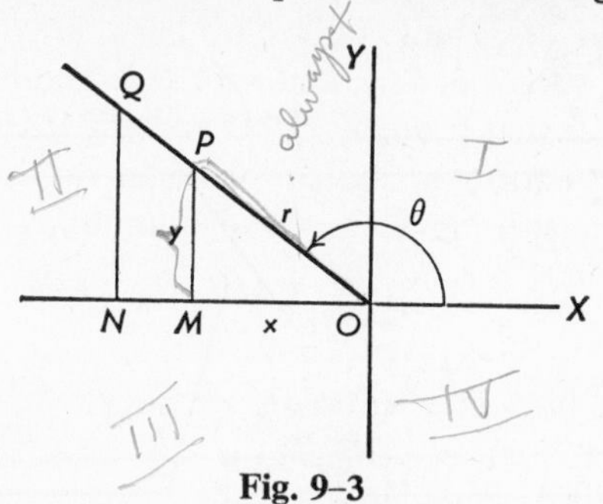

Fig. 9–3

of the angle lies in the second quadrant. Which quadrant the terminal side of an angle lies in depends, of course, upon the measure of the angle. The following discussion applies to all cases.

Select any point P on the terminal side of the angle θ except the vertex. This point has associated with it three numbers: its *abscissa*, its *ordinate*, and its *distance from the origin* (always positive), denoted, respectively, by x, y, and r. From these three numbers, six ratios can be formed. These ratios are the values of the six trigonometric functions referred to above and exhibited as follows:

$$\begin{aligned}
\text{sine } \theta &= \frac{y}{r} = \frac{\text{ordinate}}{\text{distance}} && \text{(written sin } \theta) \\
\text{cosine } \theta &= \frac{x}{r} = \frac{\text{abscissa}}{\text{distance}} && \text{(written cos } \theta) \\
\text{tangent } \theta &= \frac{y}{x} = \frac{\text{ordinate}}{\text{abscissa}} && \text{(written tan } \theta) \\
\text{cotangent } \theta &= \frac{x}{y} = \frac{\text{abscissa}}{\text{ordinate}} && \text{(written cot } \theta) \\
\text{secant } \theta &= \frac{r}{x} = \frac{\text{distance}}{\text{abscissa}} && \text{(written sec } \theta) \\
\text{cosecant } \theta &= \frac{r}{y} = \frac{\text{distance}}{\text{ordinate}} && \text{(written csc } \theta)
\end{aligned} \qquad [9.1]$$

Notice that the following are reciprocals:

$\sin \theta$ and $\csc \theta$, $\cos \theta$ and $\sec \theta$, $\tan \theta$ and $\cot \theta$

Formulas [9.1] constitute the rules of correspondence for the six trigonometric functions. That is, each formula is a rule that assigns to each value of the angle θ a corresponding number, expressed as a ratio of two numbers. We must check that in the case of each function the number assigned (that is, the value of the function) is uniquely determined by the value of θ. The choice of the point P was arbitrary. The question arises whether the values of sine θ, cos θ, and so forth, would be different if some other point on the terminal side of θ had been selected.

Certainly, if in Fig. 9–3 some point Q other than P were selected on the terminal side of θ, the values of x, y, and r for Q would be different from those of P. But due to the fact that triangles OPM and OQN are similar, the *ratios* of the values of x, y, and r for Q are equal to similar ratios of the values of x, y, and r for P. For example, using P and the definition in [9.1], we have

$$\sin \theta = \frac{MP}{OP}.$$

Using Q and applying the same definition, we have

$$\sin \theta = \frac{NQ}{OQ}.$$

But, since corresponding sides of similar triangles are proportional,

$$\frac{NQ}{OQ} = \frac{MP}{OP}.$$

Therefore, sin θ is the same whether the point P or any other point on the terminal side is used to define it. The same thing can be shown to be true for the other five expressions defined in [9.1]. In other words, these six expressions depend for their values *only on the angle* θ and not at all upon which point on its terminal side is selected as point P. Indeed, the values of these expressions depend only upon the *measure of* θ.

Trigonometry deals with the properties and applications of the six functions—sine, cosine, tangent, cotangent, secant, and cosecant—that we have just defined. The rules for these functions, given in [9.1], should be thoroughly memorized.

The sine function associates with each angle a real number between -1 and 1, inclusive, because

$$-1 \leqq \frac{y}{r} \leqq 1.$$

Thus, the *domain* of the sine function is the set of all angles, and its range is a set of real numbers from -1 to 1, inclusive. The *range* can be shown, by the method used below in discussing the tangent function, to be the set of *all* real numbers from -1 to 1, inclusive. The cosine function has the same domain and range as those of the sine.

For each of the remaining four trigonometric functions, the domain consists of almost, but not quite, all angles. For example, an angle of measure 90° does not belong to the domain of either the tangent or secant function. Indeed, all angles whose measures are *odd* multiples of 90° must be excluded from the domains of the tangent and secant, since for such angles any point on the terminal side has $x = 0$, and x occurs in the *denominator* in the values of both tangent and secant functions (see [9.1]). For a similar reason, *even* multiples of 90° are excluded from the domains of the cotangent and cosecant functions.

An angle may be constructed such that a point on its terminal side has y/x equal to *any preassigned real number n*. To do this, locate the point with coordinates $(1, n)$ and draw the ray from the origin through this point (see Fig. 9–4). For any angle θ in standard position with this ray as terminal side, we have

$$\tan \theta = \frac{y}{x} = n.$$

Thus, the *range* of the tangent function is the set of *all* real numbers. A similar argument shows that the range of the cotangent function is also the set of all real numbers.

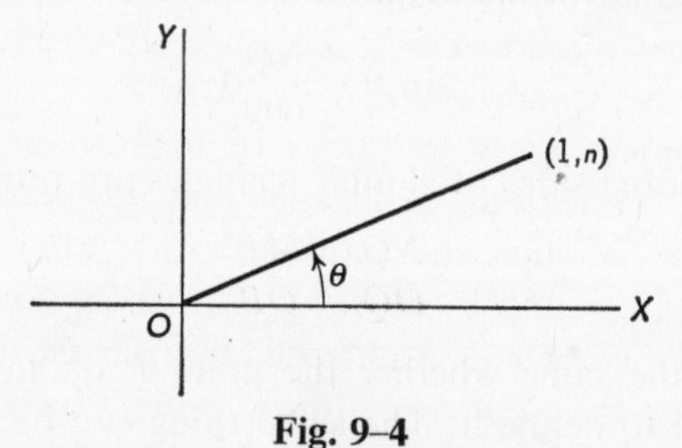

Fig. 9–4

The reader should use the definitions $\sec \theta = r/x$ and $\csc \theta = r/y$ to convince himself that the range for each of the secant and cosecant functions is the set of real numbers whose absolute values are 1 or greater, that is, the set of real numbers that are less than or equal to -1, or equal to or greater than 1.

The following table summarizes these results. In this summary the symbol n denotes a real number.

Function	Domain	Range
sine	set of all angles	$\{n \mid -1 \leqq n \leqq 1\}$
cosine	set of all angles	$\{n \mid -1 \leqq n \leqq 1\}$
tangent	set of all angles except *odd* multiples of 90°	$\{n \mid n \text{ a real number}\}$
cotangent	set of all angles except *even* multiples of 90°	$\{n \mid n \text{ a real number}\}$
secant	set of all angles except *odd* multiples of 90°	$\{n \mid n \leqq -1 \text{ or } n \geqq 1\}$
cosecant	set of all angles except *even* multiples of 90°	$\{n \mid n \leqq -1 \text{ or } n \geqq 1\}$

It is clear from the definitions that all angles with the same measure have the same set of values for their trigonometric functions.

9.3 Signs of Values of the Trigonometric Functions

The value of each trigonometric function is defined as the ratio of two numbers, and hence is positive if these numbers have the same sign and is negative if they have opposite signs. Thus, $\tan \theta$, which is defined as y/x, is positive if x and y are both positive or both negative. This occurs for points in the first and third quadrants only. Thus, $\tan \theta$ is positive if the terminal side of θ lies in the first or third quadrant and is negative or zero elsewhere.

By similar reasoning, the sign of the value of any trigonometric function of an angle can be determined from the definition of the function and the quadrant in which the terminal side of the angle lies. For example, $\cos \theta = x/r$ is negative if the terminal side of θ is in the second quadrant because points in the second quadrant have x negative and r is positive.

An angle in standard position whose terminal side lies in the first quadrant is said to be in the first quadrant or to be a first quadrant angle. Similar statements hold for the other quadrants.

A device for remembering the signs of the values of the trigonometric functions for angles in various quadrants may be derived by applying the previously mentioned fact that the value of a function is positive in case the two of the quantities x, y, and r occurring in its definition have the same sign. For the *first* quadrant, since x, y, and r are all positive, *all* trigonometric functions are positive. For the *second* quadrant, y and r have the same sign, since both are positive, and hence the *sine* and *cosecant* are positive. For the *third* quadrant, x and y have the same sign, both being negative, and hence the *tangent* and *cotangent* are positive. For the *fourth* quadrant, x and r have the same sign, both being positive, and hence the *cosine* and *secant* are positive. The diagram in Fig. 9–5 depicts these results and shows which functions are positive for angles in the various quadrants. The remaining ones are negative.

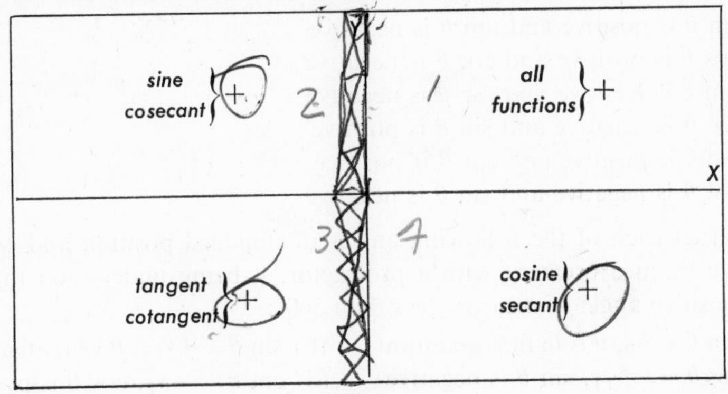

Fig. 9–5

EXERCISES

1. Is it possible for two angles to have the same initial side and the same terminal side and still not be identical? Explain.

2. What size angle does the minute hand of a clock generate from 3:00 to 5:00? Is this a positive or a negative angle?

3. What is the measure of the angle the hour hand of a clock generates from 3:00 to 8:00?

4. The flywheel of an engine makes 900 rpm. How large an angle does a spoke of the wheel generate in a second?

5. An airplane propeller is making 3000 rpm. How large an angle does it generate in a second?

Construct angles of the measures given in Exercises 6 and 7, using a protractor when necessary:

6. $38°$, $64°$, $142°$, $560°$, $-42°$, $-215°$

7. $15°$, $233°$, $465°$, $-27°$, $-130°$, $-535°$

8. Tell the algebraic sign of each of the following: $\tan 57°$, $\cos 136°$, $\sin 208°$, $\sec 313°$, $\cot 142°$, $\csc 290°$, $\tan 342°$, $\sin 98°$, $\cot 233°$, $\cos 196°$.

9. Tell the algebraic sign of each of the following: $\sec 255°$, $\tan 209°$, $\csc 143°$, $\cot 358°$, $\sin 295°$, $\tan 112°$, $\cos -9°$, $\csc -133°$, $\sec 456°$.

10. Give the algebraic signs of the values of the six trigonometric functions for each of the following angles: $124°$, $335°$, $217°$, $-28°$, $395°$, $-195°$, $610°$.

11. Tell in what quadrants the terminal side of θ can lie in each of the following cases:

(a) $\sin \theta = -2/3$ (b) $\cos \theta = 7/11$ (c) $\tan \theta = -2$
(d) $\sec \theta = -13/4$ (e) $\cot \theta = 3/7$ (f) $\csc \theta = 16/5$
(g) $\cos \theta = -0.75$ (h) $\tan \theta = 0.57$ (i) $\sec \theta = 3.62$
(j) $\cot \theta = -1.756$ (k) $\csc \theta = -2.583$ (l) $\sin \theta = 0.6583$

12. Tell in what quadrant the terminal side of θ lies if

(a) $\sin \theta$ is positive and $\tan \theta$ is negative
(b) $\cos \theta$ is positive and $\cot \theta$ is negative
(c) $\tan \theta$ is positive and $\csc \theta$ is negative
(d) $\sec \theta$ is negative and $\sin \theta$ is positive
(e) $\csc \theta$ is positive and $\cot \theta$ is positive
(f) $\cot \theta$ is negative and $\sin \theta$ is negative

13. Construct each of the following angles in standard position and compute its size by measurement with a protractor, it being understood that each is a positive angle of measure less than $360°$:

(a) $\tan \theta = 5/9$, θ is in first quadrant (b) $\sin \theta = 12/13$, θ is in quadrant II
(c) $\cos \theta = -8/11$, $\sin \theta$ is negative (d) $\cot \theta = -4/7$, $\cos \theta$ is positive

14. An angle θ in standard position has $\sin\theta = -3/5$. If the ordinate of a point on the angle's terminal side is -6, how far is the point from the origin?

15. An angle θ in standard position has $\tan\theta = 4/3$. If a point on the terminal side has -9 for abscissa, how far is the point from the origin?

Construct angles with measures listed in Exercises 16 through 19, and by making appropriate measurements, find approximate values for their trigonometric functions.

16. 73°, 137° **17.** 38°, 221°

18. 208°, 346° **19.** 118°, 665°

20. Prove that the range of the sine function is $\{n \mid -1 \leqq n \leqq 1\}$.

21. Prove that the range of the cosine function is $\{n \mid -1 \leqq n \leqq 1\}$.

22. Prove that the range of the secant function is $\{n \mid \ |n| \geqq 1\}$.

23. Use Fig. 9–3 and the definitions of the sine and cosine functions to prove: $(\sin\theta)^2 + (\cos\theta)^2 = 1$.

9.4 A Certain Type of Problem

An important and instructive type of problem is illustrated by the following examples.

Example 1

If $\sin\theta = 3/5$, construct the possible angles θ with measure between 0° and 360° and find the values of the other five functions of each angle.

SOLUTION: Since by definition $\sin\theta = y/r$, θ is an angle such that for a point on the terminal side $y/r = 3/5$. In particular, points for which $y = 3$ and $r = 5$ may be used to locate the terminal side of θ. We locate these points in Fig. 9–6 by the following considerations. Every point on a line parallel to

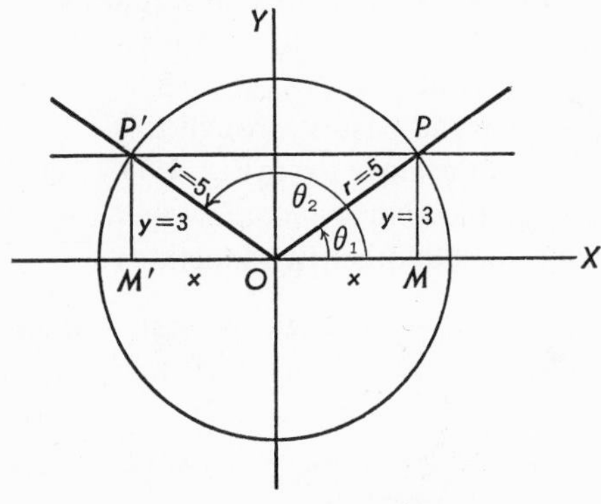

Fig. 9–6

169
144
25
13

the x axis and three units above it has $y = 3$, and every point on a circle of radius 5 with center at the origin has $r = 5$. The points P and P', where the line and the circle intersect, have both $y = 3$ and $r = 5$. Thus, joining P to the origin O, we get angle XOP as one value of θ, which we designate θ_1. Joining P' to O, we obtain angle XOP' as another value of θ, which we designate θ_2.

To find the abscissas of P and P', we apply the Pythagorean theorem to the right triangles OMP and $OM'P'$ of Fig. 9–6 and get

$$x^2 + y^2 = r^2, \quad x^2 + 9 = 25, \quad x^2 = 16.$$

Then

$$x = +4 \quad \text{or} \quad x = -4.$$

It is clear that $x = +4$ is the abscissa of P, and $x = -4$ is the abscissa of P'. Knowing the abscissa, ordinate, and distance of both P and P', one can write down the values of the remaining five functions of the two angles from the definitions of the functions. The results are listed in the table below.

	Quadrant I	**Quadrant II**
$\cos\theta$	$4/5$	$-4/5$
$\tan\theta$	$3/4$	$-3/4$
$\cot\theta$	$4/3$	$-4/3$
$\sec\theta$	$5/4$	$-5/4$
$\csc\theta$	$5/3$	$5/3$

Example 2

If $\tan\theta = -15/8$ and $\cos\theta$ is positive, construct the positive angle θ of measure less than 360° and find the values of its other five functions.

SOLUTION: Since $\tan\theta = y/x$, we must have

$$\frac{y}{x} = -\frac{15}{8}.$$

Also, since $\cos\theta$ is positive, x must be positive, for $\cos\theta = x/r$ and r is always positive. If we take $y = -15$ and $x = 8$, both conditions are satisfied. Locate the point $(8, -15)$. The ray that starts at the origin and passes through this point is the terminal side of the angle θ (see Fig. 9–7). Applying the Pythagorean theorem as before, we get $r = 17$. Hence, the values of the other five functions are:

$$\sin\theta = -15/17$$
$$\cos\theta = 8/17$$
$$\cot\theta = -8/15$$
$$\sec\theta = 17/8$$
$$\csc\theta = -17/15$$

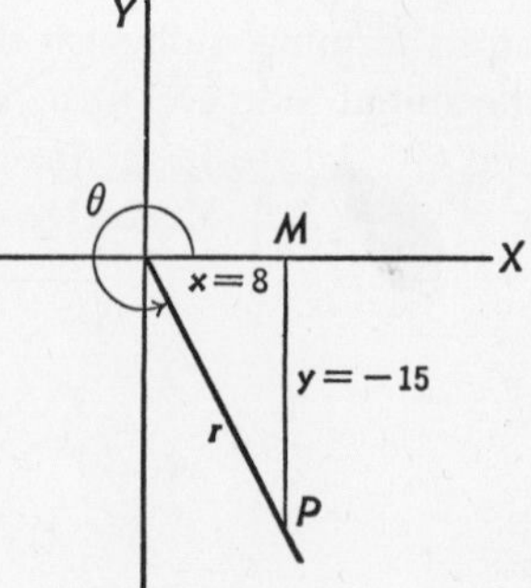

Fig. 9–7

9.5 Special Angles

The values of the trigonometric functions of certain special angles can be found by using some elementary geometry. Consider an equilateral triangle ABC as in Fig. 9–8, each of whose sides we take to be two units in length. Since an equilateral triangle is necessarily equiangular, each of its angles is of measure 60°. Now drop a perpendicular CD from C to the opposite side. In right triangles ACD and BCD, $AC = BC$, and angle A = angle B, and thus the triangles are congruent. Hence, the measure of angle ACD is one half the measure of C, or 30°, and $AD = \frac{1}{2}AB = 1$. Applying the Pythagorean theorem to right triangle ADC, we have

$$(DC)^2 = (AC)^2 - (AD)^2 = 2^2 - 1^2 = 3.$$

Thus $DC = \sqrt{3}$. Referring to triangle ADC, we have proved that in a triangle with angles 30°, 60°, and 90°, and hypotenuse 2, the sides opposite these angles are equal to 1, $\sqrt{3}$, and 2, respectively. In a 30–60–90 triangle of any size the sides are *proportional* to the three numbers 1, $\sqrt{3}$, and 2.

Let us find the values of the trigonometric functions of 30°. Construct an angle of measure 30° in standard position (see Fig. 9–9), and select a point P

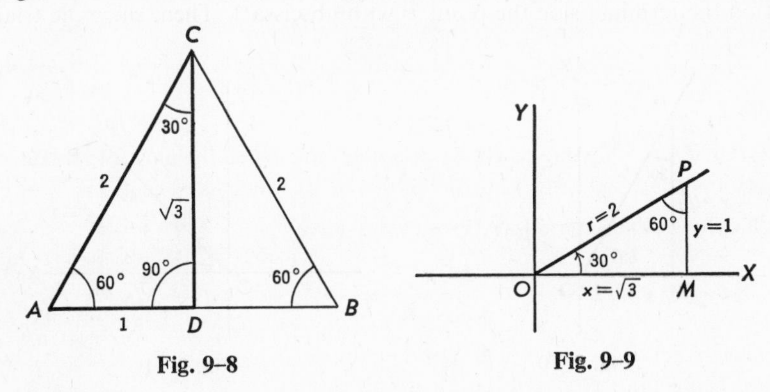

Fig. 9–8

Fig. 9–9

on its terminal side such that $OP = 2$. By dropping a perpendicular from P to the initial side we form a right triangle OPM, whose acute angles are 30° and 60°. Utilizing the property of a 30–60–90 triangle just developed, we have $x = \sqrt{3}$, $r = 2$. Hence we obtain

$$\sin 30^\circ = \frac{1}{2} \qquad \cot 30^\circ = \frac{\sqrt{3}}{1} = \sqrt{3}$$

$$\cos 30^\circ = \frac{\sqrt{3}}{2} \qquad \sec 30^\circ = \frac{2}{\sqrt{3}} = \frac{2\sqrt{3}}{3}$$

$$\tan 30^\circ = \frac{1}{\sqrt{3}} = \frac{\sqrt{3}}{3} \qquad \csc 30^\circ = \frac{2}{1} = 2$$

Construct an angle of measure 120° in standard position as in Fig. 9–10. Making use of the property of a 30–60–90 triangle mentioned above, we can select a point on the terminal side of this angle such that $x = -1$, $y = \sqrt{3}$, and $r = 2$. Hence we have

$$\sin 120° = \frac{\sqrt{3}}{2}$$

$$\cos 120° = -\frac{1}{2}$$

$$\tan 120° = \frac{\sqrt{3}}{-1} = -\sqrt{3}$$

$$\cot 120° = \frac{-1}{\sqrt{3}} = -\frac{\sqrt{3}}{3}$$

$$\sec 120° = \frac{2}{-1} = -2$$

$$\csc 120° = \frac{2}{\sqrt{3}} = \frac{2\sqrt{3}}{3}$$

Construct an angle of measure 45° in standard position as in Fig. 9–11. Select on the terminal side the point P with abscissa 1. Then, since the triangle

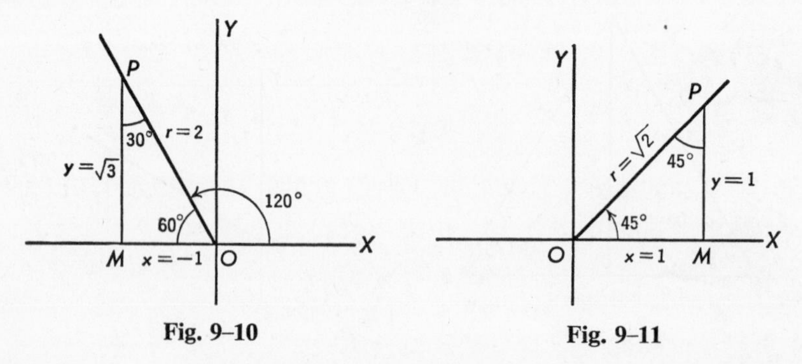

Fig. 9–10

Fig. 9–11

OMP has angle MOP and angle OPM each 45°, the triangle is isosceles, and the ordinate of P is also 1. By the Pythagorean theorem, $r^2 = x^2 + y^2 = 1 + 1 = 2$. Therefore, $r = \sqrt{2}$. Hence, we have

$$\sin 45° = \frac{1}{\sqrt{2}} = \frac{\sqrt{2}}{2} \qquad \cot 45° = \frac{1}{1} = 1$$

$$\cos 45° = \frac{1}{\sqrt{2}} = \frac{\sqrt{2}}{2} \qquad \sec 45° = \frac{\sqrt{2}}{1} = \sqrt{2}$$

$$\tan 45° = \frac{1}{1} = 1 \qquad \csc 45° = \frac{\sqrt{2}}{1} = \sqrt{2}$$

By the process employed in the preceding examples, values for the trigonometric functions can be found for any angle whose terminal side forms with the horizontal axis an angle of measure 30°, 45°, or 60°. Other examples of such angles are 150°, 240°, 315°, 390°, etc.

9.6 Quadrantal Angles

Angles with measures such as 0°, 90°, 180°, 270°, 360°, and 450°, whose terminal sides fall along one or the other of the coordinate axes, are called **quadrantal angles.** The values of their functions (if they exist) can easily be found from a figure.

Let us consider as typical an angle of measure 90°. In Fig. 9–12, choose a point P on the terminal side of 90° such that $OP = 1$. Then the point P has

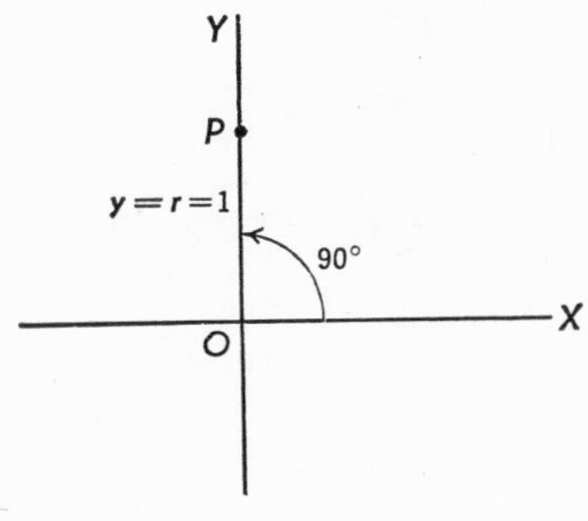

Fig. 9–12

$x = 0$, $y = 1$, and $r = 1$. Hence the values of the functions for an angle of 90° are as follows:

$$\sin 90° = 1/1 = 1$$
$$\cos 90° = 0/1 = 0$$
$$\tan 90° = 1/0 \text{ (not defined)}$$
$$\cot 90° = 0/1 = 0$$
$$\sec 90° = 1/0 \text{ (not defined)}$$
$$\csc 90° = 1/1 = 1$$

The definitions for the values of the tangent and secant functions when applied to 90° lead to the expression $1/0$. Since division by zero is *not* a permissible operation, $1/0$ is not a number; hence, tan 90° and sec 90° do not exist. That is, an angle of measure 90° does not belong to the domain of either the tangent or the secant function.

The values of the functions that exist can be found for any one of the quadrantal angles by the process we used on 90°. In each case, values of two of the functions will fail to exist. For example, an angle of measure 180° does not belong to the domain of either the cotangent or cosecant function.

EXERCISES

In Exercises 1 through 6 the value of a trigonometric function of an angle θ is given. Construct all angles θ of measure between 0° and 360°, and find the values of the remaining five trigonometric functions of each angle.

1. $\sin\theta = 4/5$ **2.** $\cos\theta = 12/13$ **3.** $\tan\theta = -3/2$
4. $\sec\theta = 13/5$ **5.** $\csc\theta = -7/4$ **6.** $\cot\theta = -2/5$

From the data given in each of Exercises 7 through 12, construct an angle and find the value of its trigonometric functions.

7. $\cot\theta = -4/3$ ($\sin\theta$ is positive)
8. $\cos\theta = -3/7$ (θ of positive measure less than 180°)
9. $\sec\theta = 17/8$ ($\tan\theta$ is negative)
10. $\csc\theta = -25/7$ ($\cos\theta$ is negative)
11. $\tan\theta = 2$ (θ not in quadrant I)
12. $\sec\theta = 3/2$ (θ not in quadrant I)
13. If $\csc A = m/n$, m and n both positive, $m > n$, and A acute, find the values of the other functions of A.
14. If $\tan\theta = -\dfrac{\sqrt{15}}{7}$ and θ is in the fourth quadrant, find the value of $\dfrac{\csc\theta}{\cos\theta\cot\theta}$.
15. If $\cot\theta = -4/3$ and $\csc\theta$ is negative, find the value of $2\sin\theta\cos\theta$.
16. Find the value of $\dfrac{\sin\theta - \cos\theta}{\sin\theta + \cos\theta}$, if $\cot\theta = -1/2$ and $\sec\theta$ is negative.
17. Find the value of $\sqrt{\dfrac{1-\cos\theta}{1+\cos\theta}}$, if $\sin\theta = 24/25$ and $\sec\theta$ is positive.
18. Is it possible to determine θ uniquely if all that is known about θ is the value of $\sin\theta$?

Construct an appropriate figure and find the values of the trigonometric functions for each of the angles in Exercises 19 through 33.

19. 60° **20.** 135° **21.** 225° **22.** 240° **23.** 150°
24. 210° **25.** 180° **26.** 360° **27.** 315° **28.** 300°
29. 0° **30.** 270° **31.** 450° **32.** 585° **33.** −225°

34. By constructing appropriate figures and computing values of the functions involved, obtain the values of:
(a) $\sin 120° \cos 30° + \cos 120° \sin 30°$
(b) $\cos 315° \cos 60° - \sin 315° \sin 60°$
(c) $\cos 270° \cos 150° + \sin 270° \sin 150°$
(d) $\sin 330° \cos 180° - \cos 330° \sin 180°$

35. By constructing appropriate figures and obtaining values of the functions involved, compute the values of:

(a) $2 \sin 240° \cos 240°$ (b) $(\cos 330° + \sin 330°)^2$

(c) $\dfrac{\tan 210° + \tan 135°}{1 - \tan 210° \tan 135°}$ (d) $\dfrac{\tan 300° - \tan 225°}{1 + \tan 300° \tan 225°}$

36. Find all measures of θ between 0° and 360° corresponding to each of the following:

(a) $\sin \theta = \frac{1}{2}$ (b) $\cos \theta = 1$ (c) $\tan \theta = -1$

(d) $\sec \theta = -2$ (e) $\cot \theta = 0$ (f) $\csc \theta = -\sqrt{2}$

37. Find all measures of θ between 0° and 360° corresponding to each of the following:

(a) $\tan \theta = \sqrt{3}$ (b) $\cos \theta = \dfrac{\sqrt{2}}{2}$ (c) $\csc \theta = -2$

(d) $\sec \theta = -\sqrt{2}$ (e) $\sin \theta = -1$ (f) $\cot \theta = -\dfrac{\sqrt{3}}{3}$

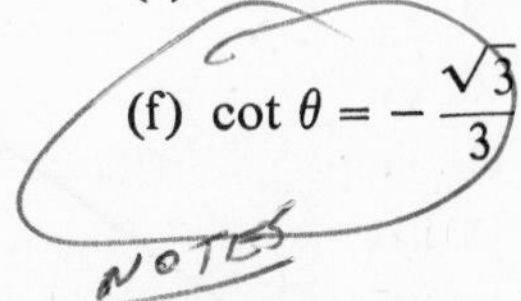

9.7 Trigonometric Functions of Positive Acute Angles

In case the angle θ is a positive acute angle (an angle of measure between 0° and 90°), the quantities x, y, and r—all being positive—can be regarded as the lengths of the adjacent side, opposite side, and hypotenuse, respectively, of a right triangle of which θ is one of the acute angles, as shown in Fig. 9–13. Hence, for *positive acute angles*, the values of the trigonometric functions may be stated by equations [9.2] below, where we use the name of a side to denote its length.

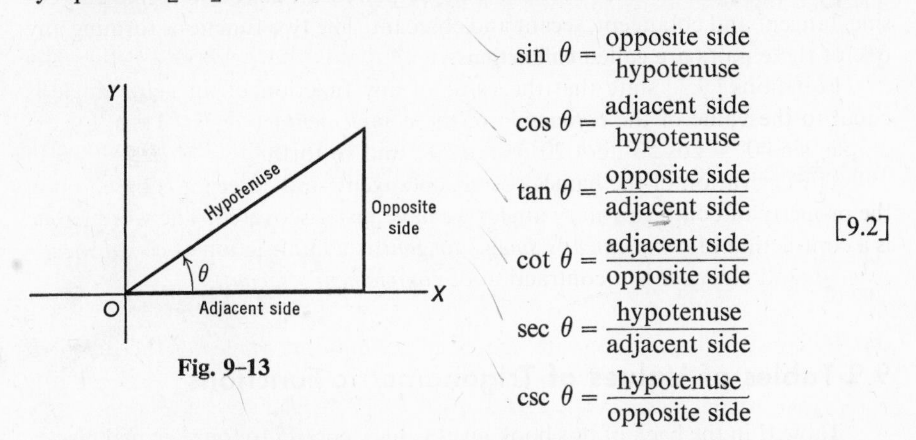

Fig. 9–13

$$\sin \theta = \frac{\text{opposite side}}{\text{hypotenuse}}$$
$$\cos \theta = \frac{\text{adjacent side}}{\text{hypotenuse}}$$
$$\tan \theta = \frac{\text{opposite side}}{\text{adjacent side}}$$
$$\cot \theta = \frac{\text{adjacent side}}{\text{opposite side}} \qquad [9.2]$$
$$\sec \theta = \frac{\text{hypotenuse}}{\text{adjacent side}}$$
$$\csc \theta = \frac{\text{hypotenuse}}{\text{opposite side}}$$

Note that these statements of the definitions apply to *positive acute angles only*. However, they are very useful and should be carefully memorized.

9.8 Complementary Angles

Some interesting relations exist between values of trigonometric functions of any two positive acute angles the sum of whose measures is 90°. Such angles are called **complementary.** Let A and B be any two complementary angles. A right triangle can be constructed with its acute angles equal in measure to A and B.

Let the triangle in Fig. 9–14 be such a triangle. Notice that the side opposite angle A is adjacent to angle B and the side adjacent to A is opposite B. Here and hereafter we use the same symbol to denote both a side and the length of that side, and the same symbol to denote an angle and the measure of that angle.

From definitions [9.2] we have

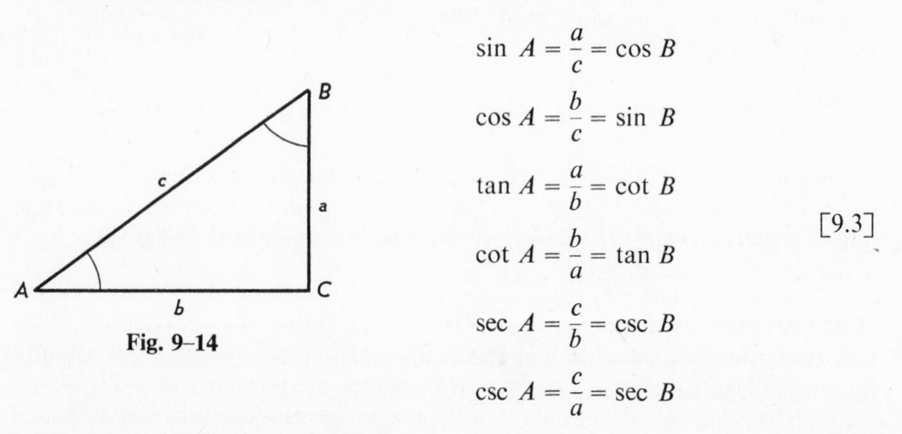

Fig. 9–14

$$\begin{aligned}
\sin A &= \frac{a}{c} = \cos B \\
\cos A &= \frac{b}{c} = \sin B \\
\tan A &= \frac{a}{b} = \cot B \\
\cot A &= \frac{b}{a} = \tan B \\
\sec A &= \frac{c}{b} = \csc B \\
\csc A &= \frac{c}{a} = \sec B
\end{aligned} \qquad [9.3]$$

The six trigonometric functions may be paired off as follows: sine and cosine, tangent and cotangent, secant and cosecant. The two functions forming any one of these pairs are called **cofunctions.**

Equations [9.3] state that the value of any function of an acute angle is equal to the value of the *cofunction* of the *complementary angle*. Thus, for example, $\sin 40° = \cos 50°$, $\cot 20° = \tan 70°$, and so forth.

The derivation of the names cosine, cotangent, and cosecant is based upon the property of complementary angles we have just discovered. The word *cosine* is a contraction of *complement's sine*, *cotangent* is a contraction of *complement's tangent*, and *cosecant* is a contraction of *complement's secant*.

9.9 Tables of Values of Trigonometric Functions

Table II in the back of this book gives values, correct to four decimal places, of the six trigonometric functions of acute angles listed every 10 min. Notice that in this table, angles of measure less than 45° are listed in the columns at the left of the page, and the size of the angles increases as one reads down the page. Angles of measure between 45° and 90° are listed in the columns at the right side of the page, and the size of the angles increases as one reads up the page. Moreover, the labelings **Sin, Cos,** etc., at the top of the columns apply to angles less than 45°, while the labelings at the bottom of the columns apply to angles greater than 45°. In this way, each entry in the table does double duty and serves as the value of two different functions, which are in each case cofunctions. Thus, the relations between cofunctions of complementary angles stated by equations [9.3] of Section 9.8 permit the construction of a table of trigonometric functions occupying half as much space as it would otherwise. The use of the columns labeled **Radians** will be explained later.

The following examples will show how Table II is used to find the values of trigonometric functions of an angle whose measure is expressed in terms of degrees and a multiple of 10 min.

Example 1

Find the value of sin 32° 10′.

SOLUTION: In Table II in the back of the book we read down the column headed **Degrees** until we come to 32° 10′. Then we go horizontally to the right until we come to the column headed **Sin.** There we find the entry 0.5324, the 5 being read from the line above. Hence,

$$\sin 32^\circ\, 10' = 0.5324.$$

We observe in passing that the entry 0.5324 serves also as the value of cos 57° 50′, the cofunction of the complement of 32° 10′.

Example 2

Find the value of cot 75° 40′.

SOLUTION: In Table II we go up the column at the *right*, designated by the word **Degrees** at the *bottom* of the page, until we come to 75° 40′. Then we go horizontally to the left until we come to the column designated at the *bottom* of the page by **Cot.** There we find the entry 0.2555. Hence,

$$\cot 75^\circ\, 40' = 0.2555.$$

9.10 Some Elementary Applications of Trigonometry

One of the uses of trigonometry is in the process of **indirect measurement.** Indirect measurement, as we shall use the term, means finding the value of a distance or an angle without applying to it directly any measuring instrument such as a foot ruler or a protractor. Some distances, such as the length of a house, are easy to measure directly. Others, such as the height of an unscalable mountain peak or the distance to the moon, are not amenable to direct measure. Frequently, distances and angles that are not directly measurable may be calculated by measuring directly other, related distances and angles and then applying trigonometry. In particular, if the unknown distance or angle forms a part of a right triangle, and if enough other parts of the triangle can be measured to determine it, then trigonometry can be applied to find the part desired. We shall illustrate the process by a simple example.

Since we shall need them in the statement of some problems, we now define the two terms **angle of elevation** and **angle of depression.** In Fig. 9–15 an observer

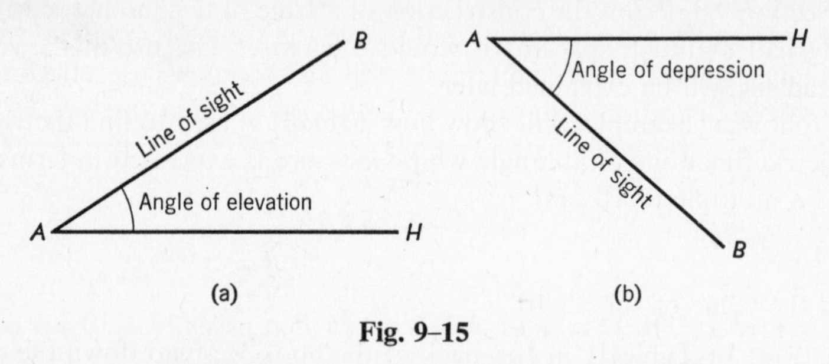

Fig. 9–15

at A views an object at B. The positive acute angle HAB, formed by the line of sight AB and the horizontal line AH through the eye of the observer and in the same vertical plane as B, is called the *angle of elevation* or *angle of depression* of the object according as the observer has to *elevate* or to *depress* his gaze from the horizontal to see the object.

Example

A tower casts a shadow 208.5 ft long when the angle of elevation of the tower as seen from the end of the shadow is 25° 40′. (This angle is also the angle of elevation of the sun.) Find the height of the tower.

SOLUTION: The situation is portrayed in Fig. 9–16. In the right triangle ABC we know the angle A is 25° 40′ and the adjacent side b is of length 208.5 ft, and

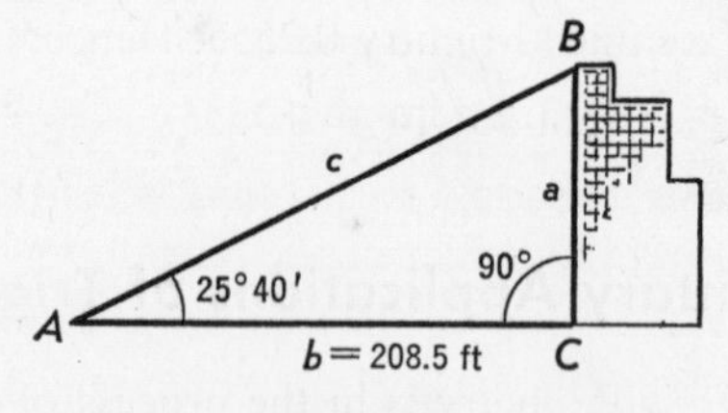

Fig. 9–16

desire to find the opposite side a. We choose a function of angle A whose definition is in terms of the side we want to find and the side we know. The tangent, whose value is defined as $\dfrac{\text{opposite side}}{\text{adjacent side}}$, is such a function. We have

COSINE A = SINE OF ITS COMPLEMENT

COFUNCTION OF θ = FUNCTION OF (90° − θ)

$$\tan 25^\circ 40' = \frac{a}{208.5},$$

$$a = 208.5 \tan 25^\circ 40'.$$

The value of $\tan 25^\circ 40'$ is found in Table II to be 0.4806. Hence,

$$a = 208.2(0.4806) = 100.2,$$

and thus the tower is 100.2 ft high.

Notice from the example given that to find the value of an unknown side of a right triangle when an acute angle and a side are known, we use a trigonometric function whose definition is in terms of the *known side* and the *side we want to find.*

EXERCISES

1. Find a value for θ in each of the following cases:
(a) $\sin \theta = \cos 3\theta$. (b) $\tan(\theta - 20^\circ) = \cot \theta$. (c) $\sec(2\theta + 10^\circ) = \csc 2\theta$.

2. Find a value for x in each of the following cases:
(a) $\cot 4x = \tan 2x$. (b) $\sin(x + 18^\circ) = \cos 2x$. (c) $\csc(3x - 50^\circ) = \sec x$.

3. Find the values of the following from Table II: $\sin 35^\circ 30'$, $\cot 18^\circ 20'$, $\cos 68^\circ 40'$, $\csc 32^\circ$, $\sec 72^\circ 50'$, $\tan 8^\circ 10'$.

4. Find the values of the following from Table II: $\tan 28^\circ 40'$, $\sin 68^\circ 30'$, $\cos 41^\circ 20'$, $\sec 28^\circ 10'$, $\cot 75^\circ$, $\csc 52^\circ 50'$.

Exercises 5 to 10 refer to Fig. 9–17.

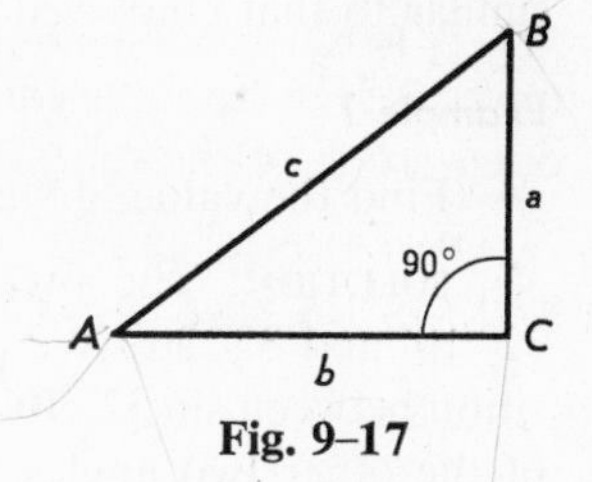

Fig. 9–17

5. If $A = 34^\circ 20'$ and $c = 200$, find a.

6. If $A = 42^\circ 40'$ and $c = 350$, find b.

7. If $B = 62^\circ 30'$ and $b = 52$, find a.

8. If $B = 57^\circ 20'$ and $a = 76$, find b.

9. If $A = 29^\circ 50'$ and $a = 86.7$, find b and c.

10. If $B = 61^\circ 10'$ and $b = 48.3$, find a and c.

11. A telephone pole casts a shadow 50.5 ft long when the angle of elevation of the sun is $16^\circ 40'$. Find the height of the pole.

12. The angle of elevation of the top of a building as viewed from a point on the ground 112.5 ft from the base of the building is $33^\circ 20'$. Find the height of the building.

13. A straight highway makes an angle of 4° with the horizontal. How much does the highway rise in a distance of 100 ft measured along the road?

14. A straight sidewalk is inclined to the horizontal at an angle of $5^\circ 20'$. Find how far one must walk along the sidewalk to change his elevation by 6 ft.

15. An observer at a point O on a straight coast running north and south sights a ship in a direction 29° 30′ east of north. The ship is reported at the same time to be directly east of a point M. The point M is 28.2 miles north of O. Find the distance of the ship from each of the points O and M.
16. From an airplane at an altitude of 6000 ft, the pilot observes the angle of depression of a building to be 25° 10′. How far is the building from a point on the ground directly beneath the plane?
17. From the top of a building 485 ft high, the angle of depression of a man on the ground is 18° 20′. How far is the man from the base of the building?
18. A triangular city lot has two of its sides perpendicular to each other. The side of the lot opposite the right angle is 130 ft long and makes an angle of 49° 50′ with one of the other sides. Find the lengths of the other two sides.
19. The distance CB through a swamp is desired. A line AC of length 350.2 yd is laid off at right angles to CB. Angle BAC is measured and found to be 53° 40′. Find the length of CB.

9.11 Interpolation

We have seen that for an acute angle whose measure is expressed in terms of degrees and an integral multiple of 10 min, the values of the trigonometric functions can be found directly in Table II. If the number of minutes in the measure of an angle is not a multiple of 10, it is necessary to employ a process known as *interpolation*. The following examples illustrate the method, which is similar to that employed in the case of logarithms.

Example 1

Find the value of sin 32° 13′.

SOLUTION: The angle 32° 13′ is not listed in the table, but it lies between 32° 10′ and 32° 20′. We assume that sin 32° 13′ occupies the same relative position between sin 32° 10′ and sin 32° 20′ that 32° 13′ does between the measures of the other two angles. The work done in getting the proper value is shown below.

$$10'\left[\begin{array}{l} 3'\left[\begin{array}{l}\sin 32^\circ 10' = 0.5324 \\ \sin 32^\circ 13' = \quad ?\end{array}\right] c \\ \quad \sin 32^\circ 20' = 0.5348 \end{array}\right] 24$$

To locate sin 32° 13′ in the proper relative position, we form the proportion

$$\frac{c}{24} = \frac{3}{10}, \qquad \text{or} \quad c = 0.3(24) = 7.2.$$

We take for the value of the correction the nearest integer to 7.2, which is 7.

This correction is *added* to the last digit in the value of the sine of the angle that is just *smaller* than our angle. This gives us

$$\sin 32° 13' = 0.5331.$$

Notice that this number occupies a position $\frac{3}{10}$ of the way from 0.5324 to 0.5348, just as 32° 13′ lies $\frac{3}{10}$ of the way from 32° 10′ to 32° 20′.

Example 2

Find the value of cot 67° 47′.

SOLUTION:

$$10\left[\begin{array}{l} 7\left[\begin{array}{l}\cot 67° 40' = 0.4108 \\ \cot 67° 47' = \quad ?\end{array}\right] c \\ \cot 67° 50' = 0.4074\end{array}\right] 34$$

We form the proportion

$$\frac{c}{34} = \frac{7}{10}, \qquad \text{or} \quad c = 0.7(34) = 23.8.$$

We take c to be 24, and this time we *subtract* the correction from the cotangent of the angle that is just smaller than our angle. This gives us

$$\cot 67° 47' = 0.4084.$$

Note: In case the value of the correction c is *exactly halfway* between two integers, for example, 8.5, we follow an old computer's rule and call it 8 or 9, whichever will make the last digit in the value of the function even.

It is very important to notice that for functions, whose values *increase* as the angle increases, as do the sine, tangent, and secant, the correction is *added.* For the cosine, cotangent, and cosecant, whose values *decrease* as the angle increases, the correction is *subtracted.* In each case the correction is always combined with the function of the *smaller angle*.

9.12 Finding the Measure of an Angle

Table II in the back of the book may be used to find the measure of an acute angle if the value of one of its functions is known. The process is illustrated by the following examples.

Example 1

If $\sin \theta = 0.5225$, find θ.

SOLUTION: We locate the number 0.5225 in the "Sin" column in Table II, and by going horizontally to the left to the "Degrees" column, we observe that it corresponds to an angle of 31° 30′. Therefore, $\theta = 31° 30'$.

Example 2

If $\tan\theta = 0.4115$, find a value for θ.

SOLUTION: We attempt to find 0.4115 in the "Tan" column of Table II. This we are unable to do, but we do locate two numbers in this column between which our number lies. A process of interpolation is applied to these entries to determine the value of θ.

$$10\left[\begin{array}{l} d\left[\begin{array}{ll}\tan 22^\circ\, 20' & = 0.4108 \\ \tan\theta & = 0.4115\end{array}\right] 7 \\ \quad \tan 22^\circ\, 30' = 0.4142\end{array}\right] 34$$

By proportion, we have

$$\frac{d}{10} = \frac{7}{34}.$$

Therefore,

$$d = 10(7/34) = 2'.$$

Adding this $2'$ to $22^\circ\, 20'$, we get $\theta = 22^\circ\, 22'$.

Example 3

If $\cos\theta = 0.3804$, find a value for θ.

SOLUTION:

$$10\left[\begin{array}{l} d\left[\begin{array}{ll}\cos 67^\circ\, 30' & = 0.3827 \\ \cos\theta & = 0.3804\end{array}\right] 23 \\ \quad \cos 67^\circ\, 40' = 0.3800\end{array}\right] 27$$

By proportion,

$$\frac{d}{10} = \frac{23}{27}, \quad \text{or} \quad d = 10\left(\frac{23}{27}\right) = 9'.$$

Adding this $9'$ to $67^\circ\, 30'$, we get

$$\theta = 67^\circ\, 39'.$$

Note: In case d may be approximated equally accurately by either of two numbers, one even and the other odd, we agree to take the even one. Thus, we approximate $8.5'$ by $8'$.

Notice that in all interpolations we work from the *smaller* angle.

9.13 Finding the Measure of an Angle of a Right Triangle

We have already solved problems in which we had to find the length of one or more sides of a right triangle when we knew an acute angle and a side of the triangle. In this section we illustrate the process of finding an angle if we know the lengths of two sides.

Example

In right triangle ABC of Fig. 9–18, $a = 200$ and $b = 354$. Find the remaining parts of the triangle.

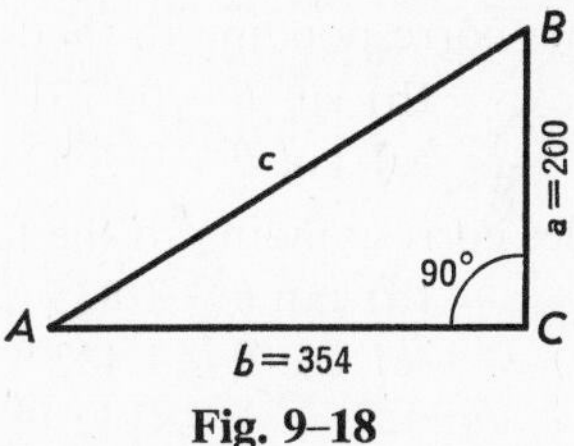

Fig. 9–18

SOLUTION: We first find angle A. We have

$$\cot A = 354/200 = 1.770.$$

Using Table II, we have

$$10\left[d\left[\begin{array}{l}\cot 29^\circ\, 20' = 1.780\\ \cot A \quad\;\; = 1.770\end{array}\right]10\atop \cot 29^\circ\, 30' = 1.767\right]13$$

$$\frac{d}{10} = \frac{10}{13}, \qquad \text{or} \quad d = 10\left(\frac{10}{13}\right) = 8'.$$

Therefore,

$$A = 29^\circ\, 28'.$$

Immediately, we get $B = 90^\circ - 29^\circ\, 28' = 60^\circ\, 32'$. To get the remaining side c, we use the cosecant function and obtain

$$\frac{c}{a} = \csc A, \qquad \text{or} \quad c = a \csc A = 200 \csc 29^\circ\, 28'.$$

The interpolation for finding csc 29° 28′ is displayed as follows:

$$10\left[8\left[\begin{array}{l}\csc 29^\circ\, 20' = 2.041\\ \csc 29^\circ\, 28' = \quad ?\end{array}\right]x\atop \csc 29^\circ\, 30' = 2.031\right]10$$

$$\frac{x}{10} = \frac{8}{10}, \quad x = 8.$$

$$\csc 29^\circ\, 28' = 2.033.$$

Therefore,

$$c = 200(2.033) = 406.6.$$

EXERCISES

1. Find the values of the following:

(a) sin 27° 42′ (b) cos 35° 27′ (c) tan 68° 18′
(d) cot 38° 29′ (e) sec 71° 16′ (f) csc 57° 25′

2. Find the values of the following:
(a) $\tan 34° 23'$ (b) $\cos 27° 36'$ (c) $\sin 75° 12'$
(d) $\cot 29° 56'$ (e) $\csc 83° 47'$ (f) $\sec 43° 44'$

3. Find measures of angles corresponding to the following:
(a) $\cos \theta = 0.8672$ (b) $\sin \theta = 0.9231$ (c) $\tan \theta = 0.2674$
(d) $\sec \theta = 1.705$ (e) $\cot \theta = 0.2542$ (f) $\csc \theta = 2.564$

4. Find measures of angles corresponding to the following:
(a) $\sec \theta = 3.854$ (b) $\tan \theta = 1.825$ (c) $\sin \theta = 0.4285$
(d) $\cos \theta = 0.3267$ (e) $\csc \theta = 1.482$ (f) $\cot \theta = 2.742$

Exercises 5 through 15 are based on triangles labeled like Fig. 9–19, with a right angle at C.

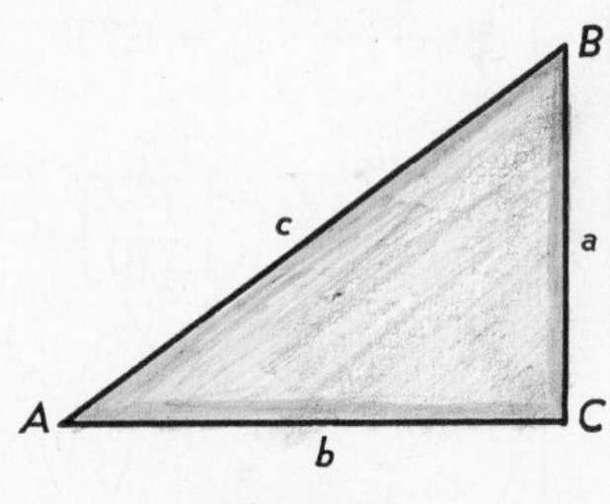

Fig. 9–19

5. $B = 72° 46'$, $a = 75$. Find b.
6. $B = 55° 32'$, $b = 150$. Find the remaining parts of the triangle.
7. $A = 28° 54'$, $a = 280$. Find the remaining parts of the triangle.
8. $B = 75° 18'$, $a = 126.7$. Find the remaining parts of the triangle.
9. $A = 41° 27'$, $c = 18.83$. Find the remaining parts of the triangle.
10. $a = 16$, $b = 12$. Find A.
11. $b = 43$, $c = 60$. Find B.
12. $a = 650$, $c = 1000$. Find the remaining parts of the triangle.
13. $a = 428$, $b = 539$. Find the remaining parts of the triangle.
14. $a = 65.7$, $b = 83.2$. Find the remaining parts of the triangle.
15. $b = 18.5$, $c = 37.9$. Find the remaining parts of the triangle.
16. A ladder 20 ft long leans against a building in such a way as to make an angle of 58° 43′ with the ground. How far up the building does the end of the ladder reach?
17. What is the angle of inclination of a roadbed that rises 7 ft in each 100 ft measured horizontally? (Such a road is said to have a 7 percent grade.)
18. The height of the Empire State Building is 1250 ft. What is the angle of elevation of its top as seen from a point on the ground ½ mile from its base?

19. At a certain instant the angle of depression of a railroad station as seen from an airplane is 67° 23′. If the altitude of the plane is 8000 ft, how far must it fly to be directly over the station?

20. From the top of a lighthouse 212 ft above the surface of the water, the angle of depression of a boat is observed to be 8° 17′. How far is the boat from the lighthouse?

21. An observer in a blimp 3000 ft above the surface of the ocean observes that the angle of depression of a submarine barely below the surface is 23° 36′. How long is the straight-line distance from the blimp to the submarine?

22. A vertical cliff 70 ft high rises at the water's edge. From a buoy anchored some distance offshore, the angle of elevation of the top of the cliff is 16° 23′. Neglecting sag, how long must a cable be to reach from the top of the cliff to the buoy? How far is the buoy from the water's edge?

23. In order to determine the distance between two points P and Q, between which the ground is very uneven, a surveyor lays off the distance PR 300 ft long in a direction perpendicular to PQ. Angle PRQ is measured with a transit to be 66° 24′. Use these data to compute PQ.

24. A portion of a tunnel under a river is straight for 150 yd and descends 32 ft in this distance. What angle does this part make with the horizontal? What is the horizontal distance between the ends of this part of the tunnel?

9.14 Solution of Further Problems by Means of Right Triangles

We have already in previous sections seen applications of trigonometry to problems involving indirect measure. The procedure followed was to represent relevant features of a situation by a right triangle and then solve the triangle for certain of its parts. In this section we have some more instances

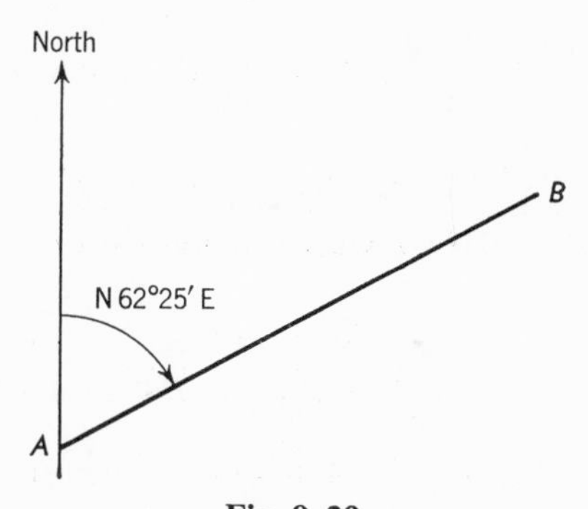

Fig. 9–20

of problems whose solution involves the use of right triangles. In some cases two triangles have to be considered simultaneously.

We need the concept of **bearing,** which occurs in surveying and in navigation. The bearing of a point B as viewed from a point A is defined as the positive measure of the acute angle which the line joining A to B makes with a north-south line through A. This angle is indicated as being measured east or west from either north or south; for example, the bearing in Fig. 9–20 is N 62° 25′ E, and is considered to be a positive acute angle.

Example

At a certain point A on level ground the angle of elevation of the top of a tower is observed to be 32° 40′. At another point B in line with A and the base of the tower, and 50 ft closer to the tower, the angle of elevation of the top is observed to be 67° 13′. Find the height of the tower.

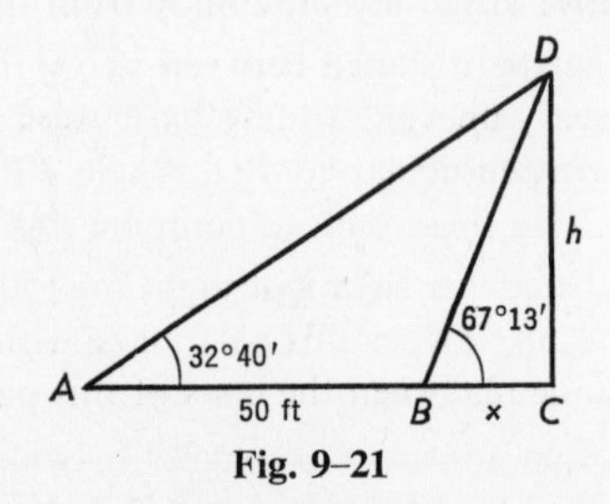

Fig. 9–21

SOLUTION: In Fig. 9–21, which portrays the situation, we have two right triangles ACD and BCD, but not enough is known to solve either triangle alone. However, they can be solved simultaneously. We get from triangle BCD,

$$\frac{x}{h} = \cot B, \quad \text{or} \quad x = h \cot B.$$

From triangle ACD, we have

$$\frac{50 + x}{h} = \cot A, \qquad 50 + x = h \cot A.$$

By substitution for x, we get

$$50 + h \cot B = h \cot A.$$

Solving for h, we have

$$h = \frac{50}{\cot A - \cot B}.$$

Now substituting the values of the angles and looking up the trigonometric functions in Table II, we have

$$h = \frac{50}{\cot 32^\circ 40' - \cot 67^\circ 13'} = \frac{50}{1.560 - 0.4200} = \frac{50}{1.140} = 43.86.$$

Therefore, the tower is 43.86 ft high.

EXERCISES

1. In making a survey, the bearing of a point B from a point A is found to be N 43° 33′ W, and the distance between the two points is 2000 ft. How far is B north of A? How far west?
2. At 2:00 P.M. a ship is 14 nautical miles directly east of a lighthouse. The ship is sailing due north with a speed of 24 knots (24 nautical miles per hour). What is the bearing of the lighthouse from the ship at 3:30 P.M.?
3. The bearing of a lighthouse from a ship is S 27° 42′ W. The ship is 15 miles off the east-west coast upon which the lighthouse is located. How far is the ship from the lighthouse?

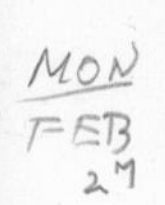

4. Find the perimeter of a regular pentagon inscribed in a circle of radius 10 in.
5. A circle is circumscribed about a regular decagon, each side of which is 7 in. Find the radius of the circle.
6. A ship is 16 miles due south of a tanker. In what direction should the ship sail to pass to the east of the tanker and 3 miles from it at the closest point?
7. At a certain instant a transport sailing east at a rate of 20 mph is 30 miles due north of a destroyer sailing north at the rate of 28 mph. What is the bearing of the transport from the destroyer 30 min later?
8. From the top of a Coast Guard observation tower 200 ft high, the angles of depression of two boats due east are observed to be 8° 40′ and 5° 10′, respectively. Find the distance between the boats.
9. From the top of a cliff 300 ft high, the angles of depression of two travelers in the valley below and in line with the base of the cliff are measured to be 20° 40′ and 7°, respectively. Find the distance between the two travelers.
10. The angle of elevation of the top of a mountain peak as observed from a point P on a level plain below is 17° 45′. From another point Q in line with P and the base of the mountain, and 500 ft closer to the mountain, the angle of elevation is 26°. Find the height of the peak.
11. A building 40 ft high stands upon the same horizontal plain as a bell tower. The angle of elevation of the top of the tower and the angle of depression of its base, both measured from the top of the building, are 57° 35′ and 35° 18′, respectively. Find the height of the tower.

12. A furniture factory 65 ft high has a vertical sign on top of the roof. From a point on the ground some distance from the building the angles of elevation of the top and the bottom of the sign are 27° 55′ and 23° 8′, respectively. Find the height of the sign.

13. At the same instant two observers located 2 miles apart measure the angle of elevation of an airplane that is between them and directly over the line joining them. The two angles are 42° 20′ and 52° 40′. Find the altitude of the airplane.

14. Two observation stations are located 10 miles apart on a straight north-south coastline. The bearings of a ship as measured from these two stations are S 52° 10′ E and N 74° 15′ E, respectively. Find the distance from the ship to the shore.

15. As observed from a balloon 3500 ft above the surface of a lake, the angle of depression of a point on one shore of the lake is 27° 18′ and that of a point on the other side and in the same vertical plane with the balloon and the first point is 16° 42′. Find the distance across the lake.

9.15 Vectors

It is a familiar fact that the effect of a push applied to an object depends both on the strength of the push and on the direction in which it is exerted. A push of definite magnitude applied in a definite direction is called a *force*. We can represent a force by a line segment with an arrowhead on one end to indicate direction. The length of the segment represents the magnitude of the force and the direction of the segment represents the direction of the force. Such a directed line segment is called a **vector.** The direction of a vector is usually defined by giving the angle that the vector makes with some fixed reference line (see Fig. 9–22). Other quantities that possess the two attributes of magnitude and direction, and hence can be represented by vectors, are *velocities* and *accelerations*.

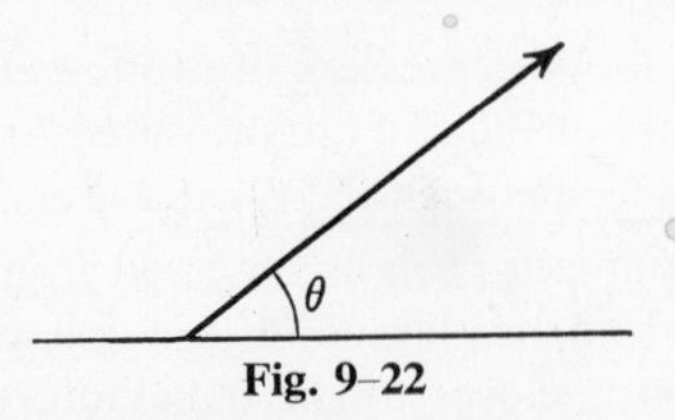

Fig. 9–22

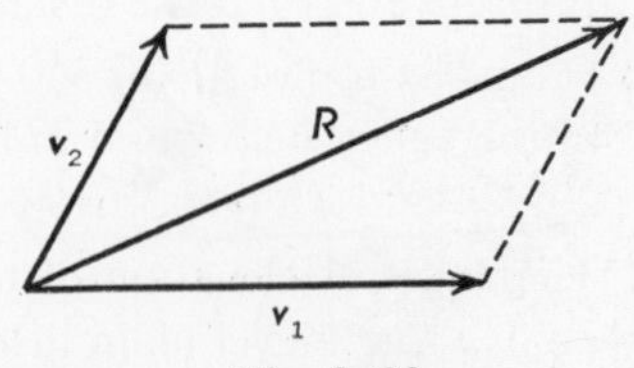

Fig. 9–23

Two vectors v_1 and v_2 are added by the following method. Construct the two vectors v_1 and v_2 with their origins at the same point as in Fig. 9–23. Complete the parallelogram on the two line segments as sides. The *diagonal R* of this parallelogram, directed as indicated in the figure, is called the **sum** or **resultant** of the two vectors v_1 and v_2. It is shown in physics that if the original vectors represent forces, then R represents the single force that is equivalent to the two forces represented by v_1 and v_2. A similar interpretation holds for velocities and accelerations.

If R is the resultant of v_1 and v_2, then v_1 and v_2 are called **components** of R. Two vectors have a unique resultant, but a single vector has many pairs of components.

An alternate construction for the resultant of the vectors v_1 and v_2 is to construct v_1, and then construct v_2 with its origin at the tip of v_1, as in Fig. 9–24. The resultant R is the vector with origin at the origin of v_1 and tip at the tip of v_2.

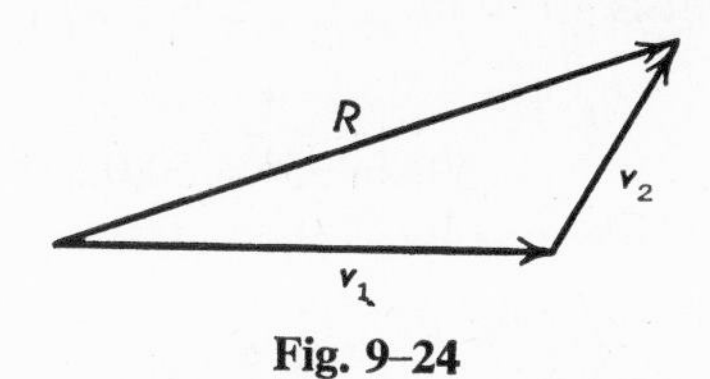

Fig. 9–24

The following examples illustrate the use of trigonometry in solving problems involving vectors.

Example 1

Two forces, one of 110 lb in a horizontal direction and the other of 70 lb in a vertical direction, are acting at a point. What single force would produce the same effect?

SOLUTION: The answer to this question is given by the resultant of the vectors representing the two forces. We find the magnitude and direction of this resultant by applying trigonometry to Fig. 9–25. We have

$$\tan A = {}^{70}\!/_{110} = 0.6364, \qquad A = 32° \ 28'.$$

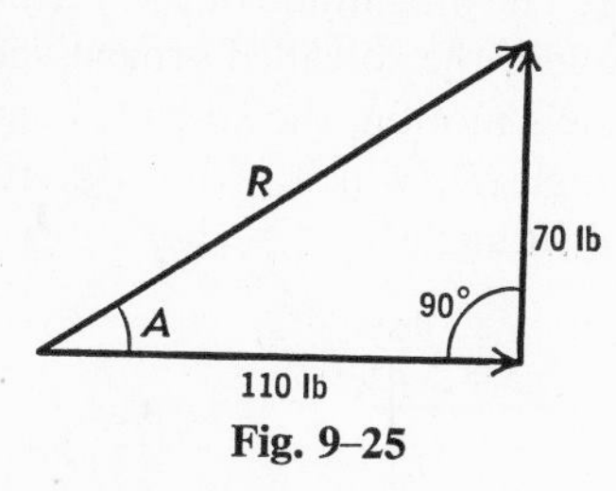

Fig. 9–25

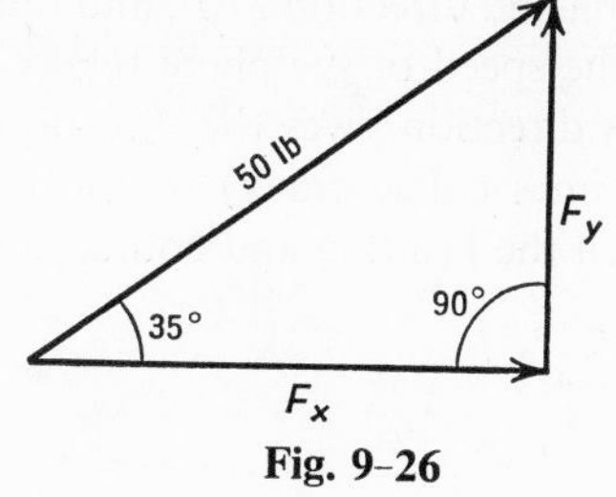

Fig. 9–26

Then

$$\frac{R}{70} = \csc 32° \ 28', \qquad R = 70 \csc 32° \ 28',$$

$$R = 70(1.863) = 130.4.$$

Thus, a force of 130.4 lb acting at an angle of 32° 28′ with the horizontal will produce the same effect as the two given forces.

Example 2

A force of 50 lb is acting in a direction of 35° with the ground. Find the horizontal and vertical components of the force.

SOLUTION: In Fig. 9–26, F_x and F_y represent the horizontal and vertical components of the given force. From the right triangle in the figure, we get

$$\frac{F_x}{50} = \cos 35°, \qquad F_x = 50 \cos 35° = 50(0.8192) = 40.96.$$

The horizontal component is 40.96 lb.

Also,

$$\frac{F_y}{50} = \sin 35°, \qquad F_y = 50 \sin 35° = 50(0.5736) = 28.68.$$

The vertical component is 28.68 lb.

Example 3

An airplane has a heading of 270° and airspeed (AS) of 200 mph. A wind of 30 mph is blowing from 180°. Find the course and ground speed (GS) of the plane.

SOLUTION: In navigation, directions are given by angles measured from true north in an eastward or clockwise direction from 0° to 360°. These angles are regarded as positive, contrary to our usual convention regarding signs of angles. Thus, the plane that has a **heading** of 270° is pointed due west. An **air speed** of 200 mph means that the plane is operating in such a manner as would propel it through *still air* at the rate of 200 miles per hour. The 30 mph wind is blowing from due south. The vector representing the actual motion of the plane relative to the ground is the *resultant* of the *air speed vector*, magnitude 200 mph and direction 270°, and the *wind vector*. The magnitude of this resultant gives the speed of the plane relative to the ground, the so-called **ground speed,** and its direction gives the direction of the plane's motion, the so-called **course** (sometimes called **track**) of the plane. The angle D, which is the difference between the heading and course, is called the **drift angle.**

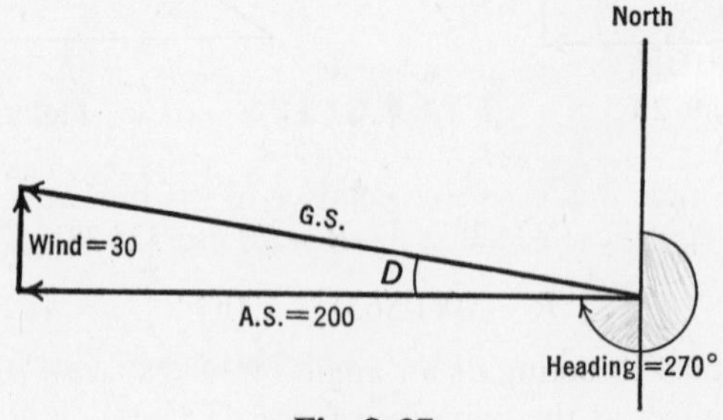

Fig. 9–27

The diagram exhibiting the vectors is given in Fig. 9–27. From the figure we have

$$\tan D = {}^{30}\!/_{200} = 0.1500, \qquad D = 8^\circ\, 32'.$$

The course of the plane is $270^\circ + 8^\circ\, 32' = 278^\circ\, 32'$. Also,

$$\frac{\text{GS}}{200} = \sec 8^\circ\, 32', \qquad \text{GS} = 200 \sec 8^\circ\, 32',$$

$$\text{GS} = 200(1.011) = 202.2.$$

The ground speed is 202.2 mph.

In Fig. 9–28 there is pictured a vector OP of magnitude r and direction θ. From this diagram we can deduce some interesting relations. If we denote the coordinates of the tip P of the vector by (x, y), we have immediately

$$x = r \cos \theta \qquad \text{and} \qquad y = r \sin \theta, \qquad [9.4]$$

$$r = \sqrt{x^2 + y^2} \qquad \text{and} \qquad \tan \theta = \frac{y}{x}. \qquad [9.5]$$

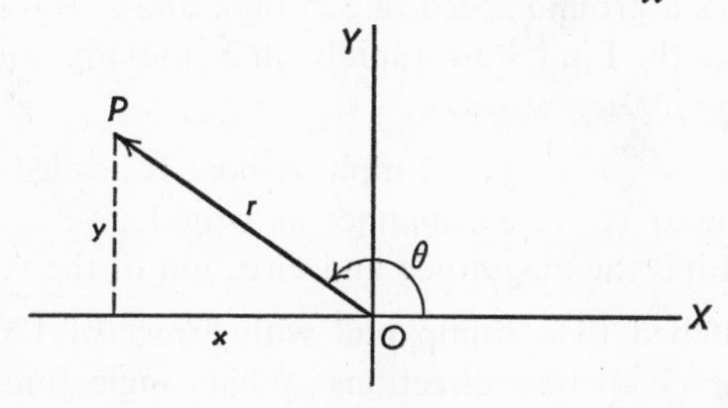

Fig. 9–28

Notice that P can be located by specifying the values of r and θ as well as by specifying the values of x and y. Indeed, r and θ are called the **polar coordinates** of P, whereas x and y are called its **Cartesian coordinates.** The formulas [9.4] express the Cartesian coordinates of a point in terms of its polar coordinates, and formulas [9.5] enable us to compute the polar coordinates of a point if its Cartesian coordinates are known. It is clear that the angle θ is not uniquely defined; adding or subtracting an integral multiple of 360° would not alter the location of P.

EXERCISES

1. Find the magnitude and direction relative to the horizontal of the resultant of each of the following pairs of horizontal and vertical forces:
   (a) $F_x = 35$ lb, $F_y = 50$ lb
   (b) $F_x = 42$ lb, $F_y = 28$ lb
   (c) $F_x = 175$ lb, $F_y = 200$ lb
   (d) $F_x = 315$ lb, $F_y = 175$ lb

2. Add vectorially the following pairs of horizontal and vertical forces, giving the magnitude of the resultant and its direction relative to the horizontal:
   (a) $F_x = 40$ lb, $F_y = 62$ lb
   (b) $F_x = 120$ lb, $F_y = 85$ lb
   (c) $F_x = 375$ lb, $F_y = 310$ lb
   (d) $F_x = 38.7$ lb, $F_y = 56.3$ lb

3. Find the horizontal and vertical components of each of the forces whose magnitudes and directions relative to the horizontal are as follows:
   (a) 300 lb, 40° (b) 225 lb, 26° 50′
   (c) 70 lb, 35° 46′ (d) 150 lb, 71° 18′

4. Resolve into horizontal and vertical components the forces with magnitudes and directions relative to the horizontal as follows:
   (a) 130 lb, 50° (b) 175 lb, 43° 10′
   (c) 220 lb, 62° 34′ (d) 312 lb, 57° 22′

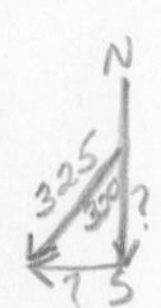

5. An airplane has a ground speed of 325 mph and is traveling in a direction 32° west of south. Find how rapidly it is moving southward and how rapidly it is moving westward.

6. The speed of a river current is 2 mph. A boat is headed directly across the stream and rowed in such a manner as would give it a speed of 5 mph in still water. Find the magnitude and direction of the velocity of the boat.

7. Two mules hitched to a stump pull with forces of 1200 lb and 1400 lb in mutually perpendicular directions. What single force (give magnitude and direction) exerted by a tractor would have the same effect?

In Exercises 8 through 11 the heading and airspeed of an airplane, and the speed and direction of the wind are given. In each find the course and ground speed of the plane.

8. Heading = 90°, AS = 160 mph; wind 25 mph from 180°.
9. Heading = 0°, AS = 180 mph; wind 35 mph from 270°.
10. Heading = 30°, AS = 200 mph; wind 32 mph from 300°.
11. Heading = 205°, AS = 220 mph; wind 40 mph from 295°.

In each of Exercises 12 through 15 the problem is to find the resultant of the two forces given. First find the horizontal and vertical components of both forces. Then add the two horizontal components to obtain a single horizontal component and add the two vertical components to obtain a single vertical component. Finally, get the resultant of the two components just obtained. In each case the angle listed is the direction relative to the horizontal.

12. F_1: 30 lb, 20° F_2: 40 lb, 80°
13. F_1: 70 lb, 15° F_2: 100 lb, 65°

14. F_1: 45 lb, 32° F_2: 90 lb, 78°

15. F_1: 80 lb, 46° F_2: 73 lb, 82°

16. Find the Cartesian coordinates of the points whose polar coordinates are: (2, 30°), (3, 225°), (5, 300°).

17. Find polar coordinates for points whose Cartesian coordinates are: $(-3, 3)$, $(-2\sqrt{3}, 2)$, $(3, -4)$.

18. The equation of a circle of radius 5 and center at the origin is $x^2 + y^2 = 25$. Find its equation in polar coordinates.

19. Find the equation in Cartesian coordinates of a curve whose equation in polar coordinates is $r = 3 \cos \theta$.

20. Find the equations in Cartesian coordinates of the curves whose equations in polar coordinates are:

(a) $\tan \theta = \sqrt{3}$ (b) $\tan \theta = r \cos \theta$
(c) $r^2 \sin \theta \cos \theta = 4$ (d) $\cos^3 \theta + \sin^3 \theta = 1/r$
(e) $\sin \theta = \cos \theta$ (f) $r = \cos^2 \theta - \sin^2 \theta$

21. Find the points of intersection, if any, of the following curves. Express your results in both Cartesian and polar coordinates:

(a) $x + 2y = 3$ and $x - y = 1$
(b) $r^2 = \sin \theta$ and $r \sin \theta = 1$
(c) $r^2 = 2r - 1$ and $\sin \theta - \cos \theta = 10/r$
(d) $2x = r^2$ and $r = 1$
(e) $2 \sin \theta \cos \theta = -1$ and $x = 1$

9.16 Functions of Large Angles in Terms of Functions of Positive Acute Angles

Angles whose measures differ by an integral multiple of 360° have exactly the same values for their trigonometric functions because their terminal sides coincide if the angles are constructed in standard position. Thus, the value of any trigonometric function of any angle is equal to the value of the same function of some angle of measure equal to or greater than 0° and less than 360°. The measure of the second angle can be obtained from that of the original by adding or subtracting 360° a sufficient number of times. For example, $\sin 460° = \sin 100°$, $\cos 1045° = \cos 325°$, $\tan (-1200°) = \tan 240°$.

Our table of trigonometric functions lists values only for angles of measure 0° to 90°. However, we shall show that values of functions of large angles may be expressed in terms of values of functions of positive acute angles, and hence the table is actually sufficient to furnish values of trigonometric functions for all angles. For this purpose we use the concept of "associated acute angle" defined in the next paragraph.

Let θ be any nonquadrantal angle in standard position. The **associated acute angle** for θ is the positive acute angle whose sides are the terminal side of θ and the x axis. Fig. 9–29 pictures several angles θ, with A denoting in each case the associated acute angle. Every angle, with the exception of the quadrantal angles, has an associated acute angle. In case θ is a positive acute angle, it is its own associated acute angle.

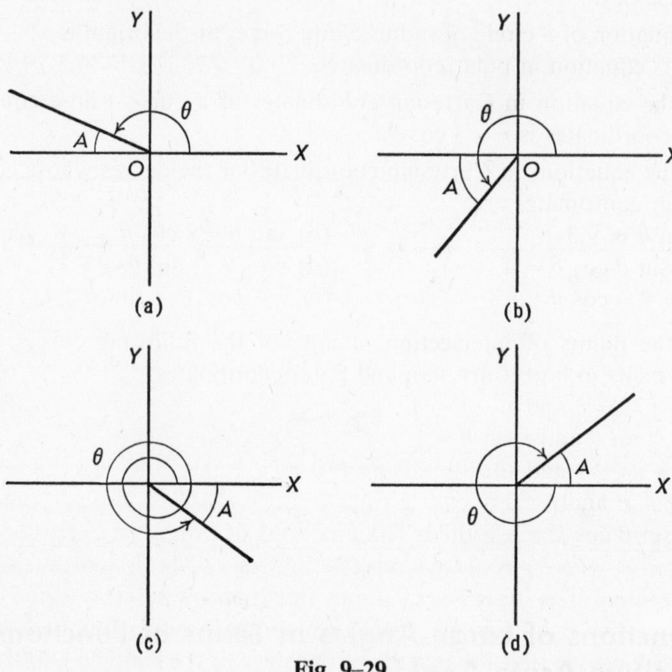

Fig. 9–29

By way of examples, the associated acute angle of 130° is 50°, that of 210° is 30°, that of 312° is 48°. Notice that these associated acute angles are obtained by taking differences in the proper order between the measure of the original angle and either 180° or 360°.

The importance of the associated acute angle concept is indicated in the following theorem.

▶ THEOREM 1. *The value of any trigonometric function of a nonquadrantal angle is equal to plus or minus the value of the same function of its associated acute angle.*

The theorem says that $\sin 150° = \sin 30°$, $\cos 252° = -\cos 72°$, $\tan 305° = -\tan 55°$, etc. The algebraic sign, plus or minus, is determined by the quadrant in which the terminal side of the original angle lies.

PROOF: Construct θ in standard position. Figure 9–30 pictures several typical values of θ. Regardless of the size of θ, if it is not quadrantal, the following construction and argument is valid. Select a point P on the terminal side

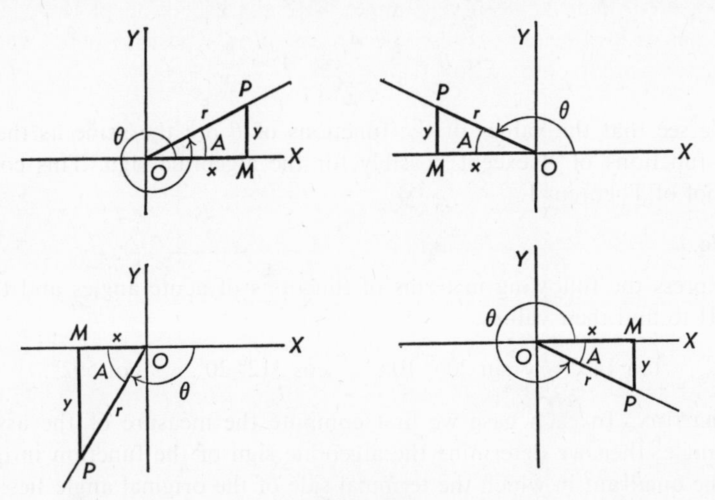

Fig. 9–30

of θ, draw a perpendicular line from P to the x axis, and call the foot of this perpendicular M. In every case a right triangle OMP is formed containing A, the associated acute angle of θ. The functions of θ may be expressed in terms of x, y, and r, where r is always positive, but one or both coordinates x and y may be negative. The functions of A may be expressed in terms of the lengths of the sides of the right triangle OMP, which are positive numbers. Referring to Fig. 9–30, we see that the lengths of the sides of the triangle OMP are equal to the *absolute values* of x, y, and r, respectively. Thus, naming the sides of the triangle with reference to angle A, we have for the lengths of these sides:

$$\text{adjacent side} = |x|, \qquad \text{opposite side} = |y|, \qquad \text{hypotenuse} = r.$$

Note: The symbol $|x|$ denotes the absolute value of x. For example, $|-5| = 5$.

Now we write the values of the trigonometric functions of θ and A in parallel columns, using the general definitions [9.1] for θ and the special definitions [9.2] for A.

$$\sin\theta = \frac{y}{r} \qquad \sin A = \frac{|y|}{r}$$

$$\cos\theta = \frac{x}{r} \qquad \cos A = \frac{|x|}{r}$$

$$\tan\theta = \frac{y}{x} \qquad \tan A = \frac{|y|}{|x|}$$

$$\cot \theta = \frac{x}{y} \qquad \cot A = \frac{|x|}{|y|}$$

$$\sec \theta = \frac{r}{x} \qquad \sec A = \frac{r}{|x|}$$

$$\csc \theta = \frac{r}{y} \qquad \csc A = \frac{r}{|y|}$$

We see that the values of the functions of θ are the same as the values of the functions of A except possibly for the algebraic sign. This completes the proof of Theorem 1.

Example

Express the following in terms of functions of acute angles and then use Table II to find their values:

$$\tan 140°, \qquad \sin 206° \, 10', \qquad \cos 312° \, 20', \qquad \cot 592°.$$

SOLUTION: In each case we first compute the measure of the associated acute angle; then we determine the algebraic sign of the function in question from the quadrant in which the terminal side of the original angle lies; finally, we use Table II to get the numerical value of the function.

Applying this process to each of the functions in our example, we get

$$\tan 140° = -\tan 40° = -0.8391$$
$$\sin 206° \, 10' = -\sin 26° \, 10' = -0.4410$$
$$\cos 312° \, 20' = \cos 47° \, 40' = 0.6734$$
$$\cot 592° = \cot 232° = \cot 52° = 0.7813$$

Let A denote a positive acute angle and consider the angles $180° - A$, $180° + A$, and $360° - A$. Since A is the associated acute angle for each of these angles, we have from Theorem 1 the following result.

▶ THEOREM 2. *The value of a trigonometric function of any one of the angles* $180° - A$, $180° + A$, *and* $360° - A$ *is equal to plus or minus the value of the same function of* A.

Examples

$$\sin (180° - A) = \sin A, \qquad \cot (180° + A) = \cot A$$
$$\cos (180° - A) = -\cos A, \qquad \tan (360° - A) = -\tan A$$

Let B denote a positive acute angle and consider the angles $90° + B$, $270° - B$, and $270° + B$. The associated acute angle for $90° + B$ is $180° - (90° + B) = 90° - B$. Likewise, the associated acute angle for both $270° - B$ and $270° + B$ is also $90° - B$. Thus, by Theorem 1, any function of any one of the angles

$90° + B$, $270° - B$, or $270° + B$ is equal to plus or minus the same function of $90° - B$. But any function of $90° - B$ is equal to the *cofunction* of B, as was shown in Section 9.8. Hence, we have the following theorem.

▶ THEOREM 3. *The value of a trigonometric function of any one of the angles $90° + B$, $270° - B$, and $270° + B$ is equal to plus or minus the value of the cofunction of B.*

Examples

$$\sin(90° + B) = \cos B, \qquad \cot(270° + B) = -\tan B$$
$$\cos(90° + B) = -\sin B, \qquad \sec(270° - B) = -\csc B$$
$$\tan(270° - B) = \cot B, \qquad \csc(270° + B) = -\sec B$$

Indeed, Theorems 2 and 3 are true for *all* values of A and B, even though our proofs apply only when A and B are positive acute angles. The verification for the general case will be made in Chapter 10 (see Exercises 17 through 32 of Section 10.11).

9.17 Functions of Negative Angles in Terms of Functions of Positive Angles

Consider the positive angle θ and the negative angle $-\theta$, whose measure has the same absolute value as that of θ. From a study of the diagrams in Fig. 9–31, it is intuitively clear that θ and $-\theta$ always have the same associated acute angle,

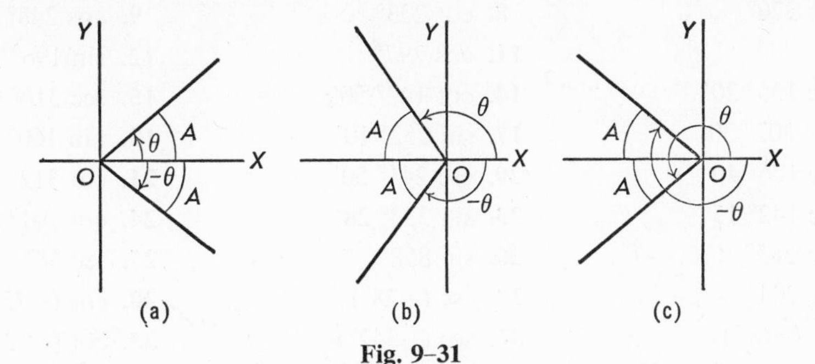

Fig. 9–31

and hence their functions can differ at most in algebraic sign. Moreover, the terminal sides of θ and $-\theta$ are always on the *same* side of the y axis and on *opposite* sides of the x axis. Hence, any points P and P' on the terminal sides of θ and $-\theta$, respectively, have the *same signs for x and r*, but *opposite signs for y*. This means that $\cos(-\theta)$ and $\sec(-\theta)$ have the *same* values as $\cos\theta$ and $\sec\theta$, but each of the other functions of $-\theta$ is equal to the *negative* of the same function of θ.

We may express these results by the following formulas:

$$\begin{aligned} \cos(-\theta) &= \cos\theta, & \sec(-\theta) &= \sec\theta \\ \sin(-\theta) &= -\sin\theta, & \csc(-\theta) &= -\csc\theta \\ \tan(-\theta) &= -\tan\theta, & \cot(-\theta) &= -\cot\theta \end{aligned} \quad [9.6]$$

A rigorous derivation of these formulas will be given in Section 10.10.

Example

Express in terms of functions of positive acute angles: $\sin(-42°)$, $\sec(-63°)$, $\cos(-130°)$, $\tan(-205°)$, $\cot(-157°)$.

SOLUTION:

$$\begin{aligned} \sin(-42°) &= -\sin 42° \\ \sec(-63°) &= \sec 63° \\ \cos(-130°) &= \cos 130° = -\cos 50° \\ \tan(-205°) &= -\tan 205° = -\tan 25° \\ \cot(-157°) &= -\cot 157° = -(-\cot 23°) = \cot 23° \end{aligned}$$

EXERCISES

Find the value of each of the functions in Exercises 1 through 42 by first expressing it in terms of a function of a positive acute angle and then using Table II.

1. sin 138° **2.** tan 214° **3.** cos 111°
4. cot 317° **5.** tan 140° **6.** sec 212°
7. csc 320° **8.** cot 223° **9.** cos 248°
10. tan 343° **11.** cos 297° **12.** sin 196°
13. csc 135° 20′ **14.** cot 142° 50′ **15.** sec 316° 40′
16. cos 202° 30′ **17.** sin 252° 10′ **18.** tan 160° 30′
19. sec 126° 40′ **20.** csc 241° 50′ **21.** cot 312° 50′
22. csc 142° 15′ **23.** sin 333° 28′ **24.** cot 201° 37′
25. tan 585° **26.** sin 858° **27.** sec 682°
28. csc 704° **29.** csc (−28°) **30.** cos (−75°)
31. sin (−62°) **32.** sec (−342°) **33.** cot (−127°)
34. tan (−236°) **35.** cos (−121°) **36.** sin (−147°)
37. csc (−218°) **38.** cos (−298°) **39.** tan (−307°)
40. sin (−665°) **41.** sec (−513°) **42.** csc (−1000°)

Express each of the functions in Exercises 43 through 66 in terms of a function of θ, assuming in each case that θ is a positive acute angle.

43. $\tan(180° - \theta)$ **44.** $\sec(180° - \theta)$ **45.** $\csc(180° - \theta)$
46. $\cot(180° - \theta)$ **47.** $\sin(180° + \theta)$ **48.** $\tan(180° + \theta)$
49. $\cos(180° + \theta)$ **50.** $\sin(360° - \theta)$ **51.** $\cos(360° - \theta)$
52. $\sec(360° - \theta)$ **53.** $\cot(360° - \theta)$ **54.** $\sec(90° + \theta)$
55. $\csc(90° + \theta)$ **56.** $\tan(90° + \theta)$ **57.** $\cot(90° + \theta)$
58. $\sin(270° - \theta)$ **59.** $\cot(270° - \theta)$ **60.** $\csc(270° - \theta)$
61. $\tan(270° - \theta)$ **62.** $\cos(270° + \theta)$ **63.** $\tan(270° + \theta)$
64. $\sec(270° + \theta)$ **65.** $\sin(270° + \theta)$ **66.** $\cot(270° + \theta)$

67. Show that theorems 2 and 3 of Section 9.16 and formulas [9.6] of Section 9.17 can be obtained from the following general theorem (to be proved in Chapter 10):

$$\text{Trig function of } (n \cdot 90° \pm \theta) = \pm \begin{cases} \text{same function of } \theta \text{ if } n \text{ is even} \\ \text{cofunction of } \theta \text{ if } n \text{ is odd} \end{cases}$$

(The two $\pm$ signs occurring do not necessarily correspond.)

9.18 Angles Corresponding to a Given Value of a Function

In Section 9.16 the problem of finding the value of a trigonometric function of any given angle was solved by using the "associated acute angle" concept. Let us now consider an example of the inverse problem. Suppose $\sin\theta = 0.5$, and we want to find θ. From a knowledge of special angles, or use of Table II, we find that one angle whose sine is 0.5 is 30°. However, 30° is not the only possible value for θ. Indeed, any angle that has 30° as associated acute angle and whose terminal side falls in the proper quadrant for its sine to be positive will have the same value for the sine as 30°. Such an angle is 150°. Thus, corresponding to $\sin\theta = 0.5$, we have $\theta = 30°$ and $\theta = 150°$. Clearly, repeatedly adding 360° to, or repeatedly subtracting 360° from, either of these angles leads to angles θ satisfying $\sin\theta = 0.5$. A few such angles are 390°, 510°, 750°, · · ·, −210°, −330°, · · ·.

In general there will be two positive angles of measure less than 360° corresponding to a permissible given value of a trigonometric function. These are found as follows. First find the associated acute angle A for the angle whose value is sought. The desired angles will then be the two angles of the set A, $180° - A$, $180° + A$, and $360° - A$ whose terminal sides lie in the proper quadrants. The proper quadrants are determined by the algebraic sign of the given function. All other angles satisfying the given condition can be found by repeatedly adding 360° to, or repeatedly subtracting 360° from, these two angles.

It may be impossible to find any value for an angle corresponding to a stated value for a function. For example, there is no value of θ for which $\sin\theta = 2$.

Example

If $\tan \theta = -1.376$, find all positive values of θ less than 360°.

SOLUTION: If A is the associated acute angle for θ, then

$$\tan A = 1.376 \qquad \text{and} \qquad A = 54° \text{ by Table II.}$$

Since $\tan \theta$ is negative, the terminal side of θ must lie in quadrant II or quadrant IV. Thus, we have

$$\theta = 180° - 54° = 126° \qquad \text{or} \qquad \theta = 360° - 54° = 306°.$$

9.19 Logarithms of Trigonometric Functions

In the solution of oblique triangles we shall need to use logarithms to find the values of such expressions as

$$\frac{24.68 \sin 32° 14'}{\sin 75° 43'}.$$

To do this, it is clear that we need values of logarithms of trigonometric functions. One way to get these would be to look up values of trigonometric functions in Table II, and then use Table III to get the logarithms of these numbers. However, Table IV lists values of *logarithms of trigonometric functions*, which enables us to go directly from the angle to the logarithm of a trigonometric function without going through the intermediate step of getting the value of the trigonometric function. We shall use examples to show how this table is used.

Example 1

Find the value of log sin 37° 24′.

SOLUTION: We locate 37° 20′ in Table IV in the **Angle** column at the left of the page. Going over horizontally to the column designated at the top by **L Sin**, we find the entry 9.7828. Just below this entry and in the column designated at the top by **d 1′**, we find 1.6, which is the change in the logarithm corresponding to a change of 1 min in the angle. Since our angle is 4′ greater than 37° 20′, we multiply 1.6 by 4, getting 6 as the result to the nearest integer. We add this 6 to the last digit of 9.7828, getting 9.7834. In this table all the characteristics have been increased by 10; hence, we have

$$\log \sin 37° 24' = 9.7834 - 10.$$

Interpolation by forming a proportion without the aid of the **d 1′** column can also be used.

Example 2

Find the value of log cot 62° 47′.

SOLUTION: We locate 62° 40′ in the **Angle** column at the right of the page. Going horizontally to the left until we come to the column designated **L Cot** at the bottom of the page, we find the entry 9.7134. In the **cd 1′** column we find that 3.1 is the change in the log cotangent due to a change in the angle of 1′. Multiplying 3.1 by 7 yields 22. We *subtract* this 22 from the last two digits of 9.7134, since the log cotangent *decreases* as the angle increases. Thus, we have

$$\log \cot 62° 47' = 9.7112 - 10.$$

Example 3

If $\log \tan \theta = 0.2450$, find θ.

SOLUTION: We look for 10.2450 in the **L Tan** column, and find the two entries 10.2444 and 10.2474 between which our logarithm lies. These two entries correspond to 60° 20′ and 60° 30′, respectively, and so θ is between these two angles. To get the number of minutes to add to 60° 20′ to give θ, we take the difference between log tan 60° 20′ and log tan θ and divide this difference by 3.0, the difference for 1′ given in the **cd 1′** column. Thus, we have as the number of minutes correction in this case $6 \div 3 = 2$. Therefore

$$\theta = 60° 22'.$$

Example 4

If $\log \cos \theta = 9.8726 - 10$, find θ.

SOLUTION: The two entries in the **L Cos** column between which our logarithm lies are 9.8733 and 9.8722, which correspond to 41° 40′ and 41° 50′, respectively. We always work from the smaller angle, and thus we take the difference between 9.8733 and our logarithm, this difference being 7. Dividing 7 by 1.1, the entry in the **d 1′** column, we get 6′ to be added to 41° 40′, which gives us

$$\theta = 41° 46'.$$

EXERCISES

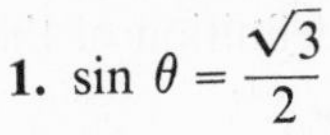

Find all positive angles less than 360° corresponding to the following:

1. $\sin \theta = \frac{\sqrt{3}}{2}$	**2.** $\cos \theta = -\frac{1}{2}$	**3.** $\tan \theta = -1$
4. $\cot \theta = \sqrt{3}$	**5.** $\cos \theta = \frac{\sqrt{2}}{2}$	**6.** $\sin \theta = -1$
7. $\tan \theta = 0.4040$	**8.** $\cot \theta = -1.280$	**9.** $\sec \theta = -2.669$
10. $\sin \theta = -0.2700$	**11.** $\cot \theta = 1.473$	**12.** $\tan \theta = 2.560$
13. $\cos \theta = -0.5398$	**14.** $\csc \theta = 2.052$	**15.** $\sin \theta = -0.5820$
16. $\cot \theta = -0.6200$	**17.** $\tan \theta = -0.3955$	**18.** $\sec \theta = 1.176$

Find the values of the following:

19. log cos 36° 20′ **20.** log sin 68° 40′ **21.** log tan 24° 26′
22. log cos 42° 33′ **23.** log cot 54° 12′ **24.** log sin 16° 54′
25. log sin 75° 8′ **26.** log tan 49° 51′ **27.** log cos 63° 46′
28. log cot 38° 17′ **29.** log sin 23° 48′ **30.** log cos 72° 35′

Find a value of θ corresponding to each of the following:

31. $\log \cos \theta = 9.7657 - 10$ **32.** $\log \tan \theta = 9.9187 - 10$
33. $\log \sin \theta = 9.6328 - 10$ **34.** $\log \cot \theta = 0.3220$
35. $\log \tan \theta = 0.1142$ **36.** $\log \cos \theta = 9.9867 - 10$
37. $\log \cot \theta = 9.9332 - 10$ **38.** $\log \sin \theta = 9.8625 - 10$
39. $\log \cos \theta = 9.2975 - 10$ **40.** $\log \tan \theta = 10.7061 - 10$
41. $\log \sin \theta = 9.4542 - 10$ **42.** $\log \cos \theta = 8.8925 - 10$

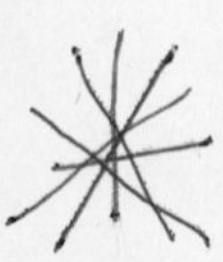

9.20 The Law of Sines

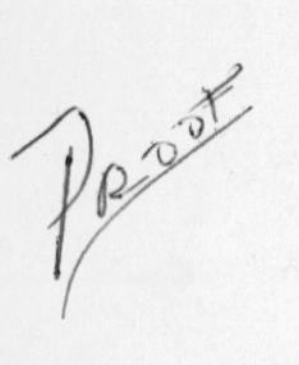

Consider any triangle. Construct a coordinate system in such a manner that a largest angle, which we denote by A, is in standard position; label the other vertices and the sides as shown in Fig. 9–32. Draw a perpendicular CD

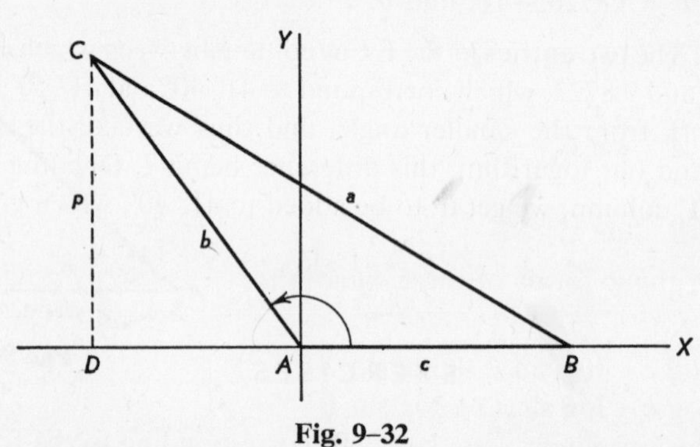

Fig. 9–32

from C to the x axis and denote its length by p. Then, by the definition of the sine function, we have

$$\frac{p}{b} = \sin A \qquad p = b \sin A.$$

Also, since BCD is a right triangle, we have

$$\frac{p}{a} = \sin B \qquad p = a \sin B.$$

Equating the two values of p, we obtain

$$a \sin B = b \sin A.$$

Division by $\sin A \sin B$ yields

$$\frac{a}{\sin A} = \frac{b}{\sin B}.$$

A similar discussion establishes

$$\frac{a}{\sin A} = \frac{c}{\sin C}.$$

This completes the derivation of the law of sines, which can be stated as follows:

$$\frac{a}{\sin A} = \frac{b}{\sin B} = \frac{c}{\sin C}. \qquad [9.7]$$

The law of sines can be used to solve oblique triangles when certain parts are given. The following example illustrates such an application when two angles and a side are given.

Example

In triangle ABC, $A = 42° 37'$, $B = 58° 42'$, and $c = 24.64$. Find the other parts of the triangle.

SOLUTION: $C = 180° - (A + B) = 180° - 101° 19'$
$C = 78° 41'$.

From the law of sines we have

$$\frac{a}{\sin A} = \frac{c}{\sin C}$$

$$\frac{b}{\sin B} = \frac{c}{\sin C}.$$

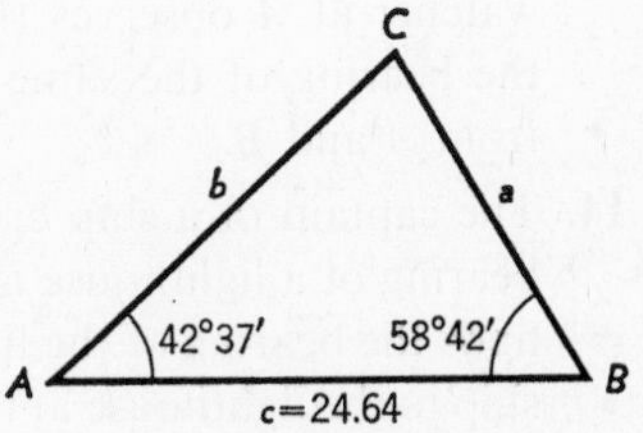

The logarithmic forms of these equations are:

$$\log a = \log c - \log \sin C + \log \sin A$$
$$\log b = \log c - \log \sin C + \log \sin B$$

Fig. 9–33

We make a skeleton outline for the computation. We then look up the necessary logarithms, combine them as directed by the logarithmic equations, and finally look up the antilogarithms. The completed solution appears as follows:

$$\begin{aligned} \log c &= 11.3916 - 10 \\ \log \sin C &= 9.9914 - 10 \\ \hline \log \text{quotient} &= 1.4002 \\ \log \sin A &= 9.8307 - 10 \\ \hline \log a &= 11.2309 - 10 \\ a &= 17.02 \end{aligned}$$

$$\begin{aligned} \log \text{quotient} &= 1.4002 \\ \log \sin B &= 9.9317 - 10 \\ \hline \log b &= 11.3319 - 10 \\ b &= 21.48 \end{aligned}$$

EXERCISES

Solve the triangles that have the parts given in Exercises 1 through 10.

1. $B = 53° 17', C = 42° 46', c = 7.468$
2. $A = 33° 15', C = 66° 35', a = 36.7$
3. $C = 46° 24', A = 72° 49', b = 236.7$
4. $A = 21° 43', B = 48° 13', b = 892.4$
5. $C = 53° 32', B = 61° 8', b = 17.58$
6. $B = 62° 43', C = 18° 24', a = 0.06247$
7. $B = 71° 25', A = 46° 33', a = 28.49$
8. $A = 22° 15', B = 69° 55', c = 469.3$
9. $A = 56° 31', C = 15° 54', b = 4826$
10. $C = 105° 12', B = 32° 6', b = 35.95$
11. A sounding is taken in a river at a point *P*. The location of *P* is recorded by giving its bearings from two points, *A* and *B*, located 200 yd apart on the river bank. The angle *BAP* is 44° 10′ and angle *ABP* is 63° 48′. Find the distances of *P* from *A* and *B*.
12. The distance *PQ* across a lake is desired. A line *PR* of length 560 yd is laid off and angles *QPR* and *PRQ* are measured to be 81° 12′ and 73° 36′, respectively. Find the distance *PQ*.
13. Two fire towers, *A* and *B*, are located 20 miles apart, *A* due north of *B*. A watcher at *A* observes the bearing of a fire to be S 55° 20′ E, and from *B* the bearing of the same fire is N 38° 30′ E. Find the distances of the fire from *A* and *B*.
14. The captain of a ship cruising a course 18° east of north observes that the bearing of a lighthouse is N 55° E. After cruising for 10.5 miles, the captain finds the bearing of the lighthouse to be N 85° E. Find the distance from the ship to the lighthouse at the time of the second observation.
15. The direction of a target *T* from a gun position *G* is 57° 30′ east of north. At an observation post *O*, 2200 yd from *G* in a direction 73° 20′ east of south, the angle *TOG* is measured to be 119° 15′. Find the range *GT*.
16. A boat on a lake sails due west from a point *A* to a point *C*. During this trip it passes a marker *B*. The bearing and distance of *B* from a point *P* on the shore due south of *A* are N 47° W and 1200 yd, respectively. The bearing of *C* from *P* is N 61° W. Find the distance *BC*.

9.21 The Ambiguous Case

If in a triangle the measures of two sides and the angle opposite one of them are specified, one of three things may be true. There may exist no triangle with the given values of the specified parts. The given values may determine the triangle uniquely up to congruence. Or there may be *two* incongruent triangles having the given values for the parts specified. The reason for the term **ambiguous** case is obvious.

Let us examine the problem geometrically to see how the various situations arise. We first assume the given angle to be acute. For definiteness, suppose the given parts are angle A, and sides a and b. Let us construct the given angle A and lay off the side b along one of its sides as indicated in Fig. 9–34. The other extremity of b is the vertex C. Let p be the length of the perpendicular dropped from C to the other side of angle A. In each case $p = b \sin A$.

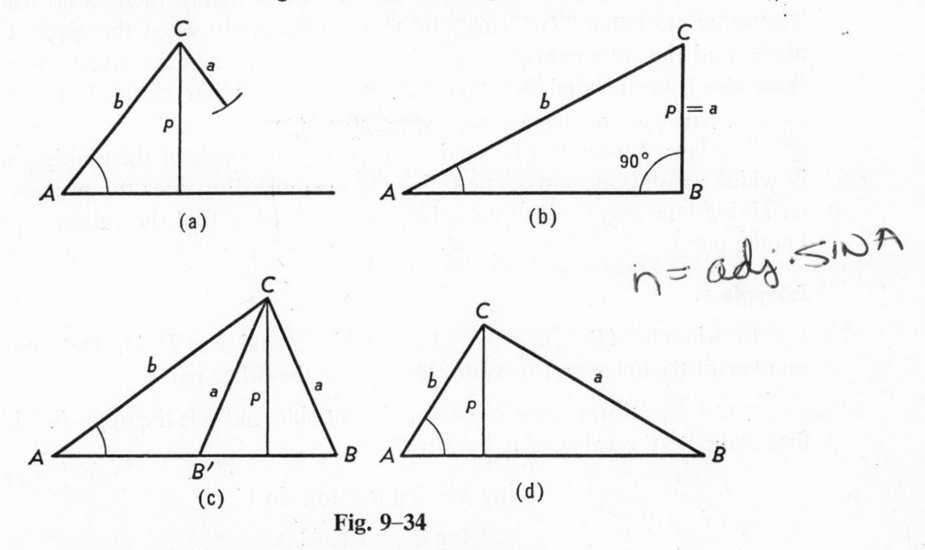

Fig. 9–34

Now one of the following situations will exist:

(i) $a < p$, in which case there is no triangle. [See Fig. 9–34(a).]

(ii) $a = p$, in which case there is one triangle, which is a right triangle. [See Fig. 9–34(b).]

(iii) $p < a < b$, in which case there are two triangles. [See Fig. 9–34(c).]

(iv) $a \geqq b$, in which case there is one triangle. [See Fig. 9–34(d).]

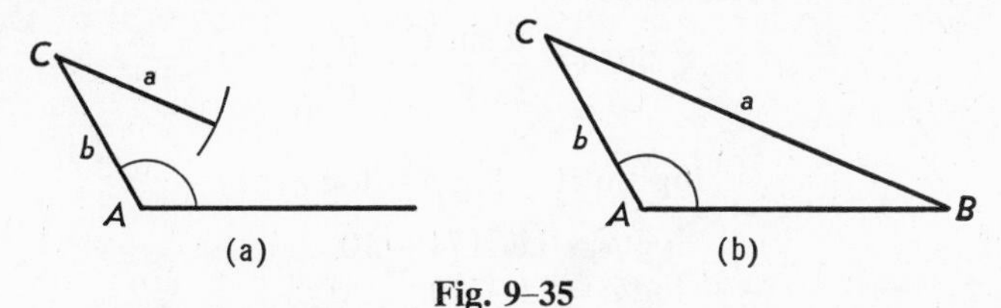

Fig. 9–35

If the given angle A is obtuse, the student can easily convince himself from a study of Fig. 9–35 that we have the two cases given on the next page.

(1) $a \leqq b$, in which case there is no triangle. [See Fig. 9–35(a).]
(2) $a > b$, in which case there is one triangle. [See Fig. 9–35(b).]

For convenience in our discussion above, we named the given parts A, a, and b. To make the statements concerning the conditions for the number of triangles applicable to every instance, regardless of what the given parts are called, we need merely to replace angle A by "given angle," side a by "opposite side," and side b by "adjacent side." Then, for the perpendicular p, we have

$$p = (\text{adjacent side}) \times (\text{sine of given angle}).$$

Statement (i) becomes "if the opposite side is less than p there is no triangle." The other statements (ii), (iii), and (iv), which apply when the given angle is acute, and the statements (1) and (2), which apply when the given angle is obtuse, can be translated into general terms in a similar manner. The student should write out the general statements at this point.

The law of sines can be used to solve any instances of the ambiguous case in which a solution exists. The following example illustrates the process of determining how many solutions exist and also how to find the values of the unknown parts.

Example

In triangle ABC, $C = 37° 22'$, $a = 34.22$, and $c = 21.43$. Determine the number of triangles and solve if possible for the other parts.

SOLUTION: In this case a is the adjacent side and c is the opposite side. We first compute the value of $p = a \sin C$.

$$\log p = \log a + \log \sin C$$

$$\begin{aligned} \log a &= 1.5343 \\ \log \sin C &= 9.7831 - 10 \\ \hline \log p &= 11.3174 - 10 \\ p &= 20.77 \end{aligned}$$

Since $p < c < a$, there are two triangles. We now proceed to solve both. We designate one triangle as ABC and the other as $A'BC$ as shown in Fig. 9–36.

From the law of sines, we get

$$\sin A = \frac{a \sin C}{c} = \frac{p}{c}.$$

Therefore,

$$\log \sin A = \log p - \log c$$

$$\begin{aligned} \log p &= 11.3174 - 10 \\ \log c &= 1.3310 \\ \hline \log \sin A &= 9.9864 - 10 \\ A &= 75° 43' \text{ or } 104° 17' \end{aligned}$$

Since there are two solutions in this case, both values are permissible, and in conformance with the notation used in Fig. 9–36, we write

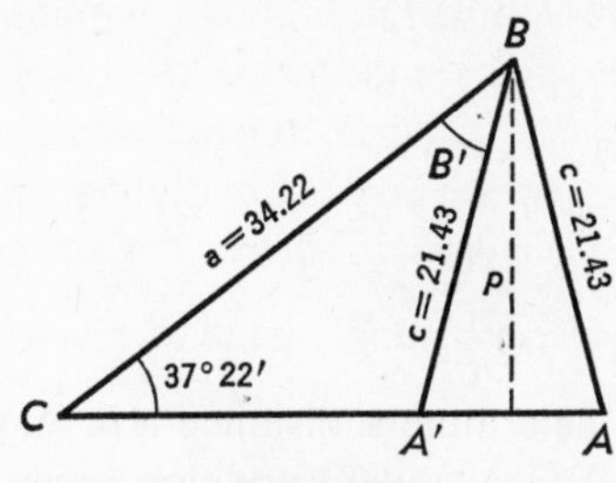

Fig. 9–36

$$A = 75° \, 43' \quad \text{and} \quad A' = 104° \, 17'.$$

In triangle ABC,

$$B = 180° - (A + C) = 66° \, 55'.$$

In triangle $A'BC$,

$$B' = 180° - (A' + C) = 38° \, 21'.$$

Applying the law of sines to each triangle, we have

$$b = \frac{c}{\sin C} \sin B \quad \text{and} \quad b' = \frac{c}{\sin C} \sin B'.$$

The logarithmic forms of these equations are

$$\log b = \log c - \log \sin C + \log \sin B,$$
$$\log b' = \log c - \log \sin C + \log \sin B'$$

$$\begin{aligned} \log c &= 11.3310 - 10 \\ \log \sin C &= 9.7831 - 10 \\ \hline \log \text{quotient} &= 1.5479 \\ \log \sin B &= 9.9638 - 10 \\ \hline \log b &= 11.5117 - 10 \\ b &= 32.49 \end{aligned} \qquad \begin{aligned} \log \text{quotient} &= 1.5479 \\ \log \sin B' &= 9.7928 - 10 \\ \hline \log b' &= 11.3407 - 10 \\ b' &= 21.92 \end{aligned}$$

EXERCISES

Test the data in Exercises 1 through 12 for the number of triangles and solve the existing triangles for the unknown parts:

1. $A = 37° \, 41'$, $b = 20.42$, $a = 11.37$

2. $B = 42° \, 55'$, $a = 12.68$, $b = 14.32$

3. $C = 52° \, 14'$, $c = 383.4$, $b = 320.7$

4. $C = 48° \, 27'$, $a = 67.83$, $c = 64.21$

5. $B = 72° 37'$, $c = 89.43$, $b = 86.2$
6. $A = 57° 45'$, $a = 415.6$, $c = 502.9$
7. $B = 112° 42'$, $c = 4679$, $b = 5672$
8. $C = 39° 56'$, $a = 962.7$, $c = 775.6$
9. $A = 64° 20'$, $a = 3.931$, $c = 4.325$
10. $A = 123° 19'$, $a = 9.678$, $b = 12.96$
11. $B = 56° 34'$, $a = 54.37$, $b = 54.37$
12. $C = 78° 50'$, $b = 65.47$, $c = 64$
13. A surveyor needs to determine a distance AB. A point C is known to be 1512 ft from B. The distance AC and the angle BAC are measured to be 543 ft and 47° 51′, respectively. Find the distance AB.
14. To determine the range GT from a gun at G to a target at T, invisible from G, an artillery battery commander with the aid of an observation plane and a map determines the following data involving a third point S: angle $SGT = 19° 16'$, $GS = 7400$ yd, and $ST = 3500$ yd. Find GT. Do you get a unique answer?

9.22 Distance between Two Points

Because we need it to obtain some important results in trigonometry, we now derive a formula for the distance between two points in a plane, in terms of their coordinates.

First of all, in the case of two points on a line with a coordinate scale (such as in Fig. 9–37), we define the distance between the two points A and B with

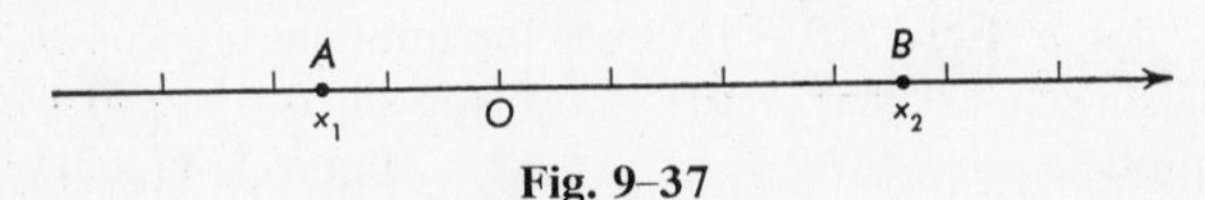

Fig. 9–37

coordinates x_1 and x_2 to be the absolute value of the difference between their coordinates:

$$\overline{AB} = |\, x_1 - x_2 \,|.$$

Let P and Q be any two points in the plane, not on the same vertical or horizontal line, and let (x_1, y_1) and (x_2, y_2) denote their coordinates (see Fig. 9–38). Let R be the point of intersection of a horizontal line through P and a vertical line through Q. By the Pythagorean theorem we have

$$\overline{PQ}^2 = \overline{PR}^2 + \overline{RQ}^2.$$

M and N, the feet of the perpendiculars to OX from P and Q, have coordinates $(x_1, 0)$ and $(x_2, 0)$, respectively, and $\overline{PR} = \overline{MN}$. But, by the definition given above, $\overline{MN} = |\, x_1 - x_2 \,|$. Therefore

$$\overline{PR}^2 = (x_1 - x_2)^2.$$

Similarly, it can be shown that

$$\overline{RQ}^2 = (y_1 - y_2)^2.$$

Therefore, if we denote the distance $\overline{PQ}$ by d, by substitution and taking the positive square root of each member, we obtain

$$d = \sqrt{(x_1 - x_2)^2 + (y_1 - y_2)^2}. \qquad [9.8]$$

It is easy to see that this formula holds also in the special cases where PQ is vertical or horizontal.

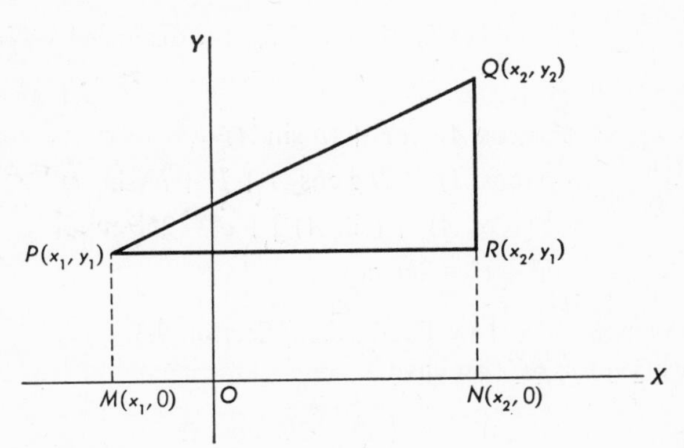

Fig. 9–38

9.23 The Cosine Law

A fundamental relation in trigonometry called the **cosine law** provides formulas for solving an oblique triangle when two sides and the included angle are known or when three sides are known.

To derive the cosine law, let ABC represent an arbitrary triangle, with a Cartesian coordinate system chosen so that angle A is in standard position and side c lies along the positive x axis (see Fig. 9–39).

If (x_1, y_1) denote the coordinates of C, we have

$$\frac{x_1}{b} = \cos A, \qquad \frac{y_1}{b} = \sin A.$$

Hence,

$$x_1 = b \cos A, \qquad y_1 = b \sin A,$$

and thus the coordinates of C are $(b \cos A, b \sin A)$.

The coordinates of B are $(c, 0)$.

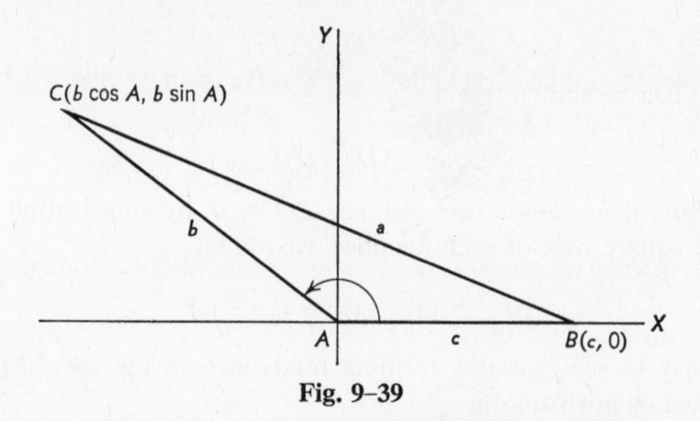

Fig. 9–39

We apply formula [9.8] of Section 9.22 for the distance between two points to obtain an expression for the square of the length of side BC:

$$\begin{aligned}\overline{BC}^2 &= (b \cos A - c)^2 + (b \sin A)^2\\ &= b^2(\cos A)^2 - 2bc \cos A + c^2 + b^2(\sin A)^2\\ &= b^2[(\cos A)^2 + (\sin A)^2] + c^2 - 2bc \cos A\\ &= b^2 + c^2 - 2bc \cos A\end{aligned}$$

since $(\cos A)^2 + (\sin A)^2 = 1$ by Exercise 23, Section 9.3.

Substituting a for $\overline{BC}$, we have

$$a^2 = b^2 + c^2 - 2bc \cos A. \qquad [9.9]$$

Formula [9.9] is one form of the cosine law. Now, angle A and its opposite side a were not assumed to possess any peculiar properties not possessed by the other angles and their opposite sides. Also equation [9.9] is symmetric in the other sides b and c; that is, if b and c are interchanged the formula remains unaltered. Thus, formula [9.9] can be interpreted as stating a relation between a side of a triangle and its opposite angle whatever side and opposite angle be taken. Translated into words, the formula states that *the square of any side of a triangle is equal to the sum of the squares of the other two sides diminished by twice the product of these two sides by the cosine of the angle opposite the first side.* The other two forms for the cosine law are

$$b^2 = c^2 + a^2 - 2ca \cos B, \qquad [9.10]$$

and

$$c^2 = a^2 + b^2 - 2ab \cos C. \qquad [9.11]$$

Notice that if the angle that occurs in a formula for the cosine law is a right angle, then the formula reduces to the Pythagorean theorem. In fact the cosine law has sometimes been called the "generalized Pythagorean theorem."

The following examples illustrate applications of the cosine law.

Example 1

If $A = 58° \, 32'$, and $b = 11$, and $c = 15$, solve triangle ABC.

SOLUTION: We use [9.9] and get

$$a^2 = 121 + 225 - 2(11)(15)(0.522) = 173.74$$

$$a = 13.18$$

Now we use the law of sines to find one of the two unknown angles.

$$\sin B = \frac{\sin A}{a} b$$

$$\log \sin B = \log \sin A - \log a + \log b$$

$$\begin{aligned} \log \sin A &= 9.9309 - 10 \\ \log a &= 1.1199 \\ \hline \log \text{quotient} &= 8.8110 - 10 \\ \log b &= 1.0414 \\ \hline \log \sin B &= 9.8524 - 10 \\ B &= 45° \, 23' \end{aligned} \qquad \begin{aligned} C &= 180° - (A + B) \\ C &= 76° \, 5' \end{aligned}$$

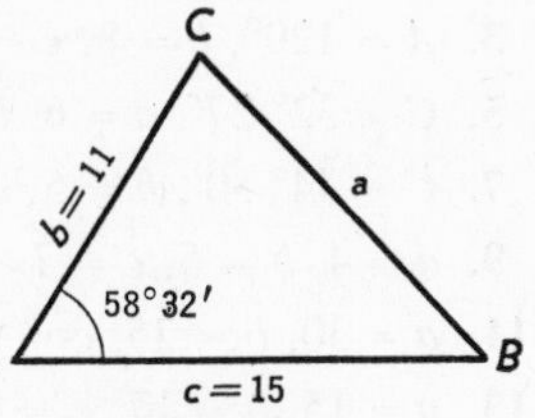

Fig. 9–40

Since there are two possible angles corresponding to $\log \sin B = 9.8524 - 10$, we have to select the proper one on the basis of relative sizes of opposite sides. In this case, since $b < a$, we must have $B < A$.

Example 2

If in triangle ABC, $a = 5$, $b = 7$, and $c = 10$, find the three angles.

SOLUTION: We use the three formulas expressing the law of cosines. Each formula is solved for the cosine of the angle in terms of the sides, as is indicated below:

$$\cos A = \frac{b^2 + c^2 - a^2}{2bc}$$

$$\cos B = \frac{c^2 + a^2 - b^2}{2ac}$$

$$\cos C = \frac{a^2 + b^2 - c^2}{2ab}$$

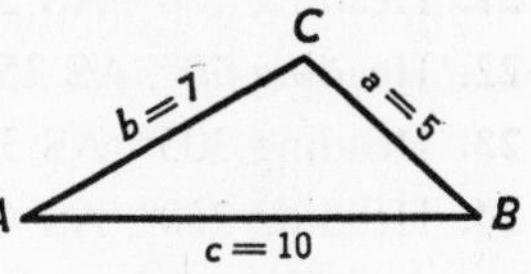

Fig. 9–41

$$\cos A = \frac{49 + 100 - 25}{140} = \frac{124}{140} = 0.8857, \qquad A = 27° \, 40'$$

$$\cos B = \frac{100 + 25 - 49}{100} = \frac{76}{100} = 0.7600, \qquad B = 40° \, 32'$$

$$\cos C = \frac{25 + 49 - 100}{70} = \frac{-26}{70} = -0.3714, \qquad C = 111° \, 48'$$

A simple check in this case is to add the three angles and see if the sum is 180°. The problem we have just solved checks perfectly. However, the student should not expect the sum of the angles obtained to be exactly 180° in every case. Slight discrepancies due to approximations frequently occur.

EXERCISES

Solve the triangles that have the given parts in Exercises 1 through 16.

1. $C = 36°, b = 21, a = 23$

2. $B = 60°, c = 15, a = 7$

3. $A = 120°, b = 8, c = 7$

4. $A = 24° 30', b = 12, c = 9$

5. $C = 32° 27', a = 6, b = 9$

6. $B = 56° 42', a = 5, c = 8$

7. $C = 44° 30', b = 5, a = 11$

8. $B = 42° 6', c = 16, a = 7$

9. $a = 4, b = 5, c = 7$

10. $a = 5, b = 7, c = 6$

11. $a = 30, b = 25, c = 20$

12. $a = 2, b = 5, c = 6$

13. $a = 15, b = 17, c = 8$

14. $a = 20, b = 40, c = 25$

15. $a = 9, b = 12, c = 20$

16. $a = 12, b = 15, c = 7$

In each of Exercises 17 through 20 are listed two forces and the angle between their directions. In each case find the magnitude of the resultant and the angle it makes with the first of the two given forces.

17. 100 lb, 40 lb; 60°

18. 80 lb, 50 lb; 120°

19. 30 lb, 60 lb; 144°

20. 150 lb, 200 lb; 74° 20′

Each of Exercises 21 through 24 gives the heading and airspeed of an airplane, and the direction the wind is from and its speed. Find the ground speed and course of the airplane (see Example 3, Section 9.15, for meaning of terms).

21. Heading 160°, AS 200 mph; wind 25 mph from 0°

22. Heading 70°, AS 250 mph; wind 30 mph from 110°

23. Heading 305°, AS 300 mph; wind 40 mph from 240°

24. Heading 230°, AS 400 mph; wind 35 mph from 220°

Trigonometric Analysis ◄ 10

10.1 Circular Functions

Each of the trigonometric functions has for its domain a set of angles and for its range a set of real numbers. We now define six functions called **circular functions** that are closely related to the trigonometric functions—in fact they are so nearly identical with the latter that they are given the same names: sine, cosine, tangent, etc. However, the circular functions have sets of *real numbers* as domains instead of sets of angles, as in the case of the trigonometric functions. It may seem strange that functions whose domains are sets of real numbers can be practically identified with functions whose domains are sets of angles, and it may appear that using the same name for two different functions will cause confusion. At any rate, let us define the circular functions and then look at the situation.

We first define two of the circular functions, the **sine** and **cosine**, by means of a circle with radius 1 and center at the origin of a coordinate reference frame as shown in Fig. 10–1. Let t be any real number—positive, negative, or zero. Beginning at the point A $(1, 0)$ where the unit circle meets the positive x axis, lay off along the circle an arc AP of length t, counterclockwise if t is positive, clockwise if t is negative.† (The measure of the length of the arc may be larger than the circumference of the circle—it will be if $t > 2\pi$.) Denote

† A precise definition of the length of an arc involves the concept of a limit and is beyond the scope of this book. The properties of circular arcs studied in plane geometry suffice for our purposes.

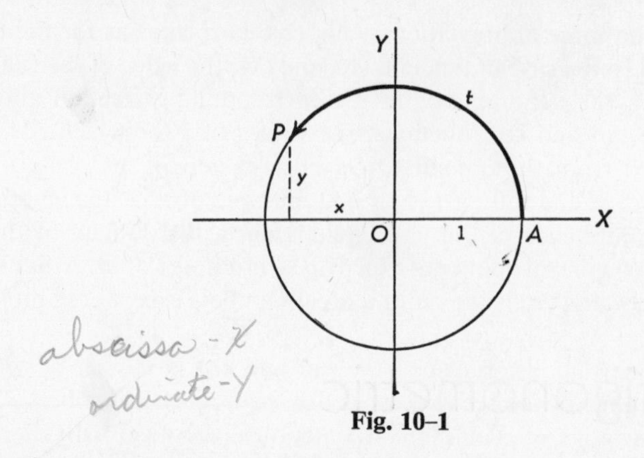

Fig. 10–1

by P the point on the circle located at the end of the arc. In this way, to each real number t there is assigned a point P on the unit circle.

This procedure can be described as winding a coordinate line around the unit circle. Any two points on the line with coordinates differing by an integral multiple of 2π would fall on the same point on the circle.

We make the following definitions:

$$\text{sine } t = \text{ordinate of } P$$
$$\text{cosine } t = \text{abscissa of } P$$

Notice that t is a variable whose scope or replacement set is the set of all real numbers. Also, since P always lies on the circle of radius 1, its ordinate and abscissa are real numbers between -1 and 1, inclusive. Thus, the scheme we have described for computing sine t assigns to each real number (each value of t) a real number in the interval -1 to 1, inclusive (the ordinate of P), and each number in the interval -1 to 1 is the ordinate of at least one point on the unit circle. That is, we have a *function*, called the **sine,** with the set of all real numbers as domain and the set of real numbers -1 to 1, inclusive, as range. Similarly, the **cosine** is a function with the same domain and range as the sine.

The other four circular functions—**tangent, cotangent, secant,** and **cosecant** are defined in terms of the sine and cosine as follows:

$$\text{tangent } t = \frac{\text{sine } t}{\text{cosine } t}$$

$$\text{cotangent } t = \frac{\text{cosine } t}{\text{sine } t}$$

$$\text{secant } t = \frac{1}{\text{cosine } t}$$

$$\text{cosecant } t = \frac{1}{\text{sine } t}$$

We shall use the same abbreviations—sin, cos, tan, etc.—as for the trigonometric functions. In the case of tan, cot, sec, and csc, the value of the function is not defined when the denominator in the corresponding fraction above is zero. Thus, for the tan and sec functions, the values of t for which $\cos t = 0$ have to be excluded from the domain. Now $\cos t$ is zero if and only if P is on the y axis, that is, if and only if t is an odd multiple of $\pi/2$, the length of a quarter of the circumference of the unit circle. Hence, the domain of the tan and sec is the set of all real numbers except *odd* multiples of $\pi/2$. Similarly, the domain of the cot and csc is the set of all real numbers except *even* multiples of $\pi/2$.

It can be shown that the range of the tan and cot is the *set of all real* numbers, and the range of the sec and csc is the set of all real numbers n, with $|n| \geqq 1$. Thus, the range of each circular function is identical with the range of the trigonometric function of the same name.

EXERCISES

1. Tell why the domain of cotangent and cosecant cannot contain even multiples of $\pi/2$.
2. Show that the range of the secant and cosecant is the set of all real numbers whose absolute values are equal to or greater than 1.
3. Make a table showing the domain and range of each circular function similar to the table given in Section 9.2 for the trigonometric functions.
4. Referring to Fig. 10–1, prove: $(\sin t)^2 + (\cos t)^2 = 1$.
5. Use Exercise 4 and the definitions given in Section 10.1 to prove:

$$1 + (\tan t)^2 = (\sec t)^2.$$

6. Prove: $1 + (\cot t)^2 = (\csc t)^2$.
7. Show that the range of the tangent is the set of all real numbers.
8. Compute the values of $\sin t$, $\cos t$, and $\tan t$ for each of the following values of t: $0, \pi/3, \pi/2, \pi, -\frac{5}{4}\pi$.
9. Compute the values of $\sin t$, $\cos t$, and $\tan t$ for each of the following values of t: $\pi/4, -\frac{2}{3}\pi, \frac{7}{6}\pi, \frac{3}{2}\pi, 2\pi$.
10. If t_1 and t_2 differ by a multiple of 2π, what can you say about the relation of the set of values of the six circular functions for t_1 to their values for t_2?
11. If t_1 and t_2 differ by an odd multiple of π, what can you say about the relation of the values of the six circular functions for t_1 to their values for t_2?
12. If θ is an angle and t a real number and $\sin t = \frac{1}{2}$, for what angles between 0° and 360° does $\sin \theta = \sin t$? Can you compute the corresponding values

of t? (Notice that $\sin \theta$ is a value of a trigonometric function and $\sin t$ is a value of a circular function.)

13. Write the definitions of all circular functions in terms of the coordinates of a point on a unit circle.

10.2 Relation of Circular to Trigonometric Functions

In the preceding section we defined the six circular functions of real numbers, whose names are the same as those of the six trigonometric functions: sine, cosine, tangent, etc. We now investigate the relationship between these two sets of functions.

If θ is an angle and t is a real number, then $\sin \theta$ denotes the value of a trigonometric function and $\sin t$ denotes the value of a circular function. Let us ask the following question: Under what circumstances is $\sin \theta = \sin t$? An answer to this question is indicated in Fig. 10–2. The arc AP of length t is

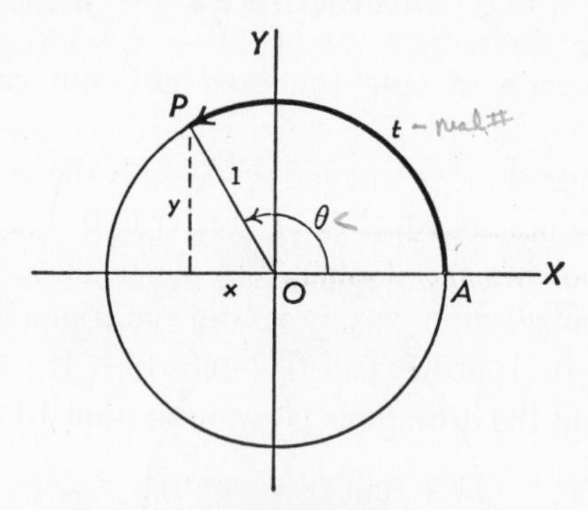

Fig. 10–2

laid off on the unit circle. Then, by definition of the circular function sine, $\sin t = y$, where y is the ordinate of P. But if θ is the angle with initial side OA and terminal side OP, subtended by the arc AP, then, by definition of trigonometric function sine, $\sin \theta = y/1 = y$. Thus, $\sin \theta = \sin t$. Similarly, the value of each of the remaining trigonometric functions of θ is equal to that of the same-named circular function of t.

For example, if $t = \frac{3}{4}\pi$, the arc AP is $\frac{3}{4}$ of a semicircle and the angle θ subtended by the arc AP has measure 135°. Hence, $\sin 135° = \sin \frac{3}{4}\pi$, $\cos 135° = \cos \frac{3}{4}\pi$, and so on for the remaining functions.

The relation between the trigonometric and the circular functions can be stated as follows: If θ is an angle with vertex at the center of a unit circle and t is the length of the arc subtending θ, then the value of each trigonometric function of θ is equal to the value of the same-named circular function of t:

$\sin \theta = \sin t$, $\cos \theta = \cos t$, $\tan \theta = \tan t$, $\cot \theta = \cot t$, $\sec \theta = \sec t$, $\csc \theta = \csc t$.

The trigonometric and circular functions have essentially the same properties. The difference between them is that they have different domains. In this chapter we shall speak mainly in terms of circular functions, but practically all results can be translated into the language of trigonometric functions.

10.3 Radian Measure

As shown in the preceding section, the correspondence between trigonometric and circular functions is achieved by associating an angle with an arc on the unit circle. Thus, if θ is the central angle that is subtended by an arc of length t, then the value of each *trigonometric* function of θ is equal to the value of the same-named *circular* function of t: $\sin \theta = \sin t$, $\cos \theta = \cos t$, and so forth. It would be convenient to have a system of angular measure such that the number of angular units in the measure of θ is equal to the number of linear units in the measure of the length of the subtending arc. There is such a system, and the unit is called a *radian*.

▶ DEFINITION. *The measure of a central angle that is subtended by an arc of length* 1 *on a unit circle is called a* **radian** (see Fig. 10–3).

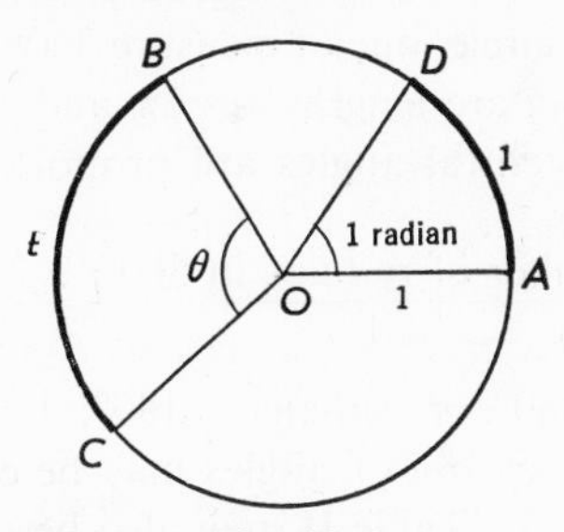

Fig. 10–3

Recall the fact from geometry that measures of central angles are proportional to the lengths of their subtending arcs. We use this fact first of all to observe that the radian is a well-defined unit. Second, apply the fact from geometry to the two angles in Fig. 10–3, one (angle AOD) of measure 1 radian with subtending arc of length 1, and the other (angle BOC) of measure θ radians with subtending arc of length t. We have

$$\frac{\theta}{1} = \frac{t}{1} \quad \text{or} \quad \theta = t.$$

That is, *the measure of an angle in radians is equal to the length of the corresponding arc on the unit circle.* For example, an arc length of 2 subtends a central angle of measure 2 radians. Thus, sin 2 can be interpreted as the value of the *circular* function sine for the real number 2 or as the value of the *trigonometric* function sine for an angle whose radian measure is 2. For either interpretation, sin 2 is the same number.

In general, if angles are measured in radians, the expressions $\sin u$, $\cos u$, $\tan u$, etc., where u is a real number, may be interpreted either as values of *trigonometric* functions of an angle of radian measure u or as values of *circular* functions of the real number u. The *values* of the functions are the same, whichever interpretation is made. This is the justification for using the same names for the circular functions as for the trigonometric functions. The context will usually indicate which class of functions is intended. Often the word "trigonometric" is applied to both classes of functions.

Another way of describing the situation is to say that the domains of the circular functions consist of the radian measures of the angles comprising the domains of the corresponding trigonometric functions.

Values of circular functions can be computed from Table II in the back of the book by using the column labeled **Radians.** For example, the value of the circular function sin 0.74 is equal to the value of the trigonometric function sine for an angle whose radian measure is 0.74. Thus, since Table II lists values of sin 0.7389 and sin 0.7418, the value of sin 0.74 can be obtained by interpolation.

The relation between radians and degrees is established by considering two central angles in a unit circle, one of measure 360° and the other of measure 1 radian. The corresponding arc lengths are 2π and 1. Hence, again using the fact that the measures of central angles are proportional to their subtending arcs, we have

$$\frac{\text{number of radians in } 360^\circ}{1} = \frac{2\pi}{1}.$$

Therefore, 2π radians $= 360^\circ$, π radians $= 180^\circ$, 1 radian $= 57^\circ\,17'\,45''$, and $1^\circ = 0.01745$ radian. The measure of angles may be changed from one system to the other by these relations. Table II may also be used for this purpose.

We now employ another fact from geometry to obtain a useful result. In Fig. 10–4 the angle θ is a central angle in each of two concentric circles, one with radius 1 and the other with radius r. If t and s are the arcs subtending θ in the two circles, it is true from geometry that $s/t = r/1$, $s = rt$. But the number of radians in the measure of θ is t. Hence, if we let θ denote the number of radians in the measure of angle θ, we have

$$s = r\theta,$$

a formula connecting the radius of a circle, the length of an arc on this circle, and the measure in radians of the corresponding central angle.

The result $s = r\theta$, or $\theta = s/r$, shows that in any circle an arc of length equal to the radius subtends a central angle of measure 1 radian.

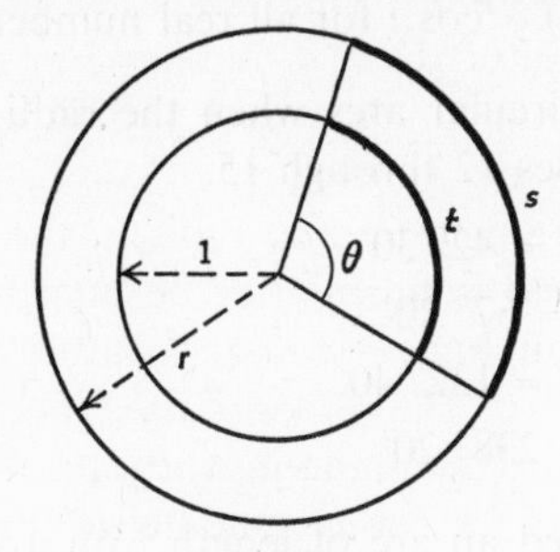

Fig. 10–4

Example

While a spoke of a flywheel of diameter 4 ft sweeps out an angle of 756° 40′, how far does an insect on the rim of the wheel ride?

SOLUTION: This is a problem to which the formula $s = r\theta$ applies. Before using the formula, we must convert the angle to radian measure. We have

$$756° \, 40' = 8 \times 90° + 36° \, 40'.$$

Now, using the two columns of Table II designated as **Degrees** and **Radians,** respectively, we find

$$\begin{aligned} 8 \times 90° = 8(1.5708) &= 12.5664 \text{ radians} \\ 36° \, 40' \qquad\qquad &= 0.6400 \text{ radian} \\ \hline 756° \, 40' \qquad\qquad &= 13.2064 \text{ radians} \end{aligned}$$

Substituting 13.2064 for θ and 2 for r in $s = r\theta$, we obtain

$$s = 2(13.2064) = 26.41.$$

Hence, the distance traveled is 26.41 ft.

EXERCISES

Use Table II and interpolation to compute the values of the following circular functions:

1. sin 0.42 **2.** tan 0.74 **3.** cos 0.35 **4.** cot 0.28

5. tan 1.21 **6.** cos 1.37 **7.** sin 4.06 **8.** cot 5.45

9. Without the use of any tables, express the measure of each of the following angles in radians: 30°, 45°, 60°, 90°, 225°, 270°, 315°.

10. Express in degrees: $\pi/4$ radians, $\pi/2$ radians, $\pi/3$ radians, $\frac{5}{4}\pi$ radians, $\frac{11}{6}\pi$ radians.

11. Show that $\cos(t + 2\pi) = \cos t$ for all real numbers t.

Find the lengths of circular arcs when the radii and central angles have the values given in Exercises 12 through 15.

12. Radius = 20 in., angle = 42° 30′

13. Radius = 9 in., angle = 67° 20′

14. Radius = 54 in., angle = 132° 40′

15. Radius = 7 ft, angle = 238° 20′

In Fig. 10–5 is depicted an arc of length t on a unit circle and the corresponding central angle θ of measure t radians. Use this figure and the fact that the length of the chord AP is less than the length of the arc AP to solve Exercises 16 through 18.

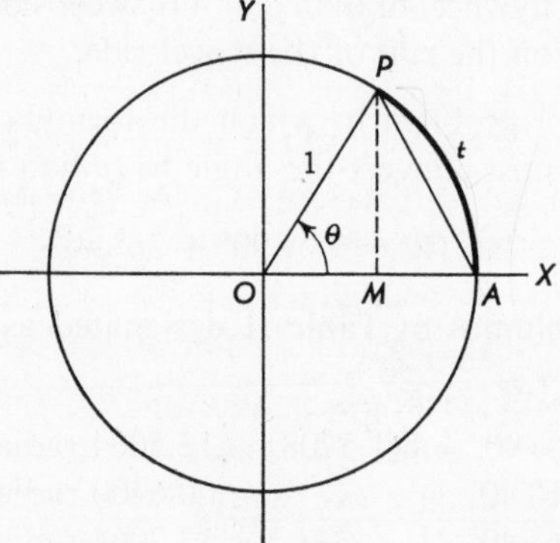

Fig. 10–5

16. Show that $\sin t < t$ for $0 < t < \pi/2$. Can you argue further that $\sin t < t$ for all $t > 0$?

17. Compute the length of the chord AP in terms of $\sin t$ and $\cos t$, and use your result to prove that $\cos t > 1 - \frac{1}{2}t^2$ for $0 < t < \pi/2$.

18. Find the length of the path AMP if $t = \pi/3$.

In Exercises 19 through 21, t denotes a real number and θ an angle.

19. If $\sin t = -\dfrac{\sqrt{3}}{2}$, find the smallest positive value of t. Also find the degree measure and the radian measure of the corresponding value of angle θ such that $\sin \theta = \sin t$.

20. If $\tan \theta = -1$, find two values of t between 0 and 2π such that $\tan t = \tan \theta$. Also find the degree measure and the radian measure of each of the corresponding values of θ.

21. If $\sin t = -\frac{\sqrt{2}}{2}$ and $\sin \theta = \sin t$, find the degree measure and the radian measure of two possible values of θ.
22. How far does the tip of the minute hand of a clock move in 25 min if the hand is 7 in. long?
23. Find the size of the central angle that is subtended by an arc 14 in. long in a circle whose radius is 10 in.
24. If a central angle of 2.5 radians intercepts an arc of 12 in. on the circumference, what is the radius of the circle?
25. Find the difference in longitude of two towns on the equator 3000 miles apart. Assume that the radius of the earth is 4000 miles.
26. Two towns on the same circle of longitude have a difference in latitude of $17° 20'$. Find the distance between the towns. (See Exercise 25.)
27. A belt passes over a pulley of radius 18 in. Find the angle generated by the pulley when a point on the belt moves 2 ft.
28. A bicycle is traveling at the rate of 1600 ft per min. If the radius of a wheel is 16 in., find the angular velocity of the wheel in radians per second.
29. A flywheel of diameter 10 ft has an angular velocity of 20 radians per sec. How far does a point on the rim of the wheel travel in a minute?
30. A pulley of radius 10 in., over which a belt passes, is rotating at the rate of 180 rpm. Find the linear speed of a point on the belt in feet per second.
31. Assume that the earth is stationary and that the moon travels in a circular path of radius 240,000 miles with the earth as center. Find the distance traveled by the moon when a line joining the moon to the earth sweeps out an angle of 35°.

10.4 Periodicity and Graphs of the Sine and Cosine Functions

Let us study the values of $\sin t$ as t is assigned a set of values that start with 0 and become increasingly large. The situation can be visualized by imagining that a point P starts at A in Fig. 10–6 and moves counterclockwise around a unit circle. The points P_1, P_2, etc. represent various positions of the point P. These points mark the ends of arcs whose lengths are values of t, and hence the ordinates of these points are, by definition, values of $\sin t$. We see that as P moves from A to B, t increases from 0 to $\pi/2$, and $\sin t$ increases from 0 to 1. As P moves from B to C, t increases from $\pi/2$ to π, and $\sin t$ decreases from 1 to 0. As P moves from C to D, t increases from π to $\frac{3}{2}\pi$, and $\sin t$ decreases from 0 to -1. As P moves from D to A, t increases from $\frac{3}{2}\pi$ to 2π, and $\sin t$ increases from -1 to 0. Then, as P continues to move around the circle, thus causing t to increase, sin t runs through the same cycle of values for every change of 2π in t. Thus, $\sin(t + 2\pi) = \sin t$ for every number t, and there is no number h smaller that 2π such that $\sin(t + h) = \sin t$ for every number t. For this reason sin t is called a **periodic function** of **period** 2π. The maximum value of sin t, which is 1, is called the **amplitude** of the sine function.

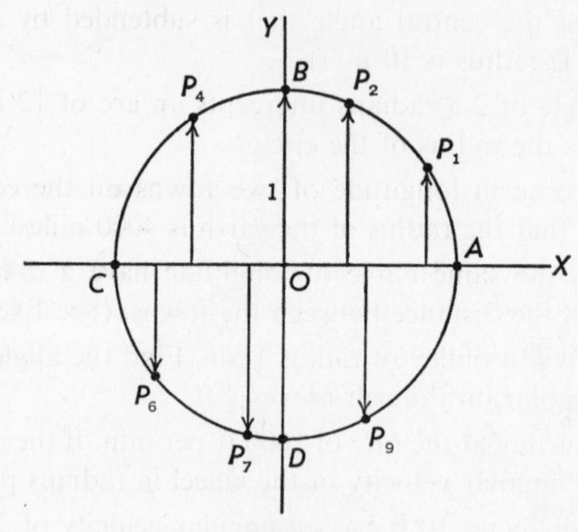

Fig. 10–6

A similar study of the cosine function can be made using the same Fig. 10–6. The abscissas of the points P_1, P_2, etc. represent values of cos t corresponding to the values of t determining these points. The cosine function also has period 2π and amplitude 1. The following table summarizes results for both sine and cosine:

Values of t	Values of sin t	Values of cos t
0 to $\frac{\pi}{2}$	0 to 1	1 to 0
$\frac{\pi}{2}$ to π	1 to 0	0 to -1
π to $3/2\pi$	0 to -1	-1 to 0
$3/2\pi$ to 2π	-1 to 0	0 to 1

All trigonometric functions are periodic, which is the main reason for their importance.

The graph of the sine function—we use the notation $y = \sin t$—can be plotted by locating a few points on the graph and drawing a smooth curve through them. These points may be plotted by obtaining values of sin t for appropriate values of t from a table of values of trigonometric functions or by using the unit circle to obtain ordinates of points as indicated in Fig. 10–7. The graph, if extended indefinitely to the left and to the right, would consist of repe-

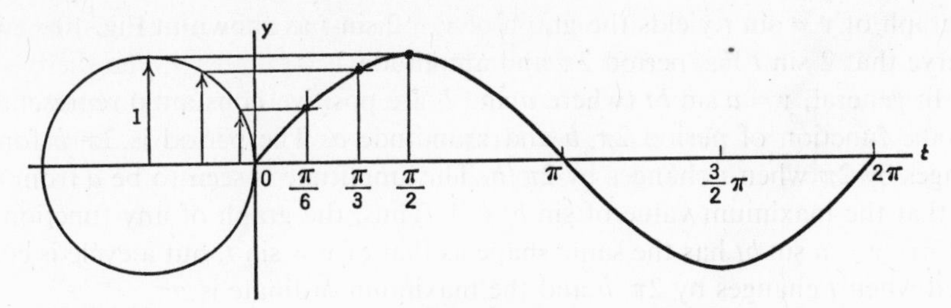

Fig. 10–7

titions of the curve shown in Fig. 10–7. This part of the whole sine curve is called a **cycle**.

To plot a graph of $y = \sin 2t$ we observe its relation to the graph of $y = \sin t$. Since $\sin t$ goes through its complete cycle of values as t changes from 0 to 2π, $\sin 2t$ goes through the same cycle as $2t$ changes from 0 to 2π, that is, as t changes from 0 to π. Thus the graph of $y = \sin 2t$ can be obtained from that of $y = \sin t$ by compressing the latter, so to speak, into one half the horizontal extent. Or, to put it another way, points of the graph of $y = \sin 2t$ may be obtained by first selecting points on the graph of $y = \sin t$ and then plotting points with the same ordinates but with abscissas one half as great. The location in this manner of a few points, such as the highest and lowest points and the points where the curve crosses the horizontal axis, is sufficient to enable one to sketch the graph by drawing a smooth curve through the points thus plotted. The graph is shown as the dotted curve in Fig. 10–8. The period of the function is π and its amplitude is 1.

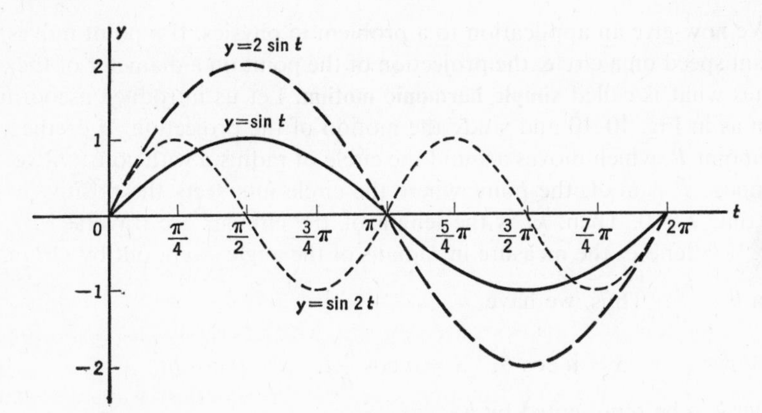

Fig. 10–8

To plot a graph of $y = 2 \sin t$ we observe that for given values of t, the ordinates in the case of this function are exactly twice those of $y = \sin t$. Hence, plotting points with the same abscissas and ordinates *twice* as large as those on

y = a sin bx   PERIOD = 2π/b

AMP. = a

the graph of $y = \sin t$ yields the graph of $y = 2 \sin t$ as shown in Fig. 10–8. We observe that $2 \sin t$ has period 2π and amplitude 2.

In general, $y = a \sin bt$ (where a and b are positive constants) represents a periodic function of period $2\pi/b$ and amplitude a. The period is $2\pi/b$ for bt changes by 2π when t changes by $2\pi/b$. The amplitude is seen to be a from the fact that the maximum value of $\sin bt$ is 1. Thus, the graph of any function of the form $y = a \sin bt$ has the same shape as that of $y = \sin t$, but a cycle is completed when t changes by $2\pi/b$ and the maximum ordinate is a.

The cosine function can be subjected to the same graphical treatment we have given for the sine function. Figure 10–9 represents the graphs of various cosine functions.

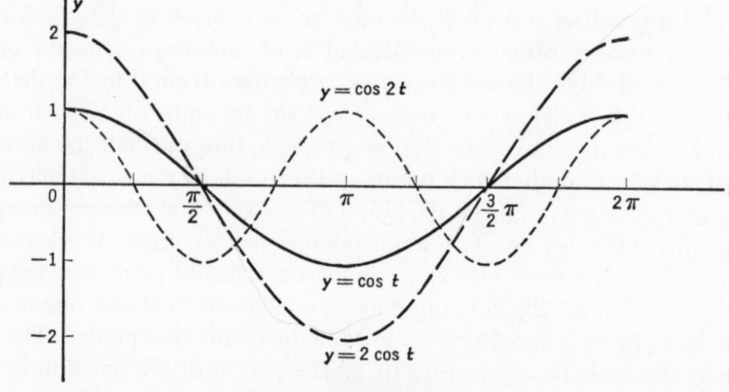

Fig. 10–9

We now give an application to a problem in physics. If a point moves with constant speed on a circle, the projection of the point on a diameter of the circle executes what is called **simple harmonic motion.** Let us introduce a coordinate system as in Fig. 10–10 and study the motion of the projection M on the x axis of the point P, which moves around the circle of radius a with constant velocity k. Suppose P is at A, the point where the circle intersects the positive x axis, when time t is 0. Then, kt is the length of the circular arc traversed by P in time t. If θ denotes the measure in radians of the angle swept out by OP in time t, then $\theta = \dfrac{kt}{a}\cdot$ Thus, we have

$$x = a \cos \theta, \quad x = a \cos \frac{k}{a}\, t, \quad x = a \cos bt,$$

if we let k/a be represented by b.

If P is at some position other than A when $t = 0$, say, at point B (see Fig. 10–11) where the length of the arc AB is d, then

$$\theta = \frac{kt + d}{a} = \frac{k}{a}\, t + \frac{d}{a} = bt + c,$$

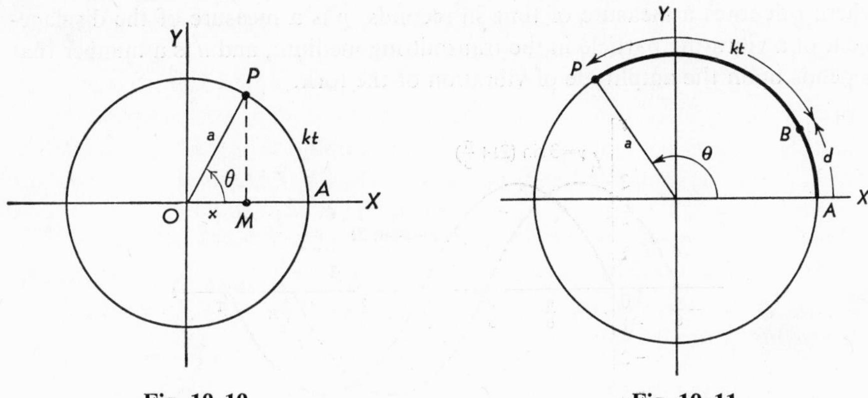

Fig. 10–10 Fig. 10–11

where $b = k/a$ and $c = d/a$. Thus, the equation for x takes the form

$$x = a \cos (bt + c).$$

To find when P is at A in this case, we set x equal to a and obtain

$$a \cos (bt + c) = a \qquad \cos (bt + c) = 1.$$

A solution is

$$bt + c = 0 \qquad \text{or} \qquad t = -\frac{c}{b}.$$

The constant $-(c/b)$ is called the **phase shift.**

The graphs of the functions $y = a \cos bt$ and $y = \cos (bt + c)$ are the same except for position. (We change our notation to the symbol y as dependent variable.) For the same values are obtained for y in both cases if t_0 is substituted for t in $y = a \cos bt$ and $t_0 - (c/b)$ is substituted for t in $y = a \cos (bt + c)$. Thus, the graph $y = a \cos (bt + c)$ can be obtained from the graph of $y = a \cos bt$ by shifting the latter horizontally $|c/b|$ units, to the *left* if c/b is positive and to the *right* if c/b is negative. A similar statement holds for the relation of the graphs of $a \sin bt$ and $a \sin (bt + c)$.

Figure 10–12 shows the graphs of $y = 3 \sin 2t$ and $y = 3 \sin [2t + (\pi/3)]$. Notice that the graph of the latter is the same as the graph of the former except that it is moved $\pi/6$ units to the left.

Another important application of the circular functions in physics is in the study of sound. The source of a sound instigates a to-and-fro motion of particles in the transmitting medium, which is usually air. This vibration is periodic and can be described mathematically by use of the circular functions. For example, if a tuning fork of pitch middle C is put into vibration, the equation describing the vibration (and thus in a sense the sound itself) is of the form

$$y = a \sin 512\pi t$$

where t denotes a measure of time in seconds, y is a measure of the displacement of a vibrating particle in the transmitting medium, and a is a number that depends upon the amplitude of vibration of the fork.

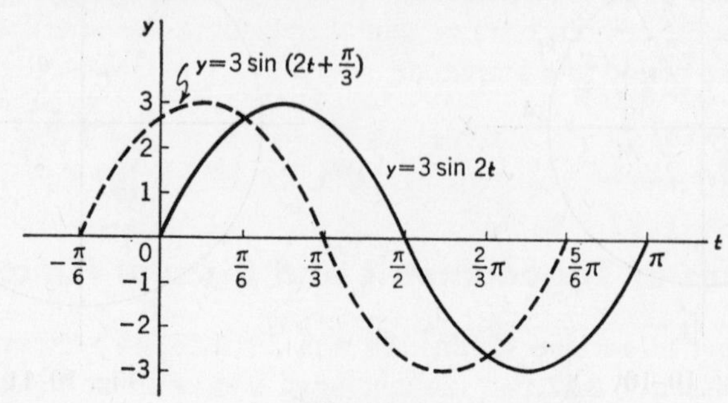

Fig. 10–12

In general, the equation

$$y = a \sin bt$$

can be interpreted as describing a "pure" sound, such as that emitted by a tuning fork. The number a is the amplitude of the function, and for a given *pitch* determines the *intensity* (or *loudness*) of the sound. The period of the function is $2\pi/b$, and the frequency of vibration, which determines the pitch, is the reciprocal, namely, $b/2\pi$.

The sound produced by a musical instrument can be represented approximately by an expression consisting of the sum of several terms of the type $a \sin (bt + c)$.

These examples illustrate the fact that the circular functions have exactly the right properties to make them useful in the study of natural phenomena that have a periodic character. These include alternating electric currents, radio waves, light rays, and many other of the most important phenomena of physics.

EXERCISES

Sketch a graph of each of the functions in Exercises 1 through 6 and state the period and amplitude in each case:

1. $y = 3 \sin t$
2. $y = \sin 3t$
3. $y = \cos 3t$
4. $y = \frac{1}{2} \cos 2t$
5. $y = 2 \sin \frac{1}{2}t$
6. $y = 4 \cos \frac{1}{3}t$

Sketch a graph of each of the functions in Exercises 7 through 12 and state the period, amplitude, and phase shift in each case.

7. $y = 2 \cos \left(t + \frac{\pi}{2}\right)$
8. $y = \cos (3t + \pi)$
9. $y = \sin \left(2t + \frac{\pi}{2}\right)$

10. $y = \frac{1}{2} \sin (3t - \pi)$ **11.** $y = 3 \cos \left(\frac{1}{2}t - \frac{\pi}{3}\right)$ **12.** $y = 4 \sin \left(\frac{1}{3}t + \frac{\pi}{6}\right)$

Plot a graph of each of Exercises 13 through 16 by graphing the separate terms on the same reference frame and then adding the ordinates. Use your graph to tell the period and amplitude.

13. $y = \sin t + \cos t$ **14.** $y = \frac{1}{2} \sin 4t + \cos 2t$
15. $y = \sin \frac{1}{2}t + 2 \cos t$ **16.** $y = \sin t + \frac{1}{2} \cos 3t$

10.5 Inverses of Trigonometric and Circular Functions

The concept of an inverse function was discussed in Section 8.16. It was pointed out in Section 8.18 that the inverse of a logarithmic function is an exponential function. Let us recall that if f is a function with domain A and range B, then, by definition, the inverse function f^{-1} has B as domain and A as range, and

$$f^{-1}(y) = x \quad \text{if and only if} \quad y = f(x),$$

where x belongs to A and y belongs to B.

If the correspondence defined by f is one-to-one, there is no difficulty because, for a given element y in B, there is *only one* x in A such that $y = f(x)$, and hence $f^{-1}(y)$ is uniquely determined. If the correspondence is not one-to-one, the situation is quite different. For example, consider the function defined by $y = x^2$ with the set of integers as domain and set of perfect square integers as range. The correspondence is not one-to-one; for instance, 2 and -2 both correspond to 4. Hence, if we try to define the inverse function, an ambiguity arises as to whether 2 or -2 is the image of 4 under the inverse function. Strictly speaking, a function has no inverse unless it is one-to-one. In this example, if we restrict the domain of $y = x^2$ to the *nonnegative* integers, we have a function which *is* one-to-one; its inverse is $x = \sqrt{y}$, with domain the set of perfect square integers and range the set of *nonnegative* integers, y representing a typical number in the domain and x its partner in the range.

We now turn to the trigonometric functions and consider first the sine. This function, which we denote by f, so that $f(x) = \sin x$, has the set of all angles as domain and the set of all real numbers -1 to 1, inclusive, as range. The function is *not* one-to-one; for example, $\sin 30° = \frac{1}{2}$ and also $\sin 150° = \frac{1}{2}$. We can obtain a function that is one-to-one by restricting the domain of the sine to be the set of all angles with degree measure $-90°$ to $90°$ [radian measure $-(\pi/2)$ to $\pi/2$], inclusive. We shall denote this function (using a capital letter) by **Sine** (or **Sin**). Thus for all values of x in the domain of definition ($-90°$ to $90°$), we have for the Sine function

$$\text{Sin}\, x = \sin x.$$

The range for the Sine is the same as that of the sine, namely -1 to 1 inclusive.

TMPH

The Sin function is one-to-one, and hence its inverse, written Sin^{-1} and read "inverse sine," can be defined as follows:

$$\text{Sin}^{-1}\, y = x \qquad \text{if and only if} \qquad y = \text{Sin}\, x,$$

where x is an angle between $-90°$ and $90°$, inclusive, and y is a number between -1 and 1, inclusive. The domain of the function Sin^{-1} is the same as the range of the function Sin, namely, the set of real numbers -1 to 1, inclusive. The range of Sin^{-1} is the same as the domain of Sin, namely, the set of angles $-90°$ to $90°$, inclusive. We denote angles by their measure.

Examples

$$\begin{array}{llll}
\text{Sin}^{-1}\left(\tfrac{1}{2}\right) & = 30° & \text{for} & \text{Sin } 30° = \tfrac{1}{2} \\
\text{Sin}^{-1}\left(-\dfrac{\sqrt{2}}{2}\right) & = -45° & \text{for} & \text{Sin } (-45°) = -\dfrac{\sqrt{2}}{2} \\
\text{Sin}^{-1}(-1) & = -90° & \text{for} & \text{Sin } (-90°) = -1 \\
\text{Sin}^{-1}\left(\dfrac{\sqrt{3}}{2}\right) & = 60° & \text{for} & \text{Sin } 60° = \dfrac{\sqrt{3}}{2}
\end{array}$$

Similar restrictions are made on the domains of the cosine and tangent functions to obtain corresponding *one-to-one* functions **Cosine** and **Tangent.** The domain of the Cosine function is defined to be the set of angles of measure 0° to 180°, inclusive, and the domain of Tangent is defined to be the set of angles of measure greater than $-90°$ and less than $90°$. Inverses of these functions, denoted by Cos^{-1} and Tan^{-1} and read "inverse cosine" and "inverse tangent," respectively, are defined as in the case of the Sine function.

Examples

$$\begin{array}{llll}
\text{Cos}^{-1}\left(\tfrac{1}{2}\right) & = 60° & \text{for} & \text{Cos } 60° = \tfrac{1}{2} \\
\text{Cos}^{-1}\left(-\dfrac{\sqrt{3}}{2}\right) & = 150° & \text{for} & \text{Cos } 150° = -\dfrac{\sqrt{3}}{2} \\
\text{Tan}^{-1}(1) & = 45° & \text{for} & \text{Tan } 45° = 1 \\
\text{Tan}^{-1}(-\sqrt{3}) & = -60° & \text{for} & \text{Tan } (-60°) = -\sqrt{3}
\end{array}$$

The following table summarizes facts concerning the Sin, Cos, and Tan functions and their inverses Sin^{-1}, Cos^{-1}, and Tan^{-1}. Notice the interchange of domain and range in case of each function and its inverse.

Function	Domain	Range
Sin	Angles $-90°$ to $90°$	Real numbers -1 to 1
Sin^{-1}	Real numbers -1 to 1	Angles $-90°$ to $90°$
Cos	Angles 0° to 180°	Real numbers -1 to 1
Cos^{-1}	Real numbers -1 to 1	Angles 0° to 180°
Tan	Angles *between* $-90°$ and $90°$	All real numbers
Tan^{-1}	All real numbers	Angles between $-90°$ and $90°$

It should be noted that the domains of the Sin, Cos, and Tan have been chosen to consist of sets of angles of least measure that will keep the ranges of these functions the same as those of sin, cos, and tan, respectively. Again we emphasize that the capitalized functions Sin, Cos, and Tan differ from their counterparts sin, cos, and tan only in that the domain of each of the former is part of the domain of its counterpart in the latter set. Sometimes the symbols **Arcsin, Arccos,** and **Arctan** are used for Sin^{-1}, Cos^{-1}, and Tan^{-1}, respectively.

Inverses of the circular functions sine, cosine, and tangent can be treated in the same manner as inverses of the corresponding trigonometric functions. The circular function sine has the set of all real numbers as domain and is not one-to-one. However, if we restrict the domain to the set of real numbers $-(\pi/2)$ to $\pi/2$, inclusive, and denote the restriction of sine to this domain by Sine (or Sin), the function Sine is one-to-one and thus has an inverse Sin^{-1}, defined precisely as in the case of the corresponding trigonometric function. That is,

$$\text{Sin}^{-1}\, y = x \qquad \text{if and only if} \qquad y = \text{Sin}\, x.$$

If radian measure is used for angles, $\text{Sin}^{-1}\, \frac{1}{2} = \pi/6$ can be interpreted either as saying that the inverse *trigonometric* function Sin^{-1} associates with $\frac{1}{2}$ the *angle* whose radian measure is $\pi/6$ or as saying that the inverse *circular* function Sin^{-1} associates with $\frac{1}{2}$ the *number* $\pi/6$.

The restrictions of domains for the circular cosine and tangent functions to obtain inverses are 0 to π, inclusive, for the cosine, and $-(\pi/2)$ to $\pi/2$, *not* inclusive, for the tangent. As a matter of notation, Cosine or Cos denotes the restriction of cosine to the domain consisting of all t, $0 \leqq t \leqq \pi$, and Tangent or Tan denotes the restriction of tangent to the domain consisting of all t, $-(\pi/2) < t < \pi/2$. The following table lists these facts.

Function	**Domain**	**Range**
Sin	Numbers $-\frac{\pi}{2}$ to $\frac{\pi}{2}$	Numbers -1 to 1
Sin^{-1}	Numbers -1 to 1	Numbers $-\frac{\pi}{2}$ to $\frac{\pi}{2}$
Cos	Numbers 0 to π	Numbers -1 to 1
Cos^{-1}	Numbers -1 to 1	Numbers 0 to π
Tan	Numbers *between* $-\frac{\pi}{2}$ and $\frac{\pi}{2}$	All real numbers
Tan^{-1}	All real numbers	Numbers between $-\frac{\pi}{2}$ and $\frac{\pi}{2}$

The graph of the inverse function Sin^{-1}, shown in Fig. 10–13(b), can be obtained from the graph of Sin by interchanging roles of the two coordinate axes. Observe that this graph is obtained from an arc of maximum length of the graph of sin with the property that no horizontal line meets this arc in more than one point [see Fig. 10–13(a)].

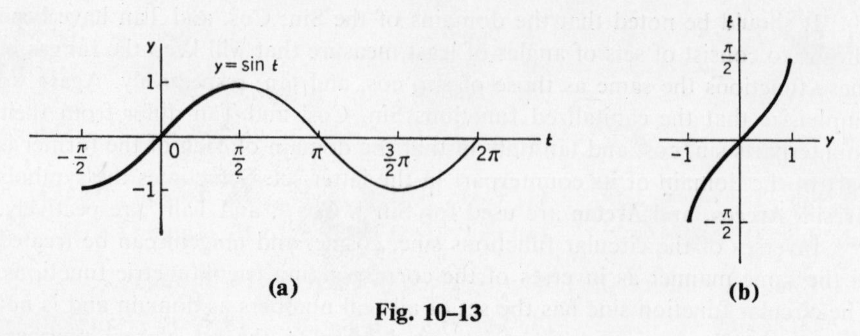

Fig. 10–13

Example 1

Find the value of $\text{Sin}^{-1}\ 0.6428$.

SOLUTION: If Sin^{-1} is interpreted as an inverse trigonometric function, we determine $\text{Sin}^{-1}\ 0.6428$ by using Table II to determine the angle between $-90°$ and $90°$ whose sine is 0.6428. The answer is $40°$ in this case.

If we interpret Sin^{-1} as an inverse circular function, we also use Table II to determine the number between $-(\pi/2)$ and $\pi/2$ whose sine is 0.6428. The answer is 0.6981.

Example 2

Compute the value of $\sin\left[\text{Cos}^{-1}\left(-\frac{3}{5}\right)\right]$.

SOLUTION: Represent $\text{Cos}^{-1}\left(-\frac{3}{5}\right)$ by θ. Then $\cos\theta = -\frac{3}{5}$ and θ lies in quadrant II. Construct θ as shown in Fig. 10–14. Then from the figure, we have

$$\sin\theta = \sin\left[\text{Cos}^{-1}\left(-\tfrac{3}{5}\right)\right] = \tfrac{4}{5}.$$

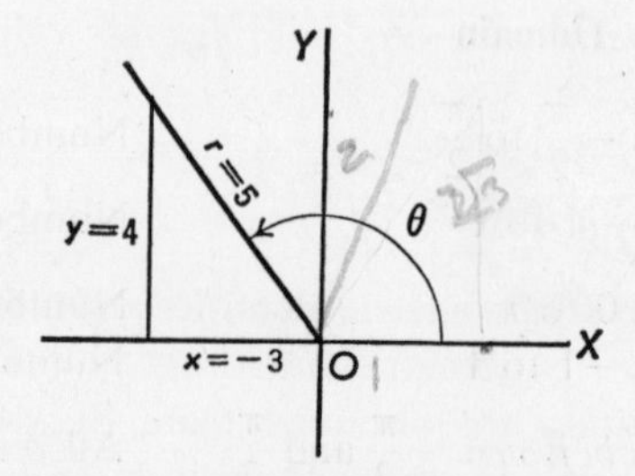

Fig. 10–14

EXERCISES

In Exercises 1 through 15 interpret the symbols first as denoting inverse trigonometric functions and then as denoting inverse circular functions and find the value in each case. Denote angles by degree measure.

1. $\text{Sin}^{-1}(-\frac{1}{2})$ **2.** $\text{Tan}^{-1}\frac{\sqrt{3}}{3}$ **3.** $\text{Cos}^{-1}\frac{1}{2}$

4. Arccos 0 **5.** Arcsin 0 **6.** $\text{Sin}^{-1} 1$

7. $\text{Tan}^{-1} 0$ **8.** $\text{Arccos}\left(-\frac{\sqrt{3}}{2}\right)$ **9.** $\text{Cos}^{-1}(-1)$

10. $\text{Sin}^{-1} 0.3090$ **11.** $\text{Cos}^{-1} 0.5150$ **12.** $\text{Tan}^{-1}(-0.4452)$

13. $\text{Sin}^{-1} 0.7238$ **14.** $\text{Cos}^{-1}(-0.8342)$ **15.** $\text{Tan}^{-1}(2.863)$

Find the value of the functions given in Exercises 16 through 27.

16. $\sin[\text{Cos}^{-1}\frac{4}{5}]$ **17.** $\text{Sin}^{-1}(\cos 30°)$ **18.** $\text{Cos}^{-1}(\tan 0°)$

19. $\tan[\text{Tan}^{-1} 2]$ **20.** $\text{Tan}^{-1}(\cot 135°)$ **21.** $\text{Cos}^{-1}(\sec 180°)$

22. $\sec[\text{Sin}^{-1}(-\frac{12}{13})]$ **23.** $\cot[\text{Cos}^{-1}(-\frac{8}{17})]$ **24.** $\cos[\text{Sin}^{-1}\frac{15}{17}]$

25. $\cos[\text{Tan}^{-1}(-\frac{4}{3})]$ **26.** $\csc[\text{Cos}^{-1}\frac{5}{9}]$ **27.** $\tan[\text{Cos}^{-1}(-\frac{5}{13})]$

28. Plot a graph of $\text{Cos}^{-1} x$.

29. Is the equation $\tan[\text{Tan}^{-1} x] = x$ satisfied by all real numbers? What about $\text{Tan}^{-1}(\tan x) = x$?

Find the solutions, if any, to the following equations:

30. $\text{Tan}^{-1}(\text{Sin } x) = \frac{\pi}{3}$ **31.** $\text{Tan}^{-1}(\text{Sin } x) = \frac{\pi}{6}$

32. $\text{Cot}^{-1}\text{ Sin Cos } x = 1$ **33.** $\text{Cot Tan } x = 2$

10.6 Trigonometric Identities

As was pointed out in Section 9.1, where the trigonometric functions were first defined, the following relations hold for all values of θ for which the functions involved exist:

$$\csc\theta = \frac{1}{\sin\theta}, \quad \sec\theta = \frac{1}{\cos\theta}, \quad \cot\theta = \frac{1}{\tan\theta}.$$

These relations are called **trigonometric identities** and clearly hold for the circular functions as well as the trigonometric functions.

Other useful identities are obtained from Fig. 10–15, where u can be interpreted either as an angle in standard position or as the length of the corresponding arc length on a unit circle. Thus, our discussion applies to both trigonometric and circular functions. In Fig. 10–15, $\sin u = y$, $\cos u = x$, and $x^2 + y^2 = 1$. Hence, we have

$$\sin^2 u + \cos^2 u = 1.†$$

† The exponents are written as shown here to indicate that the value of the function of u is squared and not u itself.

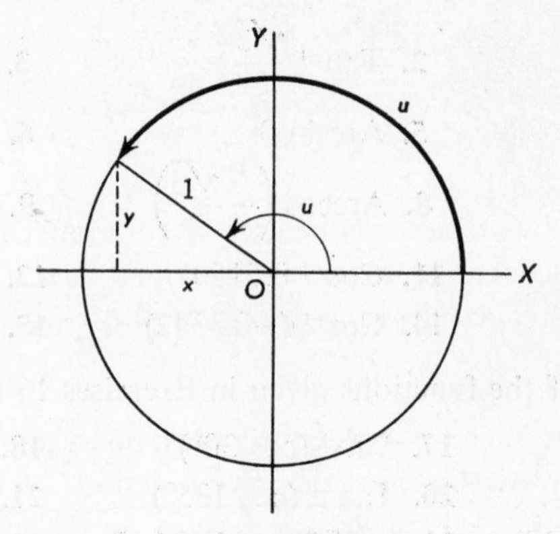

Fig. 10–15

If $x \neq 0$, we may divide $x^2 + y^2 = 1$ by x^2 and obtain

$$1 + \left(\frac{y}{x}\right)^2 = \left(\frac{1}{x}\right)^2,$$

from which, by replacing y/x by $\tan u$ and $1/x$ by $\sec u$, we have

$$1 + \tan^2 u = \sec^2 u.$$

Similarly, division of $x^2 + y^2 = 1$ by y^2 and appropriate substitution yields

$$1 + \cot^2 u = \csc^2 u.$$

By definition and substitution we obtain

$$\tan u = \frac{y}{x} = \frac{\sin u}{\cos u},$$

$$\cot u = \frac{x}{y} = \frac{\cos u}{\sin u}.$$

We collect these results in the following list. They are called the *eight fundamental identities*. They apply to both circular and trigonometric functions and hold for all values of u for which the functions involved are defined.

$$\csc u = \frac{1}{\sin u} \quad \text{or} \quad \sin u = \frac{1}{\csc u} \qquad [10.1]$$

$$\sec u = \frac{1}{\cos u} \quad \text{or} \quad \cos u = \frac{1}{\sec u} \qquad [10.2]$$

$$\cot u = \frac{1}{\tan u} \quad \text{or} \quad \tan u = \frac{1}{\cot u} \qquad [10.3]$$

$$\sin^2 u + \cos^2 u = 1 \qquad [10.4]$$

$$1 + \tan^2 u = \sec^2 u \qquad [10.5]$$

$$1 + \cot^2 u = \csc^2 u \qquad [10.6]$$

$$\tan u = \frac{\sin u}{\cos u} \qquad [10.7]$$

$$\cot u = \frac{\cos u}{\sin u} \qquad [10.8]$$

The fundamental identities may be used to compute values of trigonometric (circular) functions, to change the forms of trigonometric expressions, and to prove other identities. The following examples illustrate these applications.

Example 1

If $\cos u = -3/5$, and u is an angle in the third quadrant, use the fundamental identities to find the values of the other five functions.

SOLUTION: From [10.4], subtracting $\cos^2 u$ from both members and extracting square roots, we obtain

$$\sin u = \pm\sqrt{1 - \cos^2 u}.$$

Choosing the negative sign, since the sine of an angle in the third quadrant is negative, and substituting $-3/5$ for $\cos u$, we get

$$\sin u = -\sqrt{1 - 9/25} = -4/5.$$

From [10.2],

$$\sec u = \frac{1}{\cos u} = \frac{1}{-3/5} = -\frac{5}{3}.$$

From [10.1],

$$\csc u = \frac{1}{\sin u} = \frac{1}{-4/5} = -\frac{5}{4}.$$

From [10.7],

$$\tan u = \frac{\sin u}{\cos u} = \frac{-4/5}{-3/5} = \frac{4}{3}.$$

From [10.3],

$$\cot u = \frac{1}{\tan u} = \frac{1}{4/3} = \frac{3}{4}.$$

Example 2

Express $\sin u$ in terms of $\tan u$.

SOLUTION: We start with [10.7] and multiply both members by $\cos u$ to obtain

$$\sin u = \tan u \cos u.$$

Then, successively applying [10.2] and [10.5] to replace $\cos u$ by $1/\sec u$ and $\sec u$ by $\pm\sqrt{1 + \tan^2 u}$, we have

$$\sin u = \tan u \cos u = \frac{\tan u}{\sec u} = \frac{\tan u}{\pm\sqrt{1 + \tan^2 u}}.$$

Example 3

Simplify: $\dfrac{\tan t(\csc^2 t - 1)}{\sin t + \cot t \cos t}$.

SOLUTION: From [10.6], $\csc^2 t - 1 = \cot^2 t$. Hence we have

$$\frac{\tan t(\csc^2 t - 1)}{\sin t + \cot t \cos t} = \frac{\tan t \cot^2 t}{\sin t + \cot t \cos t}.$$

By [10.3], $\tan t \cot t = 1$, and by [10.8], $\cot t = \dfrac{\cos t}{\sin t}$. Using these relations and also [10.4], we get

$$\frac{\tan t \cot^2 t}{\sin t + \cot t \cos t} = \frac{\cot t}{\sin t + \dfrac{\cos^2 t}{\sin t}}$$

$$= \frac{\dfrac{\cos t}{\sin t}}{\dfrac{\sin^2 t + \cos^2 t}{\sin t}} = \frac{\dfrac{\cos t}{\sin t}}{\dfrac{1}{\sin t}} = \cos t$$

Example 4

Prove the identity $(\tan \theta + \cot \theta)^2 = \sec^2 \theta \csc^2 \theta$ by use of the fundamental identities.

PROOF: We prove this identity by changing the left member into the right, making use of the fundamental identities in the process.

$$(\tan \theta + \cot \theta)^2 = \left(\frac{\sin \theta}{\cos \theta} + \frac{\cos \theta}{\sin \theta}\right)^2 \qquad [10.7] \text{ and } [10.8]$$

$$= \left(\frac{\sin^2 \theta + \cos^2 \theta}{\cos \theta \sin \theta}\right)^2 = \left(\frac{1}{\cos \theta \sin \theta}\right)^2 \qquad [10.4]$$

$$= \frac{1}{\cos^2 \theta \sin^2 \theta} = \sec^2 \theta \csc^2 \theta \qquad [10.1] \text{ and } [10.2]$$

This completes the proof.

Example 5

Prove: $\dfrac{\sec^2 t - 1 + \tan^2 t \cos t}{\cos t + \cos^2 t} = \tan^2 t \sec t.$

PROOF: Again we start with the left member and transform it into the right by appropriate substitutions and suitable algebraic reductions.

$$\frac{\sec^2 t - 1 + \tan^2 t \cos t}{\cos t + \cos^2 t} = \frac{\tan^2 t + \tan^2 t \cos t}{\cos t + \cos^2 t} \qquad [10.5]$$

$$= \frac{\tan^2 t\cancel{(1 + \cos t)}}{\cos t\cancel{(1 + \cos t)}} \qquad \text{(factoring and reducing),}$$

$$= \tan^2 t \sec t \qquad [10.2]$$

There is no general rule that will always work to ensure a proof of an identity. One fact, however, is worthy of observation, namely, that each function can be expressed *rationally* in terms of sin and cos, that is, without involving any radicals. Hence, if nothing better suggests itself, replace in the member to be changed all functions by their values in terms of sines and cosines. Then work toward the other member, making whatever algebraic simplifications and further substitutions are necessary. Sometimes, to discover what substitutions are advisable, it is helpful to transform both members of the identity. Indeed, one method of proof is to transform both members to the same expression. However, even if this is done, the proof can always be written up in a form showing one member being transformed into the other. The method of proof by transforming one member into the other furnishes practice in the most usual type of application of the identities.

5, 9 11, 16, 22, 23, 27, 32, 37, 41, 44, 49.

EXERCISES

Use the fundamental identities to solve Exercises 1 through 10.

1. If $\cot u = 3/4$ and u is an acute angle, find the values of the other five functions of u.

2. If $\sin \theta = 5/13$, and θ is an angle not in the first quadrant, find the values of the remaining five functions of θ.

3. Given: $\csc t = -17/15$, $\tan t$ positive, t a real number. Find the values of the other five circular functions of t.

4. Given: $\cos t = 5/7$ and $\sin t$ negative. Find the values of the remaining circular functions of t.

5. Express $\sec u$ in terms of $\sin u$.

6. Express $\cos \theta$ in terms of $\cot \theta$.

7. Express $\csc t$ in terms of $\tan t$.

8. Express $\tan t$ in terms of $\csc t$.

9. Express each of the trigonometric functions of θ in terms of $\cos \theta$.

10. Express $\cot t$ in terms of each of the remaining five circular functions of t.

Simplify each of the expressions in Exercises 11 through 16 by use of the fundamental identities:

11. $(1 - \cos^2 \theta)(1 + \cot^2 \theta)$

12. $\cos \theta \tan \theta \csc \theta$

13. $\dfrac{(1 + \tan^2 t) \cot t}{\csc^2 t}$

14. $\dfrac{\sin t}{\cos t \tan t}$

15. $\sec t(\csc^2 t - \cot^2 t)$

16. $\tan t \cos^2 t \sec t + \cos^2 t \csc t$

Express each of the following in as simple a form as possible in terms of the functions $\sin\theta$ and $\cos\theta$ only:

17. $\csc\theta\tan\theta$

18. $\cot\theta - \csc\theta$

19. $\dfrac{\sec\theta}{\cot\theta + \tan\theta}$

20. $\dfrac{\cot\theta - \cos\theta}{1 - \sin\theta}$

Prove the following identities by transforming the left members into the right by use of the fundamental identities.

21. $\sin\theta + \cot\theta\cos\theta = \csc\theta$

22. $\cot\theta\sec^2\theta - \tan\theta = \cot\theta$

23. $\dfrac{\sin\theta + \tan\theta}{1 + \cos\theta} = \tan\theta$

24. $\dfrac{\cos\theta}{1 + \sin\theta} + \tan\theta = \sec\theta$

25. $\dfrac{\csc^2 t}{1 + \tan^2 t} = \cot^2 t$

26. $\dfrac{1}{\tan t + \cot t} = \sin t\cos t$

27. $\tan^2 t - \sin^2 t = \tan^2 t\sin^2 t$

28. $\cot^2 t - \cos^2 t = \cot^2 t\cos^2 t$

29. $\dfrac{1 + \cot A}{1 + \tan A} = \cot A$

30. $\dfrac{\cos^2 A\csc A}{1 + \csc A} + \sin A = 1$

31. $\dfrac{\sin A + \tan A}{1 + \cos A} = \tan A$

32. $\dfrac{\tan A\sin A}{\tan A - \sin A} = \dfrac{\sin A}{1 - \cos A}$

33. $\dfrac{\cot B + \cos B}{\tan B + \sec B} = \cos B\cot B$

34. $\dfrac{1 + \sin B}{\cos B} + \dfrac{\cos B}{1 + \sin B} = 2\sec B$

35. $\sin^4 x - \cos^4 x = 2\sin^2 x - 1$

36. $\sin^2 x\cot^2 x + \cos^2 x\tan^2 x = 1$

37. $\dfrac{\tan^2 x - 1}{\sin x + \cos x} = \dfrac{\sin x - \cos x}{\cos^2 x}$

38. $\dfrac{1}{\sin^2 x} + \dfrac{1}{\cos^2 x} = \dfrac{1}{\sin^2 x - \sin^4 x}$

39. $\dfrac{\dfrac{\sin^3 x}{\cos x} + \sin x\cos x}{\tan x} = 1$

40. $\dfrac{\tan x + \cot x}{\tan x - \cot x} = \dfrac{1}{1 - 2\cos^2 x}$

41. $\dfrac{\sin x + \tan x}{\sin x} + \dfrac{\cot x - \cos x}{\cos x} = \dfrac{\sin x + \cos x}{\sin x\cos x}$

42. $\dfrac{(1 - \cot\theta)^2}{\csc^2\theta} + 2\sin\theta\cos\theta = 1$

43. $\dfrac{1}{\csc\theta - \cot\theta} = \csc\theta + \cot\theta$

44. $\sin^2 t + \dfrac{1 - \tan^2 t}{\sec^2 t} = \cos^2 t$

45. $\dfrac{\sin t}{1 - \cos t} - \dfrac{1 - \cos t}{\sin t} = 2\cot t$

46. $\dfrac{1 + \sec B}{\csc B} = \sin B + \tan B$

47. $\dfrac{\csc B}{\cot B + \tan B} = \cos B$

48. $2\csc t - \cot t\cos t = \sin t + \csc t$

49. $2\sin^2\theta(\tan^2\theta + 1) + 1 = \sec^2\theta + \tan^2\theta$

50. $\dfrac{2}{\tan\theta} - \cot\theta\cos^2\theta = \sin\theta\cos\theta + \cot\theta$

51. $\dfrac{\tan\theta+\cot\theta}{1-\sin^2\theta}-\sin\theta\sec^3\theta=\sec\theta\csc\theta$

52. $\sin^4 t-\cos^4 t+2\dfrac{\cot^2 t}{\csc^2 t}=1$

53. $\sec^4 t-\tan^4 t=\dfrac{2-\cos^2 t}{1-\sin^2 t}$

54. $\dfrac{(1-\tan\theta)^2}{\csc^2\theta}+2\dfrac{\sin\theta\cos\theta}{\cot^2\theta}=\tan^2\theta$

55. $\csc^2\theta\sec\theta-\cot\theta\csc\theta+\csc\theta\sec\theta-\cot\theta=\sec\theta+\tan\theta$

10.7 Trigonometric Equations

Relations existing among the trigonometric (circular) functions such as $\sin^2\theta+\cos^2\theta=1$ and $1+\tan^2 t=\sec^2 t$ are called *identities* because they are true for *all* values of θ for which the functions are defined. Another type of relation is exemplified by $2-\sin\theta=2\cos^2\theta$, which is true for *some* but *not for all* values of θ. Such a relation is called a *trigonometric equation.* The main problem of interest in connection with trigonometric equations is to find the values of the unknown angle or number that satisfy the equation. We shall illustrate the process by the following examples.

Example 1

Solve the equation $2-\sin t=2\cos^2 t$ for all nonnegative values of t less than 2π.

SOLUTION: To express the equation in terms of one function only, we replace $\cos^2 t$ by $1-\sin^2 t$. This gives us

$$\begin{aligned}2-\sin t&=2(1-\sin^2 t)\\2-\sin t&=2-2\sin^2 t\\2\sin^2 t-\sin t&=0\end{aligned}$$

which is a quadratic equation with $\sin t$ as the unknown. Factoring the left member, we get

$$\sin t(2\sin t-1)=0.$$

Hence, setting each of the factors equal to 0 and solving for $\sin t$, we have

$$\sin t=0 \qquad \text{or} \qquad \sin t=\tfrac{1}{2}.$$

Limiting our solutions to nonnegative values less than 2π, we have

$$t=0,\quad \pi,\quad \tfrac{1}{6}\pi,\qquad \text{and}\quad \tfrac{5}{6}\pi.$$

That these numbers actually are solutions can be verified by substitution in the original equation. It is clear that indefinitely many other numbers satisfying the equation can be found by adding positive and negative multiples of 2π to these four.

Example 2

Solve the equation $4 \cos^2 \theta - 5 \sin \theta \cot \theta - 6 = 0$ for all positive angles of measure less than 360°.

SOLUTION: Replacing $\cot \theta$ by $\cos \theta / \sin \theta$, we have

$$4 \cos^2 \theta - 5 \sin \theta \frac{\cos \theta}{\sin \theta} - 6 = 0,$$

or

$$4 \cos^2 \theta - 5 \cos \theta - 6 = 0.$$

Factoring the left member of this equation, we get

$$(\cos \theta - 2)(4 \cos \theta + 3) = 0,$$

from which it follows that

$$\cos \theta = 2 \qquad \text{or} \qquad \cos \theta = -\tfrac{3}{4}.$$

Now, there is no value of θ such that $\cos \theta = 2$. To find the values of θ such that $\cos \theta = -\frac{3}{4} = -0.75$, we use Table II and obtain

$$\theta = 138° \, 35' \qquad \text{and} \qquad 221° \, 25'.$$

Example 3

Solve $\sec \theta = 2 \tan \theta - 3$ for all angles θ between 0° and 360°.

SOLUTION: Replace $\sec \theta$ by $\pm\sqrt{1 + \tan^2 \theta}$ and get

$$\pm\sqrt{1 + \tan^2 \theta} = 2 \tan \theta - 3.$$

Squaring both sides, we obtain

$$1 + \tan^2 \theta = 4 \tan^2 \theta - 12 \tan \theta + 9,$$

or

$$3 \tan^2 \theta - 12 \tan \theta + 8 = 0.$$

By means of the quadratic formula, we get

$$\tan \theta = \frac{12 \pm \sqrt{48}}{6} = 2 \pm \frac{2}{3}\sqrt{3} = 3.155 \text{ and } 0.8453.$$

Corresponding to $\tan \theta = 3.155$, $\theta = 72° \, 25'$ and $252° \, 25'$. Corresponding to $\tan \theta = 0.8453$, $\theta = 40° \, 12'$ and $220° \, 12'$.

Since at one stage in the solution we squared both members of the equation, there is a possibility that not all of these angles will satisfy our original equation. Indeed, direct substitution of each angle in the original equation reveals that 72° 25′ and 220° 12′ are solutions, while the other two angles are *not*. Hence, the solution set consists of 72° 25′ and 220° 12′.

10, 12, 115, 17, 22, 25, 29, 37

EXERCISES

24

Solve the following equations for all values of t, $0 \leqq t < 2\pi$:

1. $\sin t = \frac{\sqrt{2}}{2}$ **2.** $\cos t = -\frac{\sqrt{2}}{2}$ **3.** $\tan t = -\sqrt{3}$

4. $\sec t = 2$ **5.** $\cot t = 0$ **6.** $\sin t = -\frac{\sqrt{3}}{2}$

7. $\csc t = -\sqrt{2}$ **8.** $\cot t = -1$ **9.** $\cos t = 1$

10. $2 \sin^2 t - \sin t - 1 = 0$ **11.** $2 \cos^2 t - \cos t = 0$

12. $\sin^2 t - \cos^2 t = 0$ **13.** $\tan t - \cot t = 0$

14. $4 \cos^2 t + 15 \sin t - 13 = 0$ **15.** $3 \sin^2 t - \cos t - 1 = 0$

Solve the equations in Exercises 16 through 31 for all angles of measure 0° to 360°.

16. $\tan \theta - 3 \cot \theta = 0$ **17.** $\sec^2 \theta = 1 - \tan \theta$

18. $\tan^2 \theta - 2 \sec^2 \theta + 5 = 0$ **19.** $\sin \theta - \csc \theta = 0$

20. $\cot^2 \theta - 4 \cot \theta + 1 = 0$ **21.** $\tan \theta = \sin \theta$

22. $3 \sin^2 \theta - \cos \theta - 1 = 0$ **23.** $3 \sin^2 \theta + \sin \theta - 2 = 0$

24. $5 \sin^2 \theta - 12 \sin \theta + 4 = 0$ **25.** $\tan^2 \theta - 2 \tan \theta - 3 = 0$

26. $\sin^2 \theta - 2 \sin \theta - 2 = 0$ **27.** $\cos^2 \theta - 2 \cos \theta - 1 = 0$

28. $\sec^2 \theta - 4 \tan \theta = 0$ **29.** $2 \sin \theta - 3 \cot \theta = 0$

30. $\csc \theta - \sec \theta + 2 \cot \theta - 2 = 0$ **31.** $\sin \theta + 3 \cos \theta - 3 = 0$

Solve the following equations for all values of t, if any, in the interval $0 \leqq t < 2\pi$.

32. $\sin t = \frac{\log_{10} 7}{\log_{10} 49}$ **33.** $\log_{10} \tan t = 1$

34. $2 \log_{10} 2 = \log_{10} 5 + \log_{10} \cos \sqrt{t}$ **35.** $\log_{10} \cos t = \log_{10} 17 - 2 \log_{10} 3$

36. $\tan t = \sqrt{\frac{1 - \cos^2 t}{1 - \sin^2 t}}$ **37.** $\tan \cos t = \cot \cos t$

38. $e^{\sin t} = 1^{\sin t}$ **39.** $(\sin t + \cos t)^2 = 1 + 2 \sin t \cos t$

40. $\sin [\tan^2 t + (1 - \pi) \tan t] = 0$

10.8 Formula for cos $(u - v)$

We now derive a fundamental formula for cos $(u - v)$, where u and v can be interpreted either as angles or as numbers. For the first interpretation, the functions involved are trigonometric, and for the second, the functions involved are circular.

The derivation of the formula is given in terms of angles, but the result is clearly valid if u and v are interpreted as the numbers representing the radian measures of the angles.

If u and v denote angles, $u + v$ denotes an angle whose measure is the sum of the measures of u and v, and $u - v$ denotes an angle whose measure is the difference of the measures of u and v.

Construct angles u and v in standard position relative to a coordinate system as shown in Fig. 10–16. There is no restriction on the measures of u and v;

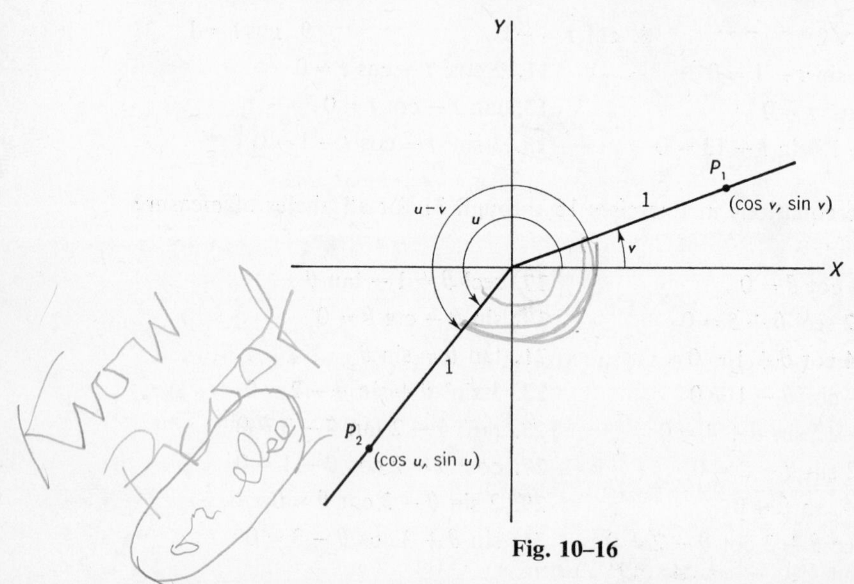

Fig. 10–16

the discussion applies to angles of any size. If angle $u - v$ is constructed with the terminal side of v as initial side, the terminal side of $u - v$ is also the terminal side of the angle with OX as initial side and measure equal to the sum of the measures v and $u - v$. Since this sum is the measure of u, the terminal side of $u - v$ coincides with the terminal side of u, as indicated in Fig. 10–16. Choose points P_1 and P_2 on the terminal sides of v and u, respectively, and at a distance 1 from the origin. From the definitions of the sine and cosine, the coordinates of P_1 and P_2 are (cos v, sin v) and (cos u, sin u), respectively. Using the formula developed in Section 9.22 for the distance between two points, we obtain

$$\overline{P_1P_2}^2 = (\cos u - \cos v)^2 + (\sin u - \sin v)^2.$$

This result simplifies to

$$\overline{P_1P_2}^2 = 2 - 2(\cos u \cos v + \sin u \sin v).$$

Now we reproduce Fig. 10–16 exactly except that the coordinate axes are rotated until the positive x axis coincides with the terminal side of v (which is also the initial side of $u - v$) as in Fig. 10–17. With respect to the coordinate

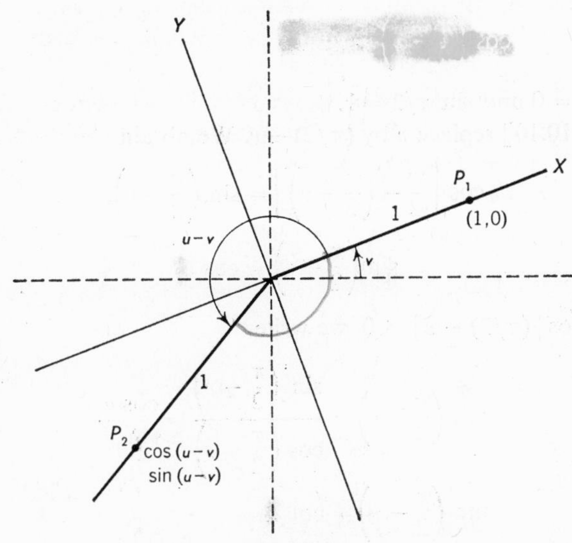

Fig. 10–17

system in the new position, the coordinates of P_1 are (1, 0) and, since $u - v$ is now in standard position, the coordinates of P_2 are $[\cos (u - v), \sin (u - v)]$. We again compute the square of the distance $\overline{P_1P_2}$ by the distance formula. This time we get

$$\overline{P_1P_2}^2 = [\cos (u - v) - 1]^2 + [\sin (u - v) - 0]^2,$$

$$\overline{P_1P_2}^2 = 2 - 2 \cos (u - v).$$

Equating the two values for $\overline{P_1P_2}^2$, we have

$$2 - 2 \cos (u - v) = 2 - 2(\cos u \cos v + \sin u \sin v).$$

Hence,

$$\cos (u - v) = \cos u \cos v + \sin u \sin v. \qquad [10.9]$$

In the derivation of formula [10.9], u and v denoted angles. As has been observed, if they are interpreted as the radian measures of the angles, the derivation goes through as before. Thus, the formula is also valid for the circular functions of real numbers, and the same will be true for the host of formulas we shall derive from it. In what follows, the letters u and v may be interpreted as angles or as real numbers. In the former case the functions are to be interpreted as trigonometric functions and in the latter case as circular functions.

10.9 Functions of $(\pi/2) - v$

Recall that formula [10.9] holds for *any* two angles (or any two real numbers) u and v. Set u equal to $\pi/2$ † in [10.9] and we obtain

$$\cos\left(\frac{\pi}{2} - v\right) = \cos\frac{\pi}{2}\cos v + \sin\frac{\pi}{2}\sin v,$$

$$\cos\left(\frac{\pi}{2} - v\right) = \sin v, \qquad [10.10]$$

since $\cos \pi/2 = 0$ and $\sin \pi/2 = 1$.

Now in [10.10] replace v by $(\pi/2) - v$. We obtain

$$\cos\left[\frac{\pi}{2} - \left(\frac{\pi}{2} - v\right)\right] = \sin\left(\frac{\pi}{2} - v\right),$$

$$\sin\left(\frac{\pi}{2} - v\right) = \cos v. \qquad [10.11]$$

Next, if $\cos[(\pi/2) - v] \neq 0$, we write

$$\tan\left(\frac{\pi}{2} - v\right) = \frac{\sin\left(\frac{\pi}{2} - v\right)}{\cos\left(\frac{\pi}{2} - v\right)} = \frac{\cos v}{\sin v},$$

$$\tan\left(\frac{\pi}{2} - v\right) = \cot v. \qquad [10.12]$$

Similarly, we can derive

$$\cot\left(\frac{\pi}{2} - v\right) = \tan v. \qquad [10.13]$$

Compare the results of this section with those of Section 9.8.

10.10 Functions of $-v$

In formula [10.9] replace u by 0. This yields

$$\cos(-v) = \cos v. \qquad [10.14]$$

To derive a similar formula for $\sin(-v)$, we replace in [10.11] the symbol v by $(\pi/2) + v$ and get

$$\sin(-v) = \cos\left(\frac{\pi}{2} + v\right) = \cos\left[v - \left(-\frac{\pi}{2}\right)\right].$$

† When occurring in connection with trigonometric functions, $\pi/2$ is to be interpreted as an angle whose radian measure is $\pi/2$; in connection with circular functions, the symbol $\pi/2$ denotes a definite real number. Throughout the remainder of the chapter a dual interpretation may be placed upon the formulas derived.

We now apply [10.9] and obtain

$$\cos\left[v - \left(-\frac{\pi}{2}\right)\right] = \cos v \cos\left(-\frac{\pi}{2}\right) + \sin v \sin\left(-\frac{\pi}{2}\right)$$

$$= \cos v \cdot 0 + (\sin v)(-1) = -\sin v.$$

Hence, by substitution we obtain

$$\sin(-v) = -\sin v. \qquad [10.15]$$

Division of [10.15] by [10.14] yields, if $\cos(-v) \neq 0$,

$$\tan(-v) = -\tan v. \qquad [10.16]$$

Formulas [10.14], [10.15], and [10.16] were obtained in Section 9.17 by an intuitive argument.

10.11 Further Addition and Subtraction Formulas

Since [10.9] is true for all angles (real numbers), it remains true if we replace v throughout by $-v$. Thus, we have

$$\cos[u - (-v)] = \cos u \cos(-v) + \sin u \sin(-v),$$

$$\cos(u + v) = \cos u \cos v - \sin u \sin v, \qquad [10.17]$$

since $\cos(-v) = \cos v$ and $\sin(-v) = -\sin v$.

Now in [10.10] replace v by $u + v$ and interchange the two members of the equation. This gives

$$\sin(u + v) = \cos\left[\frac{\pi}{2} - (u + v)\right] = \cos\left[\left(\frac{\pi}{2} - u\right) - v\right].$$

Applying [10.9] to the right member and then using [10.10] and [10.11], we have

$$\cos\left[\left(\frac{\pi}{2} - u\right) - v\right] = \cos\left(\frac{\pi}{2} - u\right)\cos v + \sin\left(\frac{\pi}{2} - u\right)\sin v$$

$$= \sin u \cos v + \cos u \sin v.$$

Thus,

$$\sin(u + v) = \sin u \cos v + \cos u \sin v. \qquad [10.18]$$

If in [10.18] we replace v by $-v$ and apply [10.14] and [10.15], we obtain

$$\sin(u - v) = \sin u \cos v - \cos u \sin v. \qquad [10.19]$$

To obtain a formula for $\tan(u + v)$, if $\cos(u + v) \neq 0$, divide [10.18] by [10.17], member for member.

$$\tan(u + v) = \frac{\sin(u + v)}{\cos(u + v)} = \frac{\sin u \cos v + \cos u \sin v}{\cos u \cos v - \sin u \sin v}.$$

Now divide the numerator and denominator on the right by $\cos u \cos v$:

$$\frac{\sin u \cos v + \cos u \sin v}{\cos u \cos v - \sin u \sin v} = \frac{\dfrac{\sin u \cos v}{\cos u \cos v} + \dfrac{\cos u \sin v}{\cos u \cos v}}{\dfrac{\cos u \cos v}{\cos u \cos v} - \dfrac{\sin u \sin v}{\cos u \cos v}}$$

$$= \frac{\tan u + \tan v}{1 - \tan u \tan v}.$$

Hence,

$$\tan (u + v) = \frac{\tan u + \tan v}{1 - \tan u \tan v}. \qquad [10.20]$$

Note: If $\cos u \cos v = 0$, then we cannot divide by this product. But since $\cos u \cos v = 0$ is equivalent to the nonexistence of $\tan u$ or $\tan v$, our derivation of [10.20] is valid in all cases in which $\tan u$, $\tan v$, and $\tan (u + v)$ are defined.

The following formula for $\tan (u - v)$ may be obtained in a similar manner from [10.9] and [10.19]:

$$\tan (u - v) = \frac{\tan u - \tan u}{1 + \tan u \tan v}. \qquad [10.21]$$

Formulas [10.17], [10.18], and [10.20] are called **addition formulas,** and formulas [10.9], [10.19], and [10.21] are called **subtraction formulas.** They are true for all values of u and v for which the functions involved are defined.

Example 1

Knowing the values of the functions of 45° and 30°, use the addition formulas to find the values of sin 75° and cos 75°.

SOLUTION: From our study of special angles, we know that

$$\sin 45° = \frac{\sqrt{2}}{2}, \quad \cos 45° = \frac{\sqrt{2}}{2}, \quad \sin 30° = \frac{1}{2}, \quad \cos 30° = \frac{\sqrt{3}}{2}.$$

Now, by [10.18],

$$\sin 75° = \sin (45° + 30°) = \sin 45° \cos 30° + \cos 45° \sin 30°$$

$$= \frac{\sqrt{2}}{2}\frac{\sqrt{3}}{2} + \frac{\sqrt{2}}{2}\frac{1}{2} = \frac{\sqrt{2}}{4}(\sqrt{3} + 1)$$

$$= \frac{1.4142}{4}(1.7320 + 1) = 0.9659.$$

Similarly, by [10.17],

$$\cos 75° = \cos 45° \cos 30° - \sin 45° \sin 30°$$

$$= \frac{\sqrt{2}}{2}\frac{\sqrt{3}}{2} - \frac{\sqrt{2}}{2}\frac{1}{2}$$

$$= \frac{\sqrt{2}}{4}(\sqrt{3} - 1) = 0.2588.$$

Example 2

Given: $\tan u = 12/5$, u a real number between $\pi/2$ and 2π, and also $\sec v = 5/3$ and $\sin v$ positive. Find the values of $\cos(u - v)$ and $\tan(u - v)$.

SOLUTION: From [10.5], Section 10.6, and the limitation on the value of u, we have

$$\sec u = -\sqrt{1 + \tan^2 u} = -\sqrt{1 + 144/25} = -13/5.$$

Hence, using [10.2], we get $\cos u = -5/13$, and by means of [10.4] we find $\sin u = -12/13$. Applying [10.2], we obtain $\cos v = 3/5$, and by [10.4], $\sin v = 4/5$. Finally, [10.7] yields $\tan v = 4/3$.

We use these values and [10.9] and [10.21] to compute the values of $\cos(u - v)$ and $\tan(u - v)$. Using [10.9], we have

$$\cos(u - v) = (-5/13)(3/5) + (-12/13)(4/5)$$
$$= \frac{-15 - 48}{65} = -\frac{63}{65}.$$

From [10.21] we have

$$\tan(u - v) = \frac{12/5 - 4/3}{1 + 12/5 \cdot 4/3} = \frac{16/15}{63/15} = \frac{16}{63}.$$

In determining the algebraic sign of a circular function for a given real number, it is helpful to visualize the quadrant in which the corresponding point on the unit circle (or the terminal side of the corresponding angle) falls.

EXERCISES

1. Use the addition formulas to find the values of sin 105° and cos 105° from the values of the functions of 60° and 45°.
2. Find the values of the sine and cosine of 36° and 25° 50′ from Table II. Then use the addition formulas to obtain values for sin 61° 50′ and cos 61° 50′.
3. By looking up values of the sine and cosine of 18° and 30° 40′ and using the addition formulas, find the values of sin 48° 40′ and also cos 48° 40′.
4. From the values of the functions of 53° 10′ and 54°, find the values of sin 107° 10′ and cos 107° 10′.
5. Use the functions of 60° and 45° to find the values of sin 15°, cos 15°, tan 105°, and tan 15°.
6. Find the values of the sine, cosine, and tangent of 18° and 65° 30′ in Table II and use them to find the values of sin 47° 30′, cos 47° 30′, tan 83° 30′, and tan 47° 30′.
7. Find the values of the sine, cosine, and tangent of 58° and 36° 30′ in Table II and use them to find the values of sin 21° 30′, cos 21° 30′, tan 21° 30′, and tan 94° 30′.

8. After locating the values of the necessary functions of 59° and 69° 10′ in Table II, find the values of the sine, cosine, and tangent of 10° 10′, and the tangent of 128° 10′.

In Exercises 9 through 12, u and v denote real numbers of smallest possible absolute value in each case, and where there is a choice between two numbers with the same absolute value, the positive one is to be chosen. Use appropriate formulas to find the values of the functions indicated.

9. $\sin(u+v)$, if $\sin u = 12/13$ and $\sin v = 3/5$.

10. $\cos(u+v)$, if $\cos u = -5/13$ and $\cos v = 12/13$.

11. $\cos(u+v)$, if $\tan u = -15/8$ and $\cos v = -4/5$.

12. $\sin(u+v)$, if $\sin u = 5/13$ and $\tan v = -3/4$.

13. If $\tan u = -12/5$, $\sin u$ positive, $\sec v = -5/3$, $\cot v$ negative, find the values of $\sin(u-v)$, $\cos(u-v)$, $\tan(u-v)$, and $\tan(u+v)$.

14. If $\cos u = 15/17$, $\sin v = 3/5$, each of u and v between $\pi/2$ and 2π, find the values of $\sin(u-v)$, $\cos(u-v)$, $\tan(u-v)$, and $\tan(u+v)$.

15. Given: $\cot u = 4/3$, $\sin v = 12/13$, each of u and v between $\pi/2$ and 2π. Find the values of the sine, cosine, and tangent of $u+v$ and $u-v$.

16. Given: $\tan u = 24/7$, $\sin u$ negative, $\sec v = -3/5$, $\csc v$ positive. Find the values of the sine, cosine, and tangent of $u+v$ and $u-v$.

Use addition and subtraction formulas to prove the trigonometric relations in Exercises 17 through 32. These relations were encountered in Section 9.16 and proved there for θ acute by a different method. Rewrite each one in terms of circular functions.

17. $\sin(90° + \theta) = \cos\theta$

18. $\cos(90° + \theta) = -\sin\theta$

19. $\cos(180° + \theta) = -\cos\theta$

20. $\sin(180° + \theta) = -\sin\theta$

21. $\sin(270° + \theta) = -\cos\theta$

22. $\cos(270° + \theta) = \sin\theta$

23. $\sin(180° - \theta) = \sin\theta$

24. $\tan(180° - \theta) = -\tan\theta$

25. $\cos(180° - \theta) = -\cos\theta$

26. $\sin(270° - \theta) = -\cos\theta$

27. $\tan(180° + \theta) = \tan\theta$

28. $\cos(270° - \theta) = -\sin\theta$

29. $\cos(360° - \theta) = \cos\theta$

30. $\sin(360° - \theta) = -\sin\theta$

31. $\tan(360° - \theta) = -\tan\theta$

32. $\tan(360° + \theta) = \tan\theta$

Prove the following identities:

33. $\tan(45° + \theta) = \dfrac{\cos\theta + \sin\theta}{\cos\theta - \sin\theta}$

34. $\sin(\pi - A - B) = \sin A \cos B + \cos A \sin B$

35. $\cos\left(\dfrac{\pi}{2} + A - B\right) = \cos A \sin B - \sin A \cos B$

36. $\cos(30° + u) + \sin(60° + u) = \sqrt{3}\cos u$

37. $\sin(20° + v) + \cos(70° + v) = 2\cos 70° \cos v$

38. $\sin(u + v) + \sin(u - v) = 2\sin u \cos v$

39. $\cos(u + v) + \cos(u - v) = 2\cos u \cos v$

40. $\tan\left(\theta + \frac{\pi}{4}\right) = \frac{1 + \tan\theta}{1 - \tan\theta}$

10.12 Functions of 2*u*

Another set of important relations in trigonometry consists of formulas that express values of trigonometric (circular) functions of twice an angle (number) in terms of trigonometric (circular) functions of the angle (number). These formulas are immediately obtained from the addition formulas. If in [10.18] we let $v = u$, we get

$$\sin(u + u) = \sin u \cos u + \cos u \sin u,$$

$$\sin 2u = 2\sin u \cos u. \qquad [10.22]$$

Similarly, replacing v by u in [10.17] and [10.20], we get

$$\cos 2u = \cos^2 u - \sin^2 u, \qquad [10.23]$$

$$\tan 2u = \frac{2\tan u}{1 - \tan^2 u}. \qquad [10.24]$$

If one knows the values of the sine, cosine, and tangent of an angle (number), formulas [10.22], [10.23], and [10.24] may be used to calculate the values of the sine, cosine, and tangent of the angle (number) which is twice the size of the original. For example, if we know the values of the functions of 1°, we can use these formulas to find the values of the functions of 2°.

Example

If $\cot u = -4/3$, u an angle, and $\csc u$ is positive, find the values of $\sin 2u$, $\cos 2u$, and $\tan 2u$.

SOLUTION: u must be in the second quadrant. By constructing u as in Fig. 10–18, one easily finds from the figure that

$$\sin u = 3/5$$
$$\cos u = -4/5$$
$$\tan u = -3/4$$

Substituting these values in [10.22], [10.23], and [10.24], we get

$$\sin 2u = 2(3/5)(-4/5) = -24/25$$
$$\cos 2u = (-4/5)^2 - (3/5)^2 = 7/25$$
$$\tan 2u = \frac{2(-3/4)}{1 - (-3/4)^2} = \frac{-3/2}{7/16} = -24/7$$

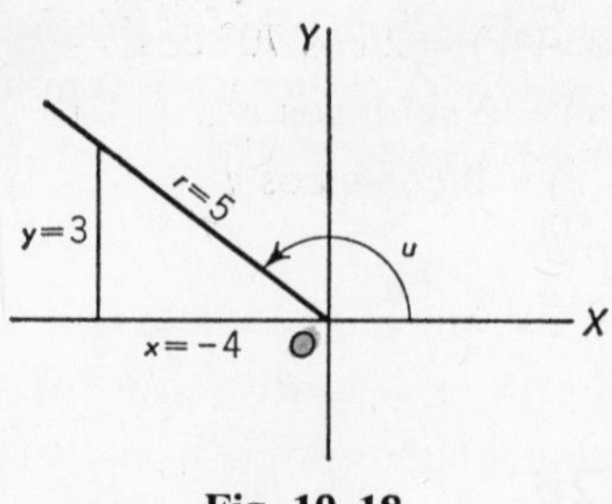

Fig. 10–18

10.13 Functions of (1/2)v

To obtain a formula that can be used to find the sine of an angle (number) half as large as one whose functions are known, we start with formula [10.23] and replace $\cos^2 u$ by $1 - \sin^2 u$ to get

$$\cos 2u = 1 - 2 \sin^2 u.$$

Solving for $\sin u$, we have

$$\sin u = \pm \sqrt{\frac{1 - \cos 2u}{2}}.$$

Finally, to emphasize that the angle (number) in the left member is half as large as that in the right, we make a change in notation by replacing $2u$ by v and u by $\frac{1}{2}v$ and get

$$\sin \frac{1}{2} v = \pm \sqrt{\frac{1 - \cos u}{2}}. \qquad [10.25]$$

To derive a similar formula for the cosine, we again start with formula [10.23] and this time replace $\sin^2 u$ by $1 - \cos^2 u$ to get

$$\cos 2u = 2 \cos^2 u - 1.$$

Solving for $\cos u$, we obtain

$$\cos u = \pm \sqrt{\frac{1 + \cos 2u}{2}}.$$

Finally, as before, we change the notation by replacing $2u$ by v and u by $\frac{1}{2}v$ and obtain

$$\cos \frac{1}{2} v = \pm \sqrt{\frac{1 + \cos v}{2}}. \qquad [10.26]$$

A similar formula for the tangent can be obtained by dividing [10.25] by [10.26] if $\cos \frac{1}{2}v \neq 0$. The result is

$$\tan \frac{1}{2} v = \pm \sqrt{\frac{1 - \cos v}{1 + \cos v}}. \qquad [10.27]$$

Note that in applying formulas [10.25], [10.26], and [10.27], one must select the proper sign in front of the radical. This sign is determined by the quadrant in which the terminal side of $(\frac{1}{2})v$ lies if v is an angle, or the quadrant in which the point determined by $(\frac{1}{2})v$ lies if v is a number. Other formulas for $\tan (\frac{1}{2})v$ are given in Exercises 43 and 44 of this section.

Example

Find the values of sin 120°, cos 120°, and tan 120° from the value of cos 240°.

SOLUTION: $\cos 240° = -\frac{1}{2}$. We use formulas [10.25], [10.26], and [10.27], and select the signs in front of the radicals on the basis of the quadrant in which the angle whose functions we are seeking lies. Since 120° lies in the second quadrant, the sine will be positive and the cosine and tangent negative. Then we have

$$\sin 120° = \sqrt{\frac{1+\frac{1}{2}}{2}} = \frac{\sqrt{3}}{2}$$

$$\cos 120° = -\sqrt{\frac{1-\frac{1}{2}}{2}} = -\frac{1}{2}$$

$$\tan 120° = -\sqrt{\frac{1+\frac{1}{2}}{1-\frac{1}{2}}} = -\sqrt{3}$$

EXERCISES

1. Using the values of the functions of 30°, find the values of the sine, cosine, and tangent of 60°.
2. Use the values of the functions of 135° to find the values of sin 270° and cos 270°.
3. From the values of the functions of 45°, find the values of the sine, cosine, and tangent of 22° 30′.
4. Given the functions of 300°, find the sine, cosine, and tangent of 150°.
5. From the values of the functions of 30° find the values of the sine, cosine, and tangent of 15°.
6. If $\sec \theta = \frac{25}{7}$ and θ is an acute angle, find the values of $\sin 2\theta$, $\cos (\theta/2)$, and $\tan (\theta/2)$.
7. If $\sin \theta = -\frac{12}{13}$ and $\cos \theta$ is negative, find values for $\sin 2\theta$, $\cos 2\theta$, and $\tan 2\theta$.
8. If $\tan 4\theta = \frac{5}{12}$ and 4θ is acute, find the values of $\sin 2\theta$, $\cos 8\theta$, and $\tan 8\theta$.

Use the values of the functions of 24° 30′ in Table II and formulas [10.22] to [10.27] to calculate the values of the functions in Exercises 9 through 14.

9. sin 49°
10. cos 49°
11. tan 49°
12. sin 12° 15′
13. cos 12° 15′
14. tan 12° 15′

If $\cot t = 7/24$ and $\pi < t < 3/2\pi$, find the values of the functions in Exercises 15 through 20.

15. $\cos 2t$

16. $\sin 2t$

17. $\sin \frac{1}{2}t$

18. $\tan 2t$

19. $\tan \frac{1}{2}t$

20. $\cos \frac{1}{2}t$

Find the values of the functions in Exercises 21 through 26.

21. $\tan [2 \operatorname{Tan}^{-1} (4/5)]$

22. $\sin [2 \operatorname{Cos}^{-1} (3/5)]$

23. $\sin [\frac{1}{2} \operatorname{Cos}^{-1} (-12/13)]$

24. $\cos [2 \operatorname{Sin}^{-1} (5/13)]$

25. $\cos [\frac{1}{2} \operatorname{Tan}^{-1} (-15/8)]$

26. $\tan [\frac{1}{2} \operatorname{Sin}^{-1} (-2/3)]$

Solve the equations of Exercises 27 through 30 for all nonnegative values of θ less than 360°.

27. $\sin 2\theta - \sin \theta = 0$

28. $\sin 2\theta + \cos \theta = 0$

29. $\cos 2\theta + \cos \theta = 0$

30. $\cos 2\theta + \sin^2 \theta = 0$

31. Derive the formula $\sin 3\theta = 3 \sin \theta - 4 \sin^3 \theta$. *Hint:* Use [10.18] and let $u = 2\theta$ and $v = \theta$.

32. Derive the formula $\cos 3\theta = 4 \cos^3 \theta - 3 \cos \theta$.

Prove the identities in Exercises 33 through 44.

33. $\cos 2u + 2 \sin^2 u = 1$

34. $(\sin \theta + \cos \theta)^2 = 1 + \sin 2\theta$

35. $\dfrac{2 \cos 2\theta}{\sin 2\theta - 2 \sin^2 \theta} = 1 + \cot \theta$

36. $\dfrac{\sin 2\theta + \sin \theta}{\cos 2\theta + \cos \theta + 1} = \tan \theta$

37. $\dfrac{\cos^4 \theta - \sin^4 \theta}{\sin 2\theta} = \cot 2\theta$

38. $\sin 2u = \dfrac{2 \tan u}{1 + \tan^2 u}$

39. $\tan 2t = \dfrac{2 \cot t}{\csc^2 t - 2}$

40. $\dfrac{\cos^2 \dfrac{t}{2} - \cos t}{\sin^2 \dfrac{t}{2}} = 1$

41. $4 \sin \theta \cos^2 \frac{1}{2}\theta = \sin 2\theta + 2 \sin \theta$

42. $\dfrac{1 - \cos \theta - \tan^2 \frac{1}{2}\theta}{\sin^2 \frac{1}{2}\theta} = \dfrac{2 \cos \theta}{1 + \cos \theta}$

43. $\tan \frac{1}{2}v = \dfrac{\sin v}{1 + \cos v}$

44. $\tan \frac{1}{2}v = \dfrac{1 - \cos v}{\sin v}$

Compute the value of each of the following:

45. $\sin [\operatorname{Arctan} 3/4 + \operatorname{Arcsin} (-5/13)]$

46. $\cos \left[\dfrac{\pi}{2} + \operatorname{Arcsin} \dfrac{2}{3}\right]$

47. $\tan [\operatorname{Tan}^{-1} 2 - \operatorname{Cos}^{-1} 3/5]$

48. $\sin [\operatorname{Cos}^{-1} (-4/5) - \operatorname{Sin}^{-1} \frac{1}{2}]$

10.14 Products of Functions in Terms of Sums

In more advanced courses in mathematics it is sometimes desirable to change the product of two trigonometric functions into a sum or difference. Formulas for doing this can readily be derived from the addition and subtraction formulas.

Let us recall the two formulas [10.18] and [10.19]:

$$\sin(u+v) = \sin u \cos v + \cos u \sin v,$$

and

$$\sin(u-v) = \sin u \cos v - \cos u \sin v.$$

Adding [10.18] and [10.19], we get

$$\sin(u+v) + \sin(u-v) = 2 \sin u \cos v$$

or

$$\sin u \cos v = \tfrac{1}{2}[\sin(u+v) + \sin(u-v)]. \qquad [10.28]$$

Similarly, by subtracting [10.19] from [10.18] and dividing by 2, we get

$$\cos u \sin v = \tfrac{1}{2}[\sin(u+v) - \sin(u-v)]. \qquad [10.29]$$

By combining formulas [10.17] and [10.9] in the same manner in which we combined [10.18] and [10.19], we are led to the results:

$$\cos u \cos v = \tfrac{1}{2}[\cos(u+v) + \cos(u-v)], \qquad [10.30]$$

$$\sin u \sin v = -\tfrac{1}{2}[\cos(u+v) - \cos(u-v)]. \qquad [10.31]$$

Example

Express $\cos 5\theta \sin 3\theta$ as a sum or difference.

SOLUTION: Using [10.29] and letting $u = 5\theta$ and $v = 3\theta$, we have

$$\cos 5\theta \sin 3\theta = \tfrac{1}{2}(\sin 8\theta - \sin 2\theta).$$

10.15 Sums and Differences of Functions in Terms of Products

In computations involving trigonometric expressions, it is sometimes desirable to change sums or differences of trigonometric functions into products. This type of transformation is the inverse of that discussed in Section 10.14. Formulas for changing sums and differences into products are easily obtained from the formulas of Section 10.14 by making appropriate changes in notation, as indicated below. Let

$$u + v = s \quad \text{and} \quad u - v = t.$$

Then, by adding and subtracting, we get

$$u = \tfrac{1}{2}(s + t) \qquad \text{and} \qquad v = \tfrac{1}{2}(s - t).$$

Replacing u and v in formulas [10.28], [10.29], [10.30], and [10.31] by their values in terms of s and t, and solving each equation for the sum or difference in terms of the product, leads to the following results:

$$\sin s + \sin t = 2 \sin \tfrac{1}{2}(s + t) \cos \tfrac{1}{2}(s - t), \qquad [10.32]$$

$$\sin s - \sin t = 2 \cos \tfrac{1}{2}(s + t) \sin \tfrac{1}{2}(s - t), \qquad [10.33]$$

$$\cos s + \cos t = 2 \cos \tfrac{1}{2}(s + t) \cos \tfrac{1}{2}(s - t), \qquad [10.34]$$

$$\cos s - \cos t = -2 \sin \tfrac{1}{2}(s + t) \sin \tfrac{1}{2}(s - t). \qquad [10.35]$$

Example

Simplify:

$$\frac{\sin 110° + \sin 20°}{\cos 110° - \cos 20°}.$$

SOLUTION: Applying [10.32] and [10.35] and letting $s = 110°$ and $t = 20°$ in each case, we have

$$\frac{\sin 110° + \sin 20°}{\cos 110° - \cos 20°} = \frac{2 \sin 65° \cos 45°}{-2 \sin 65° \sin 45°} = -\cot 45° = -1.$$

EXERCISES

Express each expression of Exercises 1 through 8 as a sum or difference.

1. $\cos 30° \cos 10°$

2. $\sin 45° \cos 15°$

3. $\cos 50° \sin 25°$

4. $\sin 70° \sin 30°$

5. $\sin 3\theta \sin \theta$

6. $\cos 4\theta \sin 2\theta$

7. $\sin \tfrac{3}{2}\theta \cos \tfrac{1}{2}\theta$

8. $\cos 7\theta \cos 3\theta$

Express each of the expressions in Exercises 9 through 16 as a product.

9. $\sin 32° + \sin 16°$

10. $\cos 25° + \cos 15°$

11. $\cos 70° - \cos 30°$

12. $\sin 55° - \sin 35°$

13. $\cos 6\theta + \cos 4\theta$

14. $\cos 7\theta - \cos 3\theta$

15. $\sin 4t - \sin 2t$

16. $\sin 11t + \sin 5t$

Simplify the expressions in Exercises 17 through 20.

17. $\dfrac{\cos 70° + \cos 20°}{\sin 70° + \sin 20°}$

18. $\dfrac{\sin 100° - \sin 40°}{\cos 100° + \cos 40°}$

19. $\dfrac{\sin 85° - \sin 35°}{\cos 85° - \cos 35°}$

20. $\dfrac{\cos 56° - \cos 22°}{\sin 56° + \sin 22°}$

be able to prove

Prove the identities in Exercises 21 through 27 by transforming the left member into the right.

21. $\dfrac{\cos 5\theta + \cos 3\theta}{\sin 5\theta - \sin 3\theta} = \cot \theta$

22. $\dfrac{\sin(\theta + 300°) - \sin(\theta + 60°)}{\cos(\theta + 30°) + \cos(\theta - 30°)} = -1$

23. $4 \sin 3t \cos 3t \sin t = \cos 5t - \cos 7t$

24. $\sin 4\theta \cos 2\theta - \sin 2\theta + \cos 4\theta \sin 2\theta = \sin 6\theta - \sin 2\theta$

25. $\dfrac{\sin A - \sin B}{\sin A + \sin B} = \dfrac{\tan \frac{1}{2}(A - B)}{\tan \frac{1}{2}(A + B)}$

26. $4 \sin 4t \cos 2t \sin t = -\cos 7t + \cos 5t - \cos 3t + \cos t$

27. $\dfrac{2 \sin 2\theta \cos \theta - \sin \theta}{\cos \theta - 2 \sin 2\theta \sin \theta} = \tan 3\theta$

28. Use appropriate formulas obtained in this chapter to prove that the general theorem stated in Exercise 67 of Section 9.17 is true for the sine, cosine, and tangent functions.

The Complex Number System ◀ 11

11.1 Introduction

The real numbers constitute a wonderful algebraic system, a complete ordered field. This system is sufficient for much of mathematics, including elementary calculus. But since the square of a real number is positive or zero, the simple equation $x^2 = -1$ does *not* have a root in the real number field. To remedy this type of deficiency, mathematicians devised the **complex number system,** a system that contains the real numbers and in which -1 has a square root. We shall give here a construction of the system of complex numbers from the reals.

The first idea we must get used to is that a pair of numbers can serve as a single number. The *rational* numbers illustrate this point. The number $\frac{2}{3}$ is written using two *integers* 2 and 3. It could just as well be written (2, 3). Indeed, if we agree to write the rational numbers $\frac{a}{b}$ in the form (a, b), all the operations with fractions can easily be carried out in this notation. This indicates that rational numbers can be represented by ordered pairs of integers. Complex numbers can be similarly treated, with the reals playing the role played by the integers in the construction of the rationals.

11.2 Definition of Complex Numbers

The set of all ordered pairs (a, b) of real numbers comprises the set of **complex numbers.**

We must define equality in this system and also the operations of addition and multiplication. In the following definitions the letters a, b, c, d denote real numbers:

Equality: $(a, b) = (c, d)$ if and only if $a = c$ and $b = d$

Addition: $(a, b) + (c, d) = (a + c, b + d)$

Multiplication: $(a, b)(c, d) = (ac - bd, ad + bc)$

The definitions of equality and addition seem natural enough, but multiplication looks a bit bizarre. The motivation for these definitions lies in the purposes the complex numbers are to serve. We want them to obey the usual associative, commutative, and distributive laws and have the other properties of a field. We want them to contain the reals as a subset. And we also want them to furnish roots for certain equations not solvable in the field of reals.

The closure, associative, commutative, and distributive laws can be checked by straightforward computations. For example, we establish the associative law for addition of complex numbers, using the associativity for addition of reals:

$$[(a, b) + (c, d)] + (e, f) = (a + c, b + d) + (e, f) \quad \text{(Definition of addition)}$$
$$= [(a + c) + e, (b + d) + f] \quad \text{(Definition of addition)}$$
$$= [a + (c + e), b + (d + f)] \quad \text{(Assoc. law for addition of reals)}$$
$$= (a, b) + (c + e, d + f) \quad \text{(Definition of addition)}$$
$$= (a, b) + [(c, d) + (e, f)] \quad \text{(Definition of addition)}$$

Thus,

$$[(a, b) + (c, d)] + (e, f) = (a, b) + [(c, d) + (e, f)].$$

The commutative law for multiplication is checked as follows:

$$(a, b)(c, d) = (ac - bd, ad + bc) \quad \text{(Definition of multiplication)}$$
$$= (ca - db, da + cb) \quad \text{(Commutative law for multiplication of reals)}$$
$$= (ca - db, cb + da) \quad \text{(Commutative law for addition of reals)}$$
$$= (c, d)(a, b) \quad \text{(Definition of multiplication)}$$

Therefore,

$$(a, b)(c, d) = (c, d)(a, b).$$

In this manner all properties for a number field, given in Chapter 2, may be checked. The additive identity is $(0, 0)$; the multiplicative identity is $(1, 0)$.

The additive inverse of (a, b) is $(-a, -b)$. If $(a, b) \neq (0, 0)$, it can be verified by direct computation that the multiplicative inverse of (a, b) is

$$\left(\frac{a}{a^2 + b^2}, \frac{-b}{a^2 + b^2}\right).$$

Thus, the complex number system is a field, since it satisfies all field axioms. Consequently, all theorems proved in Chapter 2 on the basis of the field axioms hold for the complex number system.

How can a complex number, a number of the form (a, b), be a root of the equation $x^2 = -1$? If we replace x by a pair of real numbers, the left member, x^2, of the equation becomes a number pair. How can a number *pair* be equal to a *single* real number? We shall have to look more closely at the relation between the complex number system and the real number system. We stated that we wanted the former to contain the latter as a subset. How can this be when a complex number is a pair of real numbers?

Consider the subset S of those complex numbers of the form $(a, 0)$. The sum and product of two numbers of this type are again numbers of this type:

$$(a, 0) + (c, 0) = (a + c, 0)$$
$$(a, 0)(c, 0) = (ac, 0)$$

There is a one-to-one correspondence, $a \leftrightarrow (a, 0)$, between the set of real numbers and this subset S of complex numbers. [The expression $a \leftrightarrow (a, 0)$ is read "a corresponds to $(a, 0)$."] Moreover, this correspondence preserves addition and multiplication in the following sense: If two real numbers are added, and their partners in S are also added, then the two results will be partners in the correspondence. A similar statement holds for multiplication.

For example, $6 \leftrightarrow (6, 0)$ and $2/3 \leftrightarrow (2/3, 0)$. The sum of 6 and $2/3$ is $20/3$; the sum of $(6, 0)$ and $(2/3, 0)$ is $(20/3, 0)$. Hence, since $20/3 \leftrightarrow (20/3, 0)$, we have

$$6 + 2/3 \leftrightarrow (6, 0) + (2/3, 0).$$

Similarly, the product of 6 and $2/3$ is 4; the product of $(6, 0)$ and $(2/3, 0)$ is $(4, 0)$. Hence, since $4 \leftrightarrow (4, 0)$, we have

$$6 \cdot 2/3 \leftrightarrow (6, 0) \cdot (2/3, 0).$$

In symbols, if $a \leftrightarrow (a, 0)$ and $b \leftrightarrow (b, 0)$, then

$$a + b \leftrightarrow (a, 0) + (b, 0)$$
$$ab \leftrightarrow (a, 0)(b, 0).$$

Thus, any statement in terms of addition and multiplication of real numbers has its analog in S. Since the processes of algebra can be formulated in terms of addition and multiplication, all statements concerning real numbers $a, b, c,$ and so forth can be formulated using $(a, 0)$, $(b, 0)$, $(c, 0)$, and so forth. Thus the system S can be regarded as essentially the same algebraic system as the system of real numbers; the only difference is that of notation.

The technical name for such a correspondence between algebraic systems is **isomorphism.** Thus, the correspondence $a \leftrightarrow (a, 0)$ is an isomorphism between the system of real numbers and the subset S of the set of complex numbers. The real number system and S are said to be **isomorphic.** Thus, the complex number system contains a subset that is isomorphic to the reals. In any problem involving real numbers, the real numbers a, b, c, and so forth may be replaced by their partners $(a, 0)$, $(b, 0)$, $(c, 0)$ in S, and vice versa. Indeed, we identify $(a, 0)$ with a, $(b, 0)$ with b, etc., which is possible because of the isomorphism.

Now let us rewrite the equation $x^2 = -1$ in the notation of complex numbers as $(x_1, x_2)^2 = (-1, 0)$. It is easy to verify by direct substitution that $(0, 1)$ is a root of this equation, for

$$(0, 1)^2 = (0, 1)(0, 1) = (-1, 0).$$

Thus, the complex number system contains a square root of -1.

11.3 Other Notation for Complex Numbers

Let us now consider another way of writing complex numbers, one that is perhaps more familiar to the reader. We introduce the symbol i for the complex number $(0, 1)$ discussed in the preceding section. Thus, $i^2 = (0, 1)^2 = (-1, 0)$, and we identify $(-1, 0)$ with the real number -1.

Let (a, b) be any complex number. By the definition of addition of complex numbers, we may write

$$(a, b) = (a, 0) + (0, b).$$

Now, by the definition of multiplication of complex numbers,

$$(b, 0)(0, 1) = (0, b).$$

Thus, by substitution, we get

$$(a, b) = (a, 0) + (b, 0)(0, 1).$$

Finally, if we replace $(a, 0)$ by the corresponding real number a, $(b, 0)$ by b, and $(0, 1)$ by i, we have

$$(a, b) = a + bi.$$

Computations with complex numbers can be carried out by writing them in the $a + bi$ form, using the associative, commutative, and distributive laws, and by replacing i^2, where it occurs, with -1.

Example

$$\begin{aligned}(2 + 3i)(4 + 7i) &= (2 + 3i)4 + (2 + 3i)7i \\ &= (8 + 12i) + (14i + 21i^2) \\ &= (8 + 12i) + (14i - 21) \\ &= -13 + 26i\end{aligned}$$

To see that the results of operations on complex numbers written in the $a + bi$ notation are consistent with those obtained with the (a, b) notation, consider the following:

$$(a, b) + (c, d) = (a + bi) + (c + di) = (a + c) + (b + d)i = (a + c, b + d)$$
$$(a, b)(c, d) = (a + bi)(c + di) = (ac + adi) + (bci + bdi^2)$$
$$= (ac - bd) + (ad + bc)i = (ac - bd, ad + bc)$$

Henceforth, we shall for the most part use the more familiar notation $a + bi$ for (a, b). For historical reasons, if $b \neq 0$, the complex number $a + bi$ is called **imaginary.** But a so-called *imaginary* number is not really mysterious at all. It is simply a member of a system of pairs of real numbers in which equality, addition, and multiplication are defined in a certain way.

EXERCISES

1. By use of appropriate properties of the real numbers show that addition of complex numbers is commutative.

2. Verify that the distributive law holds for complex numbers.

3. Verify that $(1, 0)$ is a multiplicative identity for the complex numbers and that $\left(\dfrac{a}{a^2 + b^2}, \dfrac{-b}{a^2 + b^2}\right)$ is the multiplicative inverse of (a, b) if $(a, b) \neq (0, 0)$.

In each of Exercises 4 through 11 perform the indicated operation, using the form of writing the complex numbers given. Then write the complex numbers in the other form, carry out the same operation, and compare results.

4. $(2, 3) + (5, 4)$

5. $(-1, 2) + (3, 4)$

6. $(-3, 2)(4, 1)$

7. $(2, -3)(4, 6)$

8. $(-3 + 2i) + (7 - 4i)$

9. $(4 + 5i) + (-7 + 2i)$

10. $(3 - 2i)(2 + 5i)$

11. $(6 - 4i)(2 - i)$

12. Define subtraction of complex numbers in terms of addition in a manner analogous to that used in Section 2.3 for reals, and compute $(a, b) - (c, d)$.

13. Define division of complex numbers in terms of multiplication in a manner analogous to that used in Section 2.3 for reals and compute $(a, b) \div (c, d)$, in case $(c, d) \neq (0, 0)$.

Use the results of Exercises 12 and 13 to carry out the operation indicated in each of Exercises 14 through 17.

14. $(7, 4) - (3, 6)$

15. $(2, 1) - (1, 5)$

16. $(3, 2) \div (1, -3)$

17. $(-4, 2) \div (3, 1)$

18. Two complex numbers of the form $a + bi$ and $a - bi$ are said to be **conjugate.** Show that the product of two conjugate complex numbers is real.

Solve the following equations:

19. $x^2 + 4 = 0$

20. $4x^2 + 9 = 0$

21. $x^2 + x + 1 = 0$

22. $2x^2 - 3x + 2 = 0$

11.4 Geometric Representation of Complex Numbers and Vectors

The development of complex numbers as ordered pairs of real numbers immediately suggests a method of representing complex numbers geometrically. The complex number $a + bi$—or (a, b)—is represented by a point whose Cartesian coordinates are (a, b), as in Fig. 11–1.

When the points of a plane are used to represent complex numbers, the plane is referred to as the **complex plane.** The horizontal axis is called the **axis of reals** and the vertical axis is called the **axis of imaginaries.**

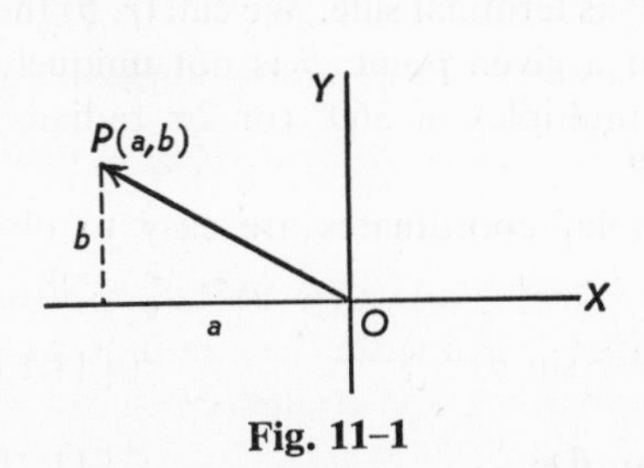

Fig. 11–1

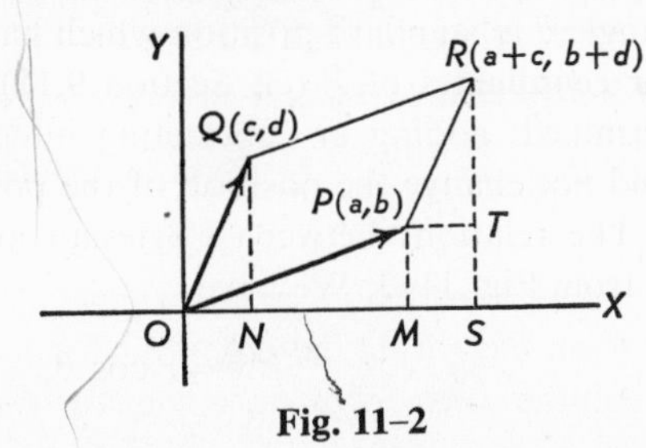

Fig. 11–2

The point P in Fig. 11–1 with coordinates (a, b), which represents the complex number $a + bi$, determines a *vector OP*, the directed line segment from the origin to the point P. Indeed, there is a one-to-one correspondence between the set of complex numbers and the set of coplanar vectors that originate at the origin of a Cartesian reference frame. Moreover, this correspondence preserves addition in the following sense: The vector corresponding to the sum $(a + c) + (b + d)i$ of the complex numbers $a + bi$ and $c + di$ is the *vector sum* of the vectors associated with the original complex numbers. This fact can be verified by geometric reasoning. Figure 11–2 gives a diagram of the situation when both vectors lie in the first quadrant. The reader should use this figure to verify for this special case the statement made above. A proof of the statement for the general case is set as an exercise.

The correspondence between complex numbers and vectors described in the preceding paragraph is called an *isomorphism* under addition. It furnishes a geometric method of adding two complex numbers: Construct the corresponding vectors, form their vector sum by the parallelogram law (cf. Section 9.15), and find the complex number corresponding to this vector sum.

Conversely, the correspondence indicates an algebraic method of adding two vectors. Coplanar vectors with a common origin can be represented by ordered pairs of real numbers, since a complex number is such a pair and to each vector there corresponds a unique complex number. Two vectors can be added by adding the corresponding ordered pairs of real numbers componentwise. We indicate this correspondence as follows, where V_1 and V_2 denote vectors and (a, b) and (c, d) are the corresponding complex numbers (ordered pairs of real numbers):

$$\text{If } V_1 \leftrightarrow (a, b) \text{ and } V_2 \leftrightarrow (c, d), \text{ then } V_1 + V_2 \leftrightarrow (a + c, b + d).$$

11.5 Polar Coordinates and Trigonometric Form of Complex Numbers

A point P in a plane (see Fig. 11–3) can be located by giving its Cartesian coordinates (x, y) or by giving its distance r from the origin and the measure of an angle θ in standard position which has OP as terminal side. We call (r, θ) the **polar coordinates** of P (cf. Section 9.15). For a given point, θ is not uniquely determined; adding or subtracting integral multiples of 360° (or 2π radians) would not change the position of the point P.

The relations between Cartesian and polar coordinates are easy to obtain from Fig. 11–3. We have

$$x = r \cos \theta, \qquad y = r \sin \theta \qquad [11.1]$$

$$r = \sqrt{x^2 + y^2}, \qquad \tan \theta = \frac{y}{x}. \qquad [11.2]$$

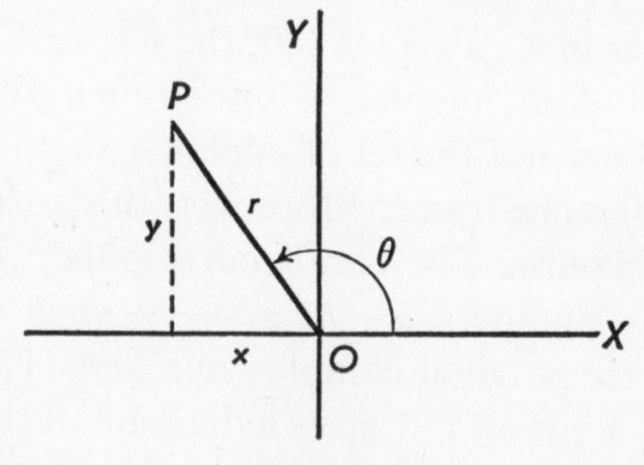

Fig. 11–3

Equations [11.1] and [11.2], which were also derived in Section 9.15, can be used to obtain Cartesian coordinates of a point from its polar coordinates, and vice versa, and also to transform equations of loci from one type of coordinate system to the other.

Example 1

Find the polar coordinates of the point P whose Cartesian coordinates are $(2, -2)$.

SOLUTION: From [11.2], since $x = 2$ and $y = -2$, we have

$$r = \sqrt{4+4} = \sqrt{8} = 2\sqrt{2} \quad \text{and} \quad \tan \theta = -\frac{2}{2} = -1.$$

Hence polar coordinates of P are $(2\sqrt{2}, 315°)$.

Now let us use these ideas to express complex numbers in a different and useful form. Let $x + yi$ be a complex number, and let P be the point that represents this number (Fig. 11–3). The coordinates of the point P are (x, y). Denote its polar coordinates by (r, θ). Then, by [11.1] we have

$$x = r \cos \theta \quad \text{and} \quad y = r \sin \theta.$$

Hence, we may write

$$x + yi = r(\cos \theta + i \sin \theta). \qquad [11.3]$$

The right member of this equation is called the **trigonometric** (or **polar**) form of the complex number $x + yi$. The number r is called its **absolute value** (or **modulus**) and the angle θ is called its **amplitude** (or **argument**). The absolute value r is determined uniquely by the relation $r = \sqrt{x^2 + y^2}$, but θ is determined by $\cos \theta = x/r$, $\sin \theta = y/r$ only to within integral multiples of 360°. To change a complex number to trigonometric form, it is helpful to plot the point representing the number.

Example 2

Write the complex number $1 + i$ in trigonometric form.

SOLUTION: If we plot the corresponding point $P(1, 1)$ (see Fig. 11–4), it is obvious that θ is a first quadrant angle such that $\tan \theta = 1$. Hence we may take θ to be of measure 45°. Moreover, $r = \sqrt{1^2 + 1^2} = \sqrt{2}$. The trigonometric form of $1 + i$ is therefore $\sqrt{2}(\cos 45° + i \sin 45°)$.

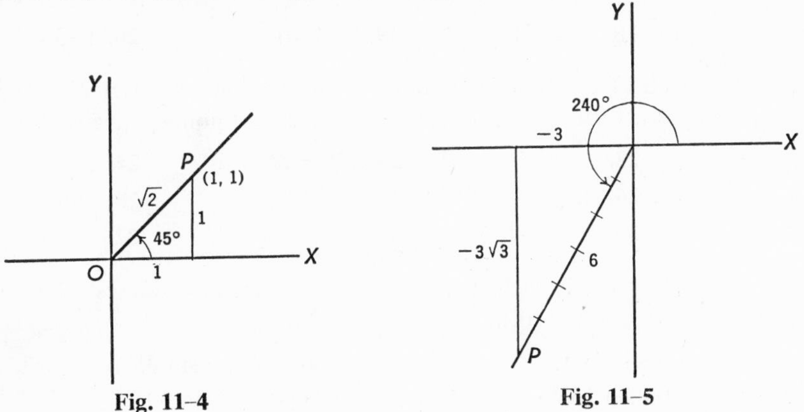

Fig. 11–4

Fig. 11–5

Example 3

Represent the number $6(\cos 240° + i \sin 240°)$ graphically and express the number in the form $x + yi$.

SOLUTION: We first construct the angle 240° in standard position (Fig. 11–5). Then, on the terminal side of the angle, we locate the point P with $r = 6$. This point P represents the given complex number. Since the coordinates of P are

$$x = 6 \cos 240° = 6(-\tfrac{1}{2}) = -3, \qquad y = 6 \sin 240° = 6\left(-\frac{\sqrt{3}}{2}\right) = -3\sqrt{3},$$

the complex number is $-3 - 3\sqrt{3}i$.

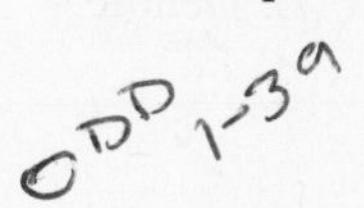

EXERCISES

Represent graphically each of the complex numbers given in Exercises 1 through 8.

1. $-2 + 3i$ **2.** $-3 + 5i$ **3.** $5 - i$ **4.** $-7 - 2i$
5. $-4 - 2i$ **6.** $-i$ **7.** -3 **8.** $2 - 5i$

Perform graphically and check algebraically the operations indicated in Exercises 9 through 12.

9. $(2 + 3i) + (5 + 2i)$ **10.** $(4 - 2i) + (-1 + 3i) + (2 - 5i)$
11. $(-3 + i) + (1 - 4i)$ **12.** $(1 + 3i) + (2 - i) + (-1 + 2i)$

Find the Cartesian coordinates of the points whose polar coordinates are given in Exercises 13 through 16.

13. $(2, 300°)$ **14.** $(3, 120°)$ **15.** $(5, 135°)$ **16.** $(4, 270°)$

Find the polar coordinates of the points whose Cartesian coordinates are given in Exercises 17 through 20.

17. $(2, 2\sqrt{3})$ **18.** $(-3, 3)$ **19.** $(-4, 0)$ **20.** $(-3\sqrt{3}, -3)$

Express each of the following complex numbers in Exercises 21 through 32 in trigonometric form, using in each case the smallest nonnegative amplitude.

21. $-2 - 2i$ **22.** $-1 + i$ **23.** i **24.** $3 - 3i$
25. -3 **26.** $2i$ **27.** $1 + \sqrt{3}i$ **28.** $-4i$
29. $-3 + 3i$ **30.** $-2 - 2\sqrt{3}i$ **31.** $-\tfrac{1}{2} + \tfrac{1}{2}\sqrt{3}i$ **32.** $-2 + 2i$

Represent graphically each of the complex numbers in Exercises 33 through 40 and express each in the form $x + yi$.

33. $5(\cos 30° + i \sin 30°)$ **34.** $10(\cos 45° + i \sin 45°)$
35. $7(\cos 135° + i \sin 135°)$ **36.** $2(\cos 90° + i \sin 90°)$

37. $6(\cos 270° + i \sin 270°)$ **38.** $3(\cos 180° + i \sin 180°)$

39. $8(\cos 300° + i \sin 300°)$ **40.** $6(\cos 210° + i \sin 210°)$

41. Devise a proof of the statement made in the third sentence of the third paragraph of Section 11.4, which will apply to all cases.

Write the Cartesian equations of Exercises 42 through 47 in terms of polar coordinates.

42. $y^2 = 4x$ **43.** $x^2 + y^2 = a^2$ **44.** $2x + 3y - 5 = 0$

45. $xy = 7$ **46.** $x^2 + y^2 - 4x = 0$ **47.** $3x^2 - y^2 - 24x + 36 = 0$

Write the polar equations of Exercises 48 through 53 in terms of Cartesian coordinates.

48. $r = a$ **49.** $r = 2 \sin \theta$ **50.** $r \cos \theta = 5$

51. $r = 4 \cos 2\theta$ **52.** $r = 6 \sin 2\theta$ **53.** $r = \dfrac{6}{1 - 2\cos\theta}$

11.6 Multiplication and Division of Complex Numbers in Trigonometric Form

Let z and w denote two complex numbers whose trigonometric forms are

$$z = r_1(\cos \theta_1 + i \sin \theta_1),$$
$$w = r_2(\cos \theta_2 + i \sin \theta_2),$$

respectively. By direct multiplication we find that

$$zw = r_1r_2[(\cos \theta_1 \cos \theta_2 - \sin \theta_1 \sin \theta_2) + i(\sin \theta_1 \cos \theta_2 + \cos \theta_1 \sin \theta_2)].$$

By the trigonometric formulas [10.17] and [10.18], this product can be written

$$zw = r_1r_2[\cos (\theta_1 + \theta_2) + i \sin (\theta_1 + \theta_2)].$$

The expression on the right is clearly the trigonometric form of the product zw. Hence, this last result can be stated in words as follows:

▶ THEOREM 1. *The absolute value of the product of two complex numbers is the product of their absolute values, while the amplitude of their product is the sum of their amplitudes.*

Suppose now that $r_2 \neq 0$, and consider the quotient $z/w = q$ of the two complex numbers given above. If the trigonometric form of the quotient q is $r(\cos \phi + i \sin \phi)$, from the relation $z = qw$, we have, by Theorem 1,

$$r_1 = rr_2 \quad \text{and} \quad \theta_1 = \phi + \theta_2.$$

Hence,

$$r = \frac{r_1}{r_2} \quad \text{and} \quad \phi = \theta_1 - \theta_2.$$

Expressed in words this result may be stated as

▶ THEOREM 2. *The absolute value of the quotient of the complex number* $r_1(\cos \theta_1 + i \sin \theta_1)$ *by the complex number* $r_2(\cos \theta_2 + i \sin \theta_2)$ *is equal to the quotient* r_1/r_2 *of their absolute values, and the amplitude of the quotient is the difference* $\theta_1 - \theta_2$ *of their amplitudes.*

11.7 De Moivre's Theorem

If n is any positive integer, then

$$[r(\cos \theta + i \sin \theta)]^n = r^n(\cos n\theta + i \sin n\theta).$$

We use mathematical induction to prove this theorem. The theorem is obviously true for $n = 1$. Now let k be any positive integer for which it is true. Then we have

$$[r(\cos \theta + i \sin \theta)]^k = r^k[\cos k\theta + i \sin k\theta].$$

On multiplying both members of this equation by $r(\cos \theta + i \sin \theta)$ and using Theorem 1 to simplify the right member, we have

$$[r(\cos \theta + i \sin \theta)]^{k+1} = r^{k+1}[\cos (k+1)\theta + i \sin (k+1)\theta].$$

Thus, the truth of the theorem for $n = k$ implies its truth for $n = k + 1$, and the proof by induction of De Moivre's theorem is complete.

Example

Find the value of $(1 + \sqrt{3}i)^5$.

SOLUTION: If we plot the point P representing the number $1 + \sqrt{3}i$ (see Fig. 11–6), we find that the absolute value of the number is 2 and its amplitude is 60°. Hence,

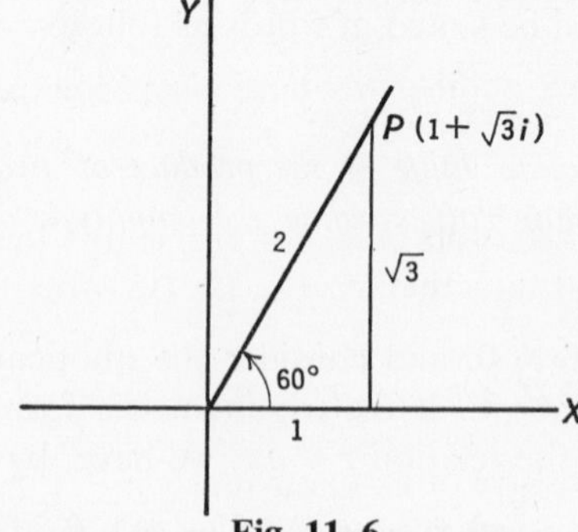

Fig. 11–6

$$(1+\sqrt{3}i)^5 = [2(\cos 60° + i \sin 60°)]^5 = 32(\cos 300° + i \sin 300°)$$

$$= 32\left[\frac{1}{2} - \frac{\sqrt{3}}{2}i\right] = 16 - 16\sqrt{3}i.$$

EXERCISES

Perform the following multiplications and divisions after first expressing the numbers in trigonometric form:

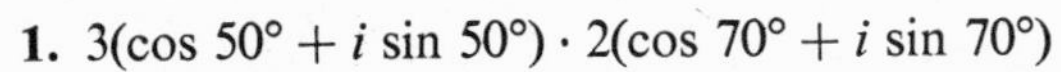

1. $3(\cos 50° + i \sin 50°) \cdot 2(\cos 70° + i \sin 70°)$
2. $\frac{1}{2}(\cos 80° + i \sin 80°) \cdot 8(\cos 55° + i \sin 55°)$
3. $(1+i)(1+\sqrt{3}i)$
4. $(\sqrt{3}+i)(1-i)$
5. $(1-\sqrt{3}i) \div (-1-i)$
6. $(1+i) \div (\sqrt{3}-i)$
7. $(-4+4i) \div (2\sqrt{3}-2i)$
8. $(-5-5\sqrt{3}i) \div (-2+2i)$
9. $\dfrac{(\sqrt{3}+i)^3}{(1-\sqrt{3}i)^2}$
10. $\dfrac{(1-i)^5}{(1+i)^3}$
11. $\dfrac{(-1+\sqrt{3}i)(-1-i)}{\sqrt{3}-i}$
12. $\dfrac{i(2+2i)}{(-3+3i)(\sqrt{3}-i)}$

Use De Moivre's theorem to raise the following numbers to the powers indicated.

13. $(\cos 18° + i \sin 18°)^{10}$
14. $\left(\dfrac{1+i}{\sqrt{2}}\right)^7$
15. $(\sqrt{3}-i)^5$
16. $[\sqrt{2}(\cos 15° + i \sin 15°)]^8$
17. $[\sqrt{2}(\cos 12° + i \sin 12°)]^{10}$
18. $(3-3i)^4$
19. $(-1-\sqrt{3}i)^3$
20. $[2(\cos 40° + i \sin 40°)]^6$

11.8 Roots of Complex Numbers

Consider the complex number w whose trigonometric form is

$$R(\cos \phi + i \sin \phi).$$

If we wish to extract the nth roots of w, our problem is to find all complex numbers $z = r(\cos \theta + i \sin \theta)$ such that $z^n = w$. By De Moivre's theorem, this leads to the equation

$$r^n[\cos n\theta + i \sin n\theta] = R(\cos \phi + i \sin \phi).$$

Since r and R are both positive or zero, obviously $r = \sqrt[n]{R}$, where r is the principal nth root of R as defined in Section 8.4, that is, for $R \neq 0$, the real positive

nth root of R. Moreover, from the relations $\cos n\theta = \cos \phi$, $\sin n\theta = \sin \phi$, we must have

$$n\theta = \phi + k \cdot 360°, \qquad \theta = \frac{\phi + k \cdot 360°}{n},$$

where k is an integer. Conversely, if these conditions are satisfied, z is an nth root of w.

Accordingly, all nth roots of the complex number

$$R(\cos \phi + i \sin \phi)$$

are given by the formula

$$\sqrt[n]{R}\left[\cos \frac{\phi + k \cdot 360°}{n} + i \sin \frac{\phi + k \cdot 360°}{n}\right]. \qquad [11.4]$$

For $k = 0, 1, 2, \cdots, n - 1$, no two of these numbers have amplitudes differing by a multiple of 360°, so that for $R \neq 0$, the numbers are all different. If, however, k has any other integral value, we obtain a number already found. We therefore have

▶ THEOREM 3. *Every complex number* $R(\cos \phi + i \sin \phi)$, *other than zero, has exactly n distinct nth roots, and these are given by the formula* [11.4] *where k assumes the values* $0, 1, 2, \cdots, n - 1$, *in turn.*

Example

Find the fourth roots of $-1 + \sqrt{3}i$.

SOLUTION: If we plot the point that represents this number (Fig. 11–7), we see that its absolute value is 2 and its amplitude is 120°. Hence,

$$-1 + \sqrt{3}i = 2[\cos 120° + i \sin 120°].$$

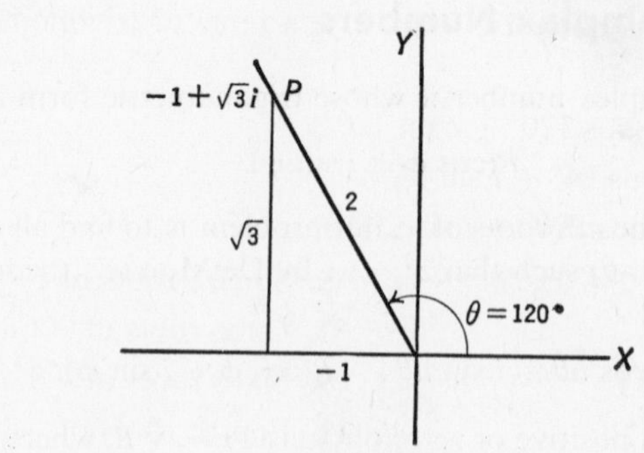

Fig. 11–7

Accordingly, the four fourth roots desired are given by

$$\sqrt[4]{2}\left[\cos\frac{120^\circ + k\cdot 360^\circ}{4} + i\sin\frac{120^\circ + k\cdot 360^\circ}{4}\right]$$
$$= \sqrt[4]{2}[\cos(30^\circ + k\cdot 90^\circ) + i\sin(30^\circ + k\cdot 90^\circ)],$$

where we are to assign to k the values 0, 1, 2, 3 in turn. The four distinct fourth roots of $-1 + \sqrt{3}i$ are therefore:

$$\sqrt[4]{2}(\cos 30^\circ + i\sin 30^\circ) = \frac{\sqrt[4]{2}}{2}(\sqrt{3} + i)$$

$$\sqrt[4]{2}(\cos 120^\circ + i\sin 120^\circ) = \frac{\sqrt[4]{2}}{2}(-1 + \sqrt{3}i)$$

$$\sqrt[4]{2}(\cos 210^\circ + i\sin 210^\circ) = \frac{\sqrt[4]{2}}{2}(-\sqrt{3} - i)$$

$$\sqrt[4]{2}(\cos 300^\circ + i\sin 300^\circ) = \frac{\sqrt[4]{2}}{2}(1 - \sqrt{3}i)$$

If k be assigned consecutive integral values greater than 3, the above values of the fourth roots of $-1 + \sqrt{3}i$ will be repeated indefinitely in cyclic order.

The complex number system encompasses all of the other number systems such as integers, rationals, reals (or more precisely isomorphic replicas of these systems) which we have previously used in this text. It represents the culmination of our development of numbers. It is a field, as is the system of rationals and also the system of reals, but it has a property not possessed by these subfields, namely, it is *algebraically closed.* The meaning of this term will be explained in the next chapter.

EXERCISES

Find all of the roots specified in Exercises 1 through 13, after first expressing the number in trigonometric form. Use a table of trigonometric functions if necessary.

1. Square roots of $9(\cos 120^\circ + i\sin 120^\circ)$

2. Cube roots of $8(\cos 84^\circ + i\sin 84^\circ)$

3. Fifth roots of $32(\cos 200^\circ + i\sin 200^\circ)$

4. Square roots of $-2 + 2\sqrt{3}i$

5. Square roots of i

6. Cube roots of $-i$

7. Cube roots of $-1 + i$

8. Fourth roots of -1

9. Sixth roots of -8

10. Cube roots of $-27i$

11. Fourth roots of $-8 + 8\sqrt{3}i$

12. Twelfth roots of $+1$

13. Fifth roots of $-16\sqrt{2} - 16\sqrt{2}i$

Find all the roots of each of the equations in Exercises 14 through 22, using tables of trigonometric functions if necessary. Express your results in the form $a + bi$.

14. $x^3 + 8i = 0$

15. $x^3 - 27 = 0$

16. $x^5 - 1 = 0$

17. $x^7 + 1 = 0$

18. $x^2 = -3 + 4i$

19. $x^3 = 1 - 2i$

20. $x^4 - 5 + 7i = 0$

21. $x^4 + x^3 + x^2 + x + 1 = 0$. *Hint:* Multiply by $x - 1$, solve resulting equation, and then discard extraneous root $x = 1$.

22. $x^5 + x^4 + x^3 + x^2 + x + 1 = 0$

23. Show that the points in the complex plane, which represent the nth roots of 1, are equally spaced on a circle of radius 1.

Theory of Equations

◄ 12

12.1 Introduction

Expressions such as

$$3x^2 + 5x - 2,$$
$$2x^3 - 3x^2 + 4x + 7,$$
$$x^5 + 2x^4 - 5x + 6,$$

are called polynomials in x. The operations of addition, subtraction, multiplication, and division of polynomials are usually studied early in high school algebra, and frequently considerable time is spent on factoring polynomials. Quadratic polynomials were encountered in Chapter 3 of this book. In the present chapter we develop some of the theory of polynomials and polynomial equations.

An expression of the form

$$a_0x^n + a_1x^{n-1} + a_2x^{n-2} + \cdots + a_{n-1}x + a_n,$$

in which the a's are numbers belonging to some number system and n is a non-negative integer, is called a **polynomial.** The a's are **coefficients,** and if $a_0 \neq 0$, the polynomial is said to be of **degree n,** and a_0 is called the **leading coefficient.** If $n = 0$ and $a_0 \neq 0$, the polynomial consists of the number a_0 and its degree is 0. The polynomial 0 does *not* have a degree. The symbol x is called a **variable** or an **indeterminate.** If x is replaced by a number from a number system to which the a's belong, we obtain a number called a **value** of the polynomial. As a matter of notation, if $P(x)$ denotes a polynomial and c is a number, then $P(c)$ denotes the value of $P(x)$ at $x = c$. Thus, a polynomial can be used to define a function, called a **polynomial function,** with the symbol x playing the role of independent variable. But it is not necessary to think of x as representing a number. Addition, subtraction, multiplication, and division of polynomials can be defined quite formally in terms of the coefficients without giving an interpretation to the symbol x. These definitions are equivalent to the rules taught in high school for performing these operations, which we assume are well known to the reader.

The number systems to which coefficients of polynomials considered in this chapter may belong are the integers, the rational numbers, the real numbers, and the complex numbers. If in the statement of a theorem on polynomials no mention is made of the coefficients, *it will be assumed that they may be any complex numbers*. For several of the theorems the coefficients must be restricted in some way.

The equation

$$a_0x^n + a_1x^{n-1} + \cdots + a_{n-1}x + a_n = 0 \qquad (a_0 \neq 0)$$

that results on equating a polynomial to zero, is called a **polynomial equation** of degree n. If $P(x)$ denotes a polynomial, a number r which substituted for x makes the polynomial have the value zero, $P(r) = 0$, is called a **root** of the polynomial $P(x)$ and a root of the corresponding polynomial equation $P(x) = 0$. Thus, if

$$P(x) = 3x^4 - 11x^2 + 2x - 8,$$

we have $P(2) = 0$, and hence 2 is a root of $P(x)$ and a root of $P(x) = 0$.

12.2 The Remainder Theorem

The set of polynomials with coefficients in a number field has many of the same properties enjoyed by the system of integers. One of these is the **division algorithm** which we state without proof:

If $P(x)$ and $D(x) \neq 0$ are polynomials with coefficients in some number field, then there exist unique polynomials $Q(x)$ and $R(x)$ with coefficients in this field such that

$$P(x) = D(x) \cdot Q(x) + R(x),$$

where $R(x) = 0$ or the degree of $R(x)$ is less than the degree of $D(x)$.

The reader is familiar with this property, and for given polynomials $P(x)$ and $D(x)$ he finds $Q(x)$, called the **quotient,** and $R(x)$, called the **remainder,** by long division. If $R(x) = 0$, $D(x)$ is called a **factor** of $P(x)$ and $P(x)$ is said to be **divisible** by $D(x)$. If $D(x)$ is of the first degree, the remainder is a constant, and we shall denote it by R.

For example, if $P(x) = 2x^4 - 5x^3 - 2x^2 + 2x - 11$ and $D(x) = x - 3$, by long division (see Section 12.4) we obtain $2x^3 + x^2 + x + 5$ as the quotient $Q(x)$ and 4 as the remainder R. Thus, we may write

$$2x^4 - 5x^3 - 2x^2 + 2x - 11 = (x - 3)(2x^3 + x^2 + x + 5) + 4,$$

or

$$P(x) = (x - 3) \cdot Q(x) + 4.$$

Now we use this example to illustrate a remarkable theorem. Substituting 3 for x in the above equation, which is an identity in x, we have

$$P(3) = 0 \cdot Q(3) + 4,$$
$$4 = P(3).$$

Thus, the remainder obtained upon dividing $P(x)$ by $x - 3$ is equal to $P(3)$. The theorem that this illustrates is known as the remainder theorem.

▶ THE REMAINDER THEOREM. *Let c denote a number. If a polynomial $P(x)$ is divided by $x - c$ to obtain a quotient $Q(x)$ and a remainder R, then $R = P(c)$.* That is, the remainder is the result of substituting c for x in $P(x)$.

PROOF: By the meaning of quotient and remainder, we have

$$P(x) = (x - c)Q(x) + R.$$

If in this identity we substitute c for x, we have

$$P(c) = 0 \cdot Q(c) + R.$$

Since $0 \cdot Q(c) = 0$, we have

$$\boxed{R = P(c)}$$

12.3 The Factor Theorem

As an immediate consequence of the remainder theorem, we obtain another important theorem called the factor theorem.

▶ THE FACTOR THEOREM. *If $P(x)$ is a polynomial in x, and if c is a root of $P(x)$, then $x - c$ is a factor of $P(x)$. Conversely, if $x - c$ is a factor of $P(x)$, then c is a root of $P(x)$.*

PROOF: If c is a root of $P(x)$, then, by the definition of a root, $P(c) = 0$. But by the remainder theorem, $P(c)$ is the remainder when $P(x)$ is divided by $x - c$. This remainder being zero, the division is exact and $x - c$ is a factor of $P(x)$. This proves the first part of the theorem.

For the converse part, $x - c$ is, by hypothesis, a factor of $P(x)$. Hence, the remainder upon dividing $P(x)$ by $x - c$ is zero. But this remainder, by the remainder theorem, is $P(c)$. Thus, we have $P(c) = 0$, which says that c is a root of $P(x)$, and the proof of the factor theorem is complete.

Example

Show that the polynomial $P(x) = x^{10} - 5x^7 + 4$ is divisible by $x - 1$.

SOLUTION: By direct substitution we find $P(1) = 0$, so 1 is a root of $P(x)$. Hence, by the factor theorem, $x - 1$ is a factor of $P(x)$. In other words, $P(x)$ is divisible by $x - 1$.

EXERCISES

In each of Exercises 1 and 2 find the quotient $Q(x)$ and the remainder $R(x)$ when the first polynomial is divided by the second.

1. $P(x) = 2x^3 - 3x^2 + 4x + 5$, $D(x) = x^2 + x + 1$

2. $P(x) = 3x^4 + 2x^3 - 4x + 3$, $D(x) = x^2 + 2x + 4$

In each of Exercises 3 through 8 use the remainder theorem to find the remainder when the first polynomial listed is divided by the second.

3. $x^{10} - 7x^3 + 5,\quad x - 1$

4. $3x^{17} - 19x^6 + 20,\quad x + 1$

5. $x^{100} + 14x^{47} + 16,\quad x + 1$

6. $2x^{23} + 5x^{10} - 4,\quad x - 1$

7. $x^5 - 17x + 7,\quad x - 2$

8. $3x^6 + 15x^3 - 11,\quad x + 2$

9. Given that 2 is a root of $3x^2 - 4x - 4$, factor this polynomial.

10. Given that -3 is a root of $x^3 + 6x^2 + 8x - 3$, factor this polynomial.

Use the quadratic formula to find roots of each of the quadratic polynomials in Exercises 11 through 16, and then use the factor theorem to factor the polynomial.

11. $6x^2 + 11x - 10$

12. $2x^2 + 3x - 2$

13. $x^2 - 3x + 1$

14. $3x^2 + x - 5$

15. $4x^2 + 3x + 2$

16. $x^2 + 4x + 5$

Use the factor theorem to prove the statements in Exercises 17 through 19.

17. $x^5 + 32$ is divisible by $x + 2$.

18. $x^{25} + a^{25}$ is divisible by $x + a$.

19. $x^{20} - a^{20}$ is divisible by $x + a$.

20. Show by the factor theorem that if n is any positive integer, $P(x) = x^{2n} - a^{2n}$ is divisible by $x - a$, also by $x + a$, and hence by $x^2 - a^2$.

Determine the value or values of k so that the polynomial $P(x)$ will be divisible by the factor indicated in Exercises 21 through 25.

21. $P(x) = x^3 + kx^2 + 2x - 5$, divisible by $x - 1$

22. $P(x) = 2x^3 + 5x^2 + kx - 16$, divisible by $x - 2$

23. $P(x) = x^4 - 2x^2 + k^2x - 6$, divisible by $x + 2$

24. $P(x) = x^4 - x^3 + kx^2 + k^2x + 4$, divisible by $x + 1$

25. $P(x) = 2x^3 + x^2 + kx + 2k^2$, divisible by $x + 1$

Determine k and l so that the polynomial $P(x)$ will be divisible by the factors indicated in Exercises 26 through 28. Find the remaining factors in each case.

26. $P(x) = 2x^3 + kx^2 + lx - 3$, divisible by $x - 1$ and $x + 3$

27. $P(x) = 3x^3 + kx^2 - 5x + l$, divisible by $x + 1$ and $x - 2$

28. $P(x) = x^4 + kx^3 + lx^2 - x + 2$, divisible by $x^2 - 1$

29. A polynomial of degree 3 has leading coefficient 1 and 2, 3, and -1 as roots. Write the polynomial.

30. A quadratic polynomial has leading coefficient 4 and $\frac{3}{4}$ and -2 as roots. Write the polynomial.

31. A quadratic polynomial $P(x)$ has $2 + i$ and $2 - i$ as roots. Moreover, $P(3) = 6$. Write the polynomial $P(x)$.

32. A cubic polynomial $P(x)$ has $1 + i$, $1 - i$ and 2 as roots, and $P(1) = -1$. Find the polynomial.

12.4 Synthetic Division

During the course of this chapter we shall frequently find it necessary to divide a polynomial $P(x)$ by a linear polynomial $x - c$. Accordingly, we shall develop a process for performing this division quickly and accurately. To illustrate the process, let us first use long division to divide

$$2x^4 - 5x^3 - 2x^2 + 2x - 11 \quad \text{by} \quad x - 3.$$

$$
\begin{array}{r|l}
 & 2x^3 + x^2 + x + 5 = Q(x) \\
x - 3 & 2x^4 - 5x^3 - 2x^2 + 2x - 11 \\
 & \underline{2x^4 - 6x^3} \\
 & \qquad\quad x^3 - 2x^2 \\
 & \qquad\quad \underline{x^3 - 3x^2} \\
 & \qquad\qquad\quad x^2 + 2x \\
 & \qquad\qquad\quad \underline{x^2 - 3x} \\
 & \qquad\qquad\qquad\quad 5x - 11 \\
 & \qquad\qquad\qquad\quad \underline{5x - 15} \\
 & \qquad\qquad\qquad\qquad\quad 4 = R
\end{array}
$$

This process can be abbreviated considerably. In the first place, we note that the first term in each line to be subtracted is identical with that just above it, and hence can be omitted. In the second place, if we are careful in our subtraction, it will be unnecessary to bring down a term from the dividend each time. With these modifications the division process then appears as follows:

$$
\begin{array}{r|l}
 & 2x^3 + x^2 + x + 5 \\
\hline
x - 3 & 2x^4 - 5x^3 - 2x^2 + 2x - 11 \\
 & \quad\; - 6x^3 \\
\cline{2-2}
 & \qquad\quad x^3 \\
 & \qquad\qquad - 3x^2 \\
\cline{2-2}
 & \qquad\qquad\quad x^2 \\
 & \qquad\qquad\qquad - 3x \\
\cline{2-2}
 & \qquad\qquad\qquad\quad 5x \\
 & \qquad\qquad\qquad\qquad - 15 \\
\cline{2-2}
 & \qquad\qquad\qquad\qquad\quad 4
\end{array}
$$

We can abbreviate this further by not writing the symbol x, but merely the coefficients, it being understood that if a power of x is missing, we write a 0 in its place. The work can then be compressed upward into three lines. Further, if the leading coefficient 2 be brought down into the third line, all but the last of these numbers are the coefficients in the *quotient*, so that the latter need not be written. The division process then assumes the following form:

$$
\begin{array}{r|rrrrr}
1 - 3 & 2 & -5 & -2 & 2 & -11 \\
 & & -6 & -3 & -3 & -15 \\
\hline
 & 2 & 1 & 1 & 5 & 4
\end{array}
$$

Finally, in the divisor we omit the coefficient 1, replace the -3 by $+3$, and *add* instead of *subtract*. We then have the following:

$$
\begin{array}{r|rrrrr}
3 & 2 & -5 & -2 & 2 & -11 \\
 & & 6 & 3 & 3 & 15 \\
\hline
 & 2 & 1 & 1 & 5 & 4
\end{array}
$$

The numbers in the third row, with the exception of the last, are the coefficients in the quotient $2x^3 + x^2 + x + 5$, while the last number 4 is the remainder R. This process is called **synthetic division.**

▶ RULE FOR SYNTHETIC DIVISION

To divide a polynomial $P(x)$ by $x - c$, we proceed as follows:

1. First arrange $P(x)$ in descending powers of x, $a_0x^n + a_1x^{n-1} + \cdots + a_n$, supplying all missing terms with zeros as coefficients.
2. Write the coefficients $a_0, a_1, \cdots, a_n$ in a horizontal line.

3. Bring down the leading coefficient a_0 into the third line; multiply a_0 by c, place the product in the second line under the next coefficient a_1, and put the sum $b_1 = ca_0 + a_1$ in the third line; multiply b_1 by c, place the product cb_1 under the next coefficient a_2, and put the sum $b_2 = cb_1 + a_2$ in the third line. Continue this process. The coefficients $a_0, b_1, \cdots, b_{n-1}$, in that order, are the coefficients in the quotient, while b_n is the remainder.

PROOF: Although the method of proof is applicable to any polynomial of positive degree, in order to ease the notation we confine our attention to the case when $P(x)$ is of degree 4.

Let $P(x) = a_0x^4 + a_1x^3 + a_2x^2 + a_3x + a_4$. Let the quotient $Q(x)$ be $b_0x^3 + b_1x^2 + b_2x + b_3$ and the remainder be R. From the identity

$$P(x) = (x - c)Q(x) + R,$$

that is,

$$a_0x^4 + a_1x^3 + a_2x^2 + a_3x + a_4 = (x - c)(b_0x^3 + b_1x^2 + b_2x + b_3) + R,$$

we have, on multiplying out the expression on the right, collecting, and equating corresponding coefficients,

$$b_0 = a_0, \quad b_1 - cb_0 = a_1, \quad b_2 - cb_1 = a_2, \quad b_3 - cb_2 = a_3, \quad R - cb_3 = a_4.$$

Hence,

$$b_0 = a_0, \quad b_1 = a_1 + cb_0, \quad b_2 = a_2 + cb_1, \quad b_3 = a_3 + cb_2, \quad R = a_4 + cb_3.$$

The b's and R, which satisfy these last relations, can be readily computed as follows:

$$\begin{array}{r|ccccc} c & a_0 & a_1 & a_2 & a_3 & a_4 \\ & & cb_0 & cb_1 & cb_2 & cb_3 \\ \hline & b_0 = a_0 & b_1 & b_2 & b_3 & R \end{array}$$

Thus, the numbers in the third line are precisely the coefficients in the quotient, and the remainder, as stated in the rule.

Example 1

Find by synthetic division the quotient and the remainder when $P(x) = x^5 - 17x^3 + 37x^2 - 11x + 7$ is divided by $x + 5$.

SOLUTION: Since $x + 5 = x - (-5)$, $c = -5$. Moreover, the x^4 term is missing, so that we must supply 0 as its coefficient. The synthetic division process in this case is as follows:

$$\begin{array}{r|rrrrrr} -5 & 1 & 0 & -17 & 37 & -11 & 7 \\ & & -5 & 25 & -40 & 15 & -20 \\ \hline & 1 & -5 & 8 & -3 & 4 & \boxed{-13} \end{array}$$

Hence, the quotient is $x^4 - 5x^3 + 8x^2 - 3x + 4$, and the remainder is -13.

By the remainder theorem if $P(x)$ is divided by $x - c$, the remainder R is $P(c)$, the result of substituting c for x in $P(x)$. Hence, synthetic division can be employed advantageously in finding the value of a polynomial $P(x)$ for $x = c$. For this reason, the process is frequently referred to as **synthetic substitution.** Indeed, the chief importance of the synthetic division process is due to the fact that the value of a polynomial corresponding to a given value of the variable can be obtained much more expeditiously by this process than by direct substitution.

Example 2

If $P(x) = 2x^3 - 5x^2 - 8x + 6$, use synthetic substitution to find the value of $P(-2)$.

SOLUTION:

$$\begin{array}{r|rrrr} -2 & 2 & -5 & -8 & 6 \\ & & -4 & 18 & -20 \\ \hline & 2 & -9 & 10 & \underline{|-14} \end{array}$$

Hence, $P(-2) = -14$.

12.5 Graph and Roots of a Polynomial

If the coefficients of a polynomial $P(x)$ are real numbers, then $P(x)$ defines a real valued function, called a **polynomial function,** with the set of real numbers as domain and rule of correspondence $y = P(x)$. The graph of this function is called the **graph of the polynomial.** As the first step in the construction of the graph a table of values for $P(x)$ is obtained. These values may be found by *direct* substitution for x or by *synthetic* substitution. Points representing the pairs of corresponding values are then plotted and a smooth curve drawn through them.

When synthetic substitution is used to make a table of values, we do not write down the coefficients of $P(x)$ repeatedly, but write them just once, as shown in the example below. A number to be substituted for x is then written in a column at the left, the numbers in the second line, as in Example 2 of Section 12.4, are carried forward mentally, and only the numbers in the third line are actually written down.

Thus, if $P(x) = 2x^3 - 5x^2 - 8x + 6$, we find the value of $P(-2)$ as follows:

x				$P(x)$
0	2	−5	−8	6
−2	2	−9	10	−14

Hence, $P(-2) = -14$. Clearly, the coefficients of the polynomial as written above in the first line are the numbers that arise when we substitute 0 for x;

so $P(0) = 6$. Similarly, we can substitute any value for x and make a table of values as follows:

x				$P(x)$
0	2	−5	− 8	6
−2	2	−9	10	−14
−1	2	−7	− 1	7
1	2	−3	−11	− 5
2	2	−1	−10	−14
3	2	1	− 5	− 9
4	2	3	4	22

Each number in the right-hand column is the value of $P(x)$ that corresponds to the value of x in the same row in the left-hand column. Thus, 6 corresponds to 0, −14 to −2, 7 to −1, etc.

A graph of the polynomial function, or briefly a graph of the polynomial, is obtained by plotting the points with coordinates (0, 6), (−2, −14), (−1, 7), (1, −5), (2, −14), (3, −9), (4, 22), and drawing a smooth curve through them (see Fig. 12–1).

If $P(x)$ is a polynomial and r is a number such that $P(r) = 0$, we recall from Section 12.1 that r is called a root of $P(x)$. If $P(x)$ is a *real* polynomial

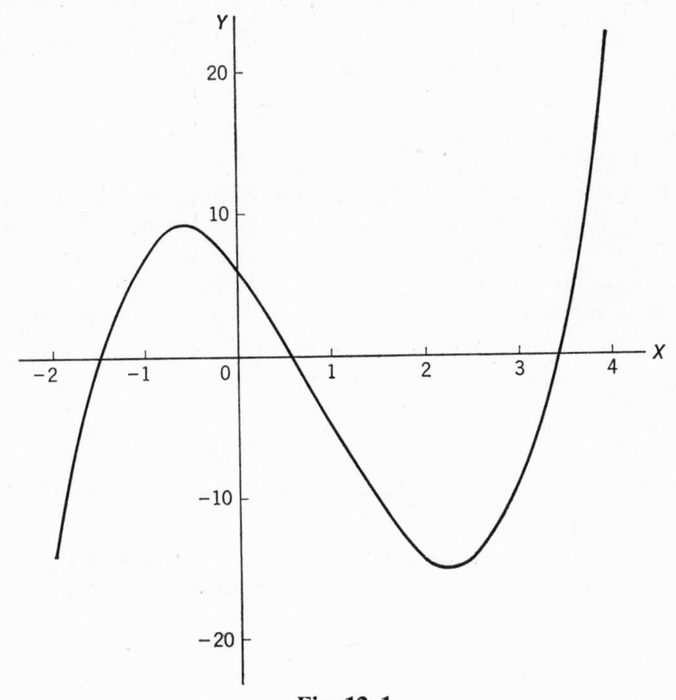

Fig. 12–1

(that is, has real coefficients), approximate values for the *real* roots can be found from the graph of $P(x)$. Indeed, the real roots are the abscissas of the points where the graph meets the horizontal axis.

The roots of the polynomial $2x^3 - 5x^2 - 8x + 6$, whose graph we have just constructed, are observed from Fig. 12–1 to be approximately -1.5, 0.6, and 3.4.

The graph of a real polynomial is a smooth unbroken curve. The geometrical picture makes plausible the following fact, which we state but do not prove:

If for two real numbers a and b, $P(a)$ and $P(b)$ have opposite signs, then the real polynomial $P(x)$ has at least one root between a and b.

This fact is useful in locating real roots of polynomials. For example, from the preceding table we note that $P(-2) = -14$, while $P(-1) = 7$. Hence, $P(x)$ has a real root between -2 and -1, which from the graph (Fig. 12–1) we observed to be approximately -1.5.

Methods of computing real roots more accurately are given later in this chapter.

If in the process of making a table of values for a polynomial by synthetic substitution, such as that on page 265, we find that for some positive number b all the partial sums arising in the substitution of b are *positive* or *zero*, then $P(x)$ has no real root greater than b. That is, b is an **upper bound** to the roots, for any number greater than b will render these partial sums positive and still greater. Hence, the last sum, which is the value of the polynomial, cannot possibly be zero. Thus, the polynomial in the example given above in this section has no real root greater than 4. Similarly, if in substituting a *negative* number $-a$, the partial sums are *alternately positive* and *negative*, then $P(x)$ has no real root less than $-a$. Thus, -2 is a **lower bound** to the roots of the polynomial in the example given above.

In making a table of values, it is usually convenient to start with $x = 0$ and proceed through positive values of x until we reach an upper bound to the roots. We then turn to negative values of x ($-1, -2$, etc.) and proceed until we reach a lower bound. The real roots of the polynomial lie between these two bounds.

EXERCISES

In Exercises 1 through 10 use synthetic division to find the quotient and the remainder when the first polynomial listed is divided by the second.

1. $x^3 - 5x^2 - 4x + 7$, $x - 3$

2. $2x^3 + x^2 - 5x - 9$, $x - 2$

3. $x^4 - 8x^2 + 4x - 10$, $x + 3$

4. $x^3 - 7x^2 + 9$, $x + 1$
5. $3x^4 + 17x^3 - 19x^2 + 7x - 5$, $x + 2$
6. $2x^4 + 13x^3 - 11x^2 + 1$, $x - \frac{1}{2}$
7. $x^3 - 0.3x^2 + 0.07x - 0.005$, $x - 0.1$
8. $2x^3 + 0.7x^2 + 0.08x - 0.061$, $x - 0.2$
9. $x^3 + 0.02x^2 + 0.0003x - 0.000004$, $x - 0.03$
10. $5x^4 - 3x^2a^2 + xa^3 + 2a^4$, $x + a$
11. If $P(x) = x^3 + 7x^2 - 9x + 5$, find by synthetic substitution:

$$P(-2), \quad P(-5), \quad P(0.1).$$

12. If $P(x) = 2x^4 - 7x^3 - 9x^2 + 3x - 7$, find by synthetic substitution:

$$P(1), \quad P(2), \quad P(3), \quad P(-1), \quad P(-2).$$

Using synthetic substitution, make a table of values for each of the polynomials in Exercises 13 through 30 and draw an accurate graph. From the graph read the real roots to one decimal place.

13. $P(x) = 2x^2 - 5x - 3$
14. $P(x) = x^2 - 2x - 7$
15. $P(x) = x^3 - 2x^2 - 5x + 6$
16. $P(x) = 2x^3 - 7x^2 - 10x + 20$
17. $P(x) = x^3 - 3x + 2$
18. $P(x) = x^3 - 3x^2 - x + 3$
19. $P(x) = x^4 - 10x^2 + 9$
20. $P(x) = x^3 + 3x - 5$
21. $P(x) = x^4 + 3x^2 - 4$
22. $P(x) = x^4 - 3x^3 - 4$
23. $P(x) = 2x^3 + 3x^2 - 36x + 7$
24. $P(x) = x^3 + x^2 + x - 7$
25. $P(x) = 2x^4 - 3x^2 + 4x - 5$
26. $P(x) = 2x^3 - 3x^2 + 6x - 5$
27. $P(x) = x^3 - x^2 - 6x$
28. $P(x) = x^5 - 4x^4 - 7x^3 - 9x + 3$
29. $P(x) = 2x^5 - 7x^4 + 6x^3 + 5x^2 - 7x + 2$
30. $P(x) = x^5 - 4x^4 + 3x^3 - x^2 + 2x + 3$

12.6 Number of Roots of a Polynomial Equation

In earlier chapters we learned that a first-degree equation has one root and that a quadratic has one or two roots. We now inquire as to the existence and number of roots of a polynomial equation of arbitrary degree $n \geqq 1$. It is not obvious that such an equation necessarily has a root at all. However, in 1799 the great German mathematician Carl Friedrich Gauss proved the following theorem.

▶ THE FUNDAMENTAL THEOREM OF ALGEBRA. *If $P(x)$ is a polynomial of the nth degree ($n \geqq 1$), there always exists a number r such that $P(r) = 0$.*

We can restate this theorem as follows: *Every polynomial equation of degree $n \geqq 1$ has at least one root.*

Notice that there is no restriction on the coefficients of the polynomial $P(x)$, nor any specification as to the kind of number the root r is. Thus, the assertion of the fundamental theorem is that a nonconstant polynomial with coefficients in the field of complex numbers has a root in the field of complex numbers. A number field having this property is said to be **algebraically closed.** The other number fields considered in this book, namely, the rationals and the reals, are not algebraically closed, as the polynomials $x^2 - 2$ and $x^2 + 1$ testify, since $x^2 - 2$ does not have a rational root and $x^2 + 1$ does not have a real root.

The proof of the fundamental theorem is beyond the scope of this book and its truth will be assumed here. On the basis of it, however, we now establish the following important theorem.

▶ THEOREM 1. *A polynomial equation of the nth degree* ($n \geqq 1$), $P(x) = 0$, *where* $P(x) = a_0x^n + a_1x^{n-1} + \cdots + a_n$, *has not more than n distinct roots.*

By the fundamental theorem we know that the equation $P(x) = 0$ has at least one root. If we denote such a root by r_1, then by the factor theorem, $x - r_1$ is a factor of $P(x)$, so that

$$P(x) = (x - r_1)P_1(x),$$

where $P_1(x)$ is a polynomial of degree $n - 1$ whose leading term is a_0x^{n-1}. If $n = 1$, $P_1(x) = a_0$. Otherwise, $P_1(x)$ also has a root r_2, and again by the factor theorem

$$P_1(x) = (x - r_2)P_2(x);$$

from which

$$P(x) = (x - r_1)(x - r_2)P_2(x).$$

Since the degree of the quotient decreases by *one* at each step, we can continue until n linear factors are separated out, and we obtain

$$P(x) = a_0(x - r_1)(x - r_2) \cdots (x - r_n). \qquad [12.1]$$

From [12.1] it follows that if c is any number different from $r_1, r_2, \cdots, r_n$, then

$$P(c) = a_0(c - r_1)(c - r_2) \cdots (c - r_n)$$

cannot be zero since none of the factors is zero. This completes the proof of Theorem 1.

The proof of Theorem 1 shows that a polynomial with complex coefficients is factorable into the product of linear factors with complex coefficients.

We have at once the following corollary.

▶ COROLLARY. *If two polynomials in the same variable, neither of degree greater than n, are equal for more than n distinct values of the variable, the polynomials are identical.*

For if the two polynomials

$$b_0x^n + b_1x^{n-1} + \cdots + b_n \quad \text{and} \quad c_0x^n + c_1x^{n-1} + \cdots + c_n$$

are equal for more than n values of x, their difference

$$F(x) = (b_0 - c_0)x^n + (b_1 - c_1)x^{n-1} + \cdots + (b_n - c_n)$$

will be zero for more than n values of x. Since $F(x) = 0$ is an equation of degree at most n, unless every coefficient of $F(x)$ is zero, we have a contradiction of Theorem 1. Therefore, every coefficient in $F(x)$ must be zero, and it follows that

$$b_0 = c_0, \quad b_1 = c_1, \quad b_2 = c_2, \quad \cdots, \quad b_n = c_n.$$

Hence, the two given polynomials are identical.

It is clear from [12.1] that $r_1, r_2, \cdots, r_n$ are roots of $P(x) = 0$. But it may happen that in the factorization of $P(x)$ in [12.1] some of the factors may be the same. If we rearrange the order of the factors if necessary, and combine like factors into a power of a single factor, we may write

$$P(x) = a_0(x - r_1)^{k_1}(x - r_2)^{k_2} \cdots (x - r_s)^{k_s}, \qquad [12.2]$$

where $k_1 + k_2 + \cdots + k_s = n$, and where $r_1, r_2, \cdots, r_s$ are all distinct. Here r_1 is said to be a root of **multiplicity** k_1; r_2 is a root of multiplicity k_2, etc. If $k_1 = 1$, r_1 is called a **simple** root of the equation; if $k_1 = 2$, r_1 is called a **double** root, etc.

Example

Find a cubic equation with -1 as a simple root and $\frac{1}{2}$ as a double root.

SOLUTION: Since -1 is a simple root and $\frac{1}{2}$ is a double root, the polynomial must have $x + 1$ and $(x - \frac{1}{2})^2$ as factors. Hence the equation is of the form

$$a_0(x + 1)(x - \tfrac{1}{2})^2 = 0,$$

where a_0 is any number not zero. To avoid fractions, we take $a_0 = 4$, and the equation is

$$(x + 1)(2x - 1)^2 = 4x^3 - 3x + 1 = 0.$$

12.7 Imaginary Roots

We now prove the following theorem.

▶ THEOREM 2. *If a polynomial equation $P(x) = 0$ with real coefficients has an imaginary root $a + bi$ $(b \neq 0)$, it has also the conjugate imaginary number $a - bi$ as a root.*

Since $a+bi$ is a root of the equation $P(x)=0$, by the factor theorem $x-(a+bi)$ is a factor of $P(x)$. If we can show that $x-(a-bi)$ also is a factor of $P(x)$, it will follow by the converse part of the factor theorem that $a-bi$ also is a root of $P(x)=0$. To do this, we show that the product of the two expressions $x-(a+bi)$ and $x-(a-bi)$,

$$[x-(a+bi)][x-(a-bi)]=(x-a)^2+b^2, \qquad [12.3]$$

is a factor of $P(x)$.

If we divide $P(x)$ by $(x-a)^2+b^2$, we obtain a remainder that is either 0 or of degree 1 at most. Since $P(x)$ and $(x-a)^2+b^2$ have coefficients in the field of real numbers, by the division algorithm we can write

$$P(x)=Q(x)[(x-a)^2+b^2]+Cx+D,$$

where the quotient $Q(x)$ and the remainder $Cx+D$ have *real* coefficients. In this identity we put $x=a+bi$. Since by hypothesis

$$P(a+bi)=0$$

and since, by [12.3], $(x-a)^2+b^2$ has the value 0 when $x=a+bi$, we have

$$0=Q(a+bi)\cdot 0+C\cdot(a+bi)+D.$$

That is,

$$(Ca+D)+Cbi=0.$$

Since a complex number is zero only if both real numbers comprising it are zero separately, we have

$$Cb=0, \qquad Ca+D=0.$$

Since by hypothesis $b\neq 0$, we have from the first of these conditions $C=0$. Then from the second condition we have also $D=0$. It follows then that the remainder is zero, and thus $P(x)$ is divisible by $(x-a)^2+b^2$ and hence by $x-(a-bi)$. Therefore $a-bi$ is a root of $P(x)=0$.

▶ COROLLARY 1. *A polynomial equation $P(x)=0$ of odd degree with real coefficients always has at least one real root.*

We prove this corollary by induction on the degree of $P(x)$. The degree of any polynomial equation of odd degree can be expressed as $2n-1$, where n is a positive integer. If $n=1$, the equation has form $a_0x+a_1=0$, which has the real root $-(a_1/a_0)$; so the corollary is true if $n=1$.

Assume that the corollary is true if $n=k$, and consider the case $n=k+1$. Thus, let $P(x)=0$ denote an equation of degree $2k+1$. If this equation has a real root, the proof is finished. Otherwise, it has an imaginary root of the form $a+bi$, and hence by Theorem 2, $a-bi$ also is a root. So, by the factor theorem applied twice, $P(x)$ is divisible by $[x - (a + bi)][x - (a - bi)] = (x - a)^2 + b^2$. Consequently, we may write

$$P(x) = [(x - a)^2 + b^2]Q(x),$$

where $Q(x)$ is a polynomial with real coefficients and degree $2k - 1$. By the inductive assumption, $Q(x)$ has a real root, which clearly is also a root of $P(x)$. Hence, the corollary is true for $n = k + 1$ whenever it is true for $n = k$. Thus, the proof of the corollary by induction is complete.

We also have another corollary.

▶ COROLLARY 2. *Every polynomial $P(x)$ with real coefficients can be expressed as a product of linear and quadratic polynomials with real coefficients.*

To prove Corollary 2, we observe that corresponding to each real root r of multiplicity m, $P(x)$ has $(x - r)^m$ as a factor. Also, the imaginary roots, if any, occur in conjugate pairs c and $\bar{c}$. The product $(x - c)(x - \bar{c})$ is a real quadratic polynomial and is a factor of $P(x)$. If we start with $P(x)$, repeated division by real factors of the two types mentioned yields at each step as quotient a polynomial with real coefficients to which the same argument as used with $P(x)$ applies. After a finite number of steps, $P(x)$ will be factored into the form specified in the corollary.

Example

Solve the cubic equation $x^3 - 3x^2 + x + 5 = 0$, given that $2 + i$ is one root.

SOLUTION: Since the equation has real coefficients, we know by Theorem 2 that $2 - i$ also is a root. Hence, $[x - (2 + i)][x - (2 - i)] = (x - 2)^2 + 1 = x^2 - 4x + 5$ is a factor of the left member. By ordinary division we find that the other factor is $x + 1$. Hence -1 is a root and the three roots are $2 + i$, $2 - i$, -1.

12.8 Factorization of Polynomials

By a **proper factorization** of a polynomial $P(x)$ we mean the expression of $P(x)$ as the product $A(x)B(x)$ of two polynomials, each of lower degree than $P(x)$. Thus, $2x^2 - 5x - 12 = (x - 4)(2x + 3)$ is an example. On the other hand, $4x + 6 = 2(2x + 3)$ is not a proper factorization, since $2x + 3$ has the same degree as $4x + 6$. In this section we are concerned with proper factorizations.

In considering factorization of a polynomial, it is necessary to have a clear understanding of what kind of numbers are to be permitted as coefficients of factors. Thus, $x^2 - 2$ can be factored as $(x - \sqrt{2})(x + \sqrt{2})$ if *real* numbers are allowed as coefficients, but it cannot be factored if we are restricted to *rational* numbers as coefficients. Similarly, $x^2 + 1$ can be factored as $(x+i)(x-i)$ if we are allowed to use *complex* coefficients, but this polynomial cannot be factored if we are restricted to *real* coefficients. A polynomial of positive degree, with coefficients in a given number field, that cannot be factored *properly* into the product of polynomials with coefficients in the given field is said to be **prime** (or **irreducible**) over that field.

In the proof of Theorem 1 it was established that any polynomial can be factored into the product of *linear* factors if *complex* coefficients are allowed. Thus, over the complex number field, the only prime polynomials are linear polynomials.

Corollary 2 to Theorem 2 says that any polynomial with *real* coefficients can be factored into the product of *linear* and *quadratic* factors if *real* coefficients are allowed. Thus, over the real number field the only prime polynomials possible are of degrees 1 or 2.

There is no parallel to the statements in the two preceding paragraphs in the case of polynomials with *rational* coefficients and the coefficients of factors limited to *rational* numbers. Indeed, it may be very difficult to determine whether or not a given polynomial with rational coefficients is irreducible over the rational field. However, in the next section we show how to find any rational **linear** factor of a polynomial with rational coefficients.

Examples

Over the rational number field, we have

$$2x^3 + x^2 - 6x - 3 = (2x + 1)(x^2 - 3).$$

Over the real number field, we have

$$2x^3 + x^2 - 6x - 3 = (2x + 1)(x + \sqrt{3})(x - \sqrt{3}).$$

Note that $x^2 - 3$ is irreducible over the rational number field but not over the real number field.

Over the real number field,

$$x^4 - 2x^3 + 3x^2 + 4x - 10 = (x + \sqrt{2})(x - \sqrt{2})(x^2 - 2x + 5).$$

Over the complex number field,

$$x^4 - 2x^3 + 3x^2 + 4x - 10 = (x + \sqrt{2})(x - \sqrt{2})[x - (1 + 2i)][x - (1 - 2i)].$$

Note that $x^2 - 2x + 5$ is irreducible over the real number field but not over the complex number field.

EXERCISES

In Exercises 1 through 8, form polynomial equations with integral coefficients and with the following numbers and no others as roots.

1. 1, 2, 3

2. 2, 1, -3

3. 1 a simple and 2 a double root

4. -1 a double and 5 a simple root

5. 2 a triple root

6. $-\frac{1}{2}$ a double and 4 a simple root

7. $\frac{1}{3}, \frac{2}{3}, 1, 3$

8. $\frac{2}{3}, \frac{1}{2}, 1, 4$

9. $2 \pm \sqrt{3}, 2$

10. $3 \pm \sqrt{2}, 4$

11. $1 \pm i, -3$

12. $-1 \pm 2i, 2$

13. Solve the equation $2x^3 - 5x^2 + 12x - 5 = 0$, given that $1 - 2i$ is one root.

14. Solve the equation $4x^3 - x^2 + 16x - 4 = 0$, given that $2i$ is one root.

15. Solve the equation $x^4 + x^3 - 2x^2 - 6x - 4 = 0$, given that $-1 - i$ is a root.

16. Find a polynomial equation of lowest degree with real coefficients and with $1 + 2i$ and -2 as roots.

17. Find a polynomial equation of lowest degree with real coefficients and with $3 - i$ and $2 + i$ as roots.

18. Find a polynomial equation of lowest degree with real coefficients and with $1 + i$ as a simple root and 2 as a double root.

Factor or list as irreducible over the *rational* number field the polynomial in each of Exercises 19 through 22.

19. $3x^2 - x - 2$

20. $2x^2 - 5x - 12$

21. $2x^2 - 4$

22. $x^2 + 3x - 1$

Factor or list as irreducible over the *real* number field the polynomial in each of Exercises 23 through 26.

23. $x^2 - 8$

24. $x^2 + x + 1$

25. $2x^2 - 3x + 5$

26. $2x^2 - 3x - 4$

27. Given that 2 is a root of $2x^3 - 2x^2 - x - 6$, factor this polynomial into factors with rational coefficients.

28. Given that $1 + i$ is a root of $2x^3 - 5x^2 + 6x - 2$, factor this polynomial into the product of linear factors.

29. If $2i$ is a root of the equation $x^3 + 3x^2 + bx + c = 0$ with real coefficients, find the values of b and c.

30. Does the graph of a polynomial of degree n with real coefficients necessarily cross the x axis n times? What is the answer if all roots of the polynomial are real?

31. Prove that no straight line can intersect the graph of a polynomial of degree n with real coefficients in more than n points. (The equation of a straight line is a linear equation.)

32. Prove Theorem 1 by induction.

12.9 Rational Roots of an Equation

Up to this point in this chapter we have established criteria by which to gain information as to the number and the character of the roots of a polynomial equation $P(x) = 0$, and have found roots in certain special circumstances. We now consider more general methods of determining roots.

Even though the coefficients of $P(x) = 0$ are real, we know that the equation need not have *all* real roots nor indeed *any* real root. We shall attempt first to find the real roots, if there are any. Real roots may be of two kinds, *rational* or *irrational.* In case the coefficients of $P(x)$ are rational, the rational roots of $P(x) = 0$ are easiest to find, and our plan will be to find them first. The irrational roots cannot, of course, be found exactly as decimals, and all we can hope to do is find them to a desired degree of approximation. A method of doing this will be presented in the next section.

We now try to find by trial the rational roots of an equation. Since there are infinitely many rational numbers, obviously the task would be a hopeless one unless we had some clue as to what rational numbers to try. Accordingly, we establish first the following theorem.

▶ THEOREM 3. *If the coefficients $a_0, a_1, \cdots, a_n$ of a polynomial equation*

$$a_0x^n + a_1x^{n-1} + \cdots + a_n = 0$$

are integers, and if p/q is a rational fraction in its lowest terms that satisfies the equation, then p is a divisor of the constant term a_n and q is a divisor of the leading coefficient a_0.

Before proceeding to a proof of the theorem, we explain first of all that when we say that p/q is a fraction in its lowest terms, we mean that p and q are integers with no common factor greater than 1. Second, we state without proof a property of integers: *Let p, q, and r be integers. If p and q have no common factor greater than* 1, *and if p is a divisor of the product qr, then p is a divisor of r.* Thus, 21 divides the product $630 = 10 \times 63$, and since 21 has no factor greater than 1 in common with 10, it must divide 63.

We now proceed with the proof of the theorem. Since by hypothesis p/q is a root of the equation $P(x) = 0$, we have by substitution,

$$a_0\frac{p^n}{q^n} + a_1\frac{p^{n-1}}{q^{n-1}} + \cdots + a_{n-1}\frac{p}{q} + a_n = 0.$$

From this we obtain, on multiplying through by q^n,

$$a_0p^n + a_1p^{n-1}q + \cdots + a_{n-1}pq^{n-1} + a_nq^n = 0. \qquad [12.4]$$

If now we subtract a_nq^n from both members, we see that every term on the left has the factor p. Thus,

$$p(a_0p^{n-1} + a_1p^{n-2}q + \cdots + a_{n-1}q^{n-1}) = -a_nq^n.$$

By hypothesis, a_0 and p are integers, and therefore the term a_0p^{n-1} is an integer, since the product of integers is an integer. Similarly, each term in the parentheses is an integer, and their sum is therefore an integer. Equation [12.4] can then be written

$$p \times \text{integer} = -a_nq^n.$$

But this is merely another way of saying that p is a *divisor* of a_nq^n. Then, since p has no factor greater than 1 in common with q^n, it follows by the property of integers stated above that p is a *divisor* of a_n.

In a similar manner, if we transpose the first term in [12.4] to the right and factor, we have

$$q(a_1p^{n-1} + a_2p^{n-2}q + \cdots + a_nq^{n-1}) = -a_0p^n,$$

from which it follows that q is a *divisor* of a_0. The proof of the theorem is thus complete.

An equation with rational fractional coefficients can be changed into an equivalent equation with integral coefficients by multiplying both members by the least common denominator of the coefficients. Theorem 3 can then be applied.

Example

Make a list of the possible rational roots of the equation

$$2x^3 - x^2 - 7x - 3 = 0,$$

and, by testing, find which, if any, are actually roots. If possible, find the remaining roots.

SOLUTION: The possible numerators are divisors of 3 and must therefore be either ± 1 or ± 3. The possible denominators must be divisors of 2 and must therefore be ± 1 or ± 2. Hence, the only possible rational roots are

$$\pm 1/1,\ \pm 3/1,\ \pm 1/2,\ \pm 3/2.$$

To find which, if any, of these are actually roots, we test them successively.

x				$P(x)$	
	2	−1	−7	−3	
1	2	1	−6	−9	not a root
−1	2	−3	−4	1	not a root
3	2	5	8	21	not a root
−3	2	−7	14	−45	not a root
$1/2$	2	0	−7	—	not a root
$-1/2$	2	−2	−6	0	$-1/2$ *is a root*
$3/2$	2	2	−4	−9	not a root
$-3/2$	2	−4	−1	—	not a root

From this table we see first of all that of the possible rational roots only one, namely, $-\frac{1}{2}$, is actually a root. Secondly, we note that in the substitution of $\frac{1}{2}$ or of $-\frac{3}{2}$ we reached a point where fractions enter. In such cases we can stop as soon as we encounter fractions, for the sum of an integer and a fraction is a fraction and cannot give zero in the last column. Finally we note that the process of substituting $-\frac{1}{2}$ can also be looked upon as a *division* of the polynomial by $x + \frac{1}{2}$, the first three numbers 2, -2, -6 in the line being the coefficients in the quotient, the last number 0 being the remainder. Hence, we have

$$2x^3 - x^2 - 7x - 3 = (x + \tfrac{1}{2})(2x^2 - 2x - 6).$$

To find the remaining roots of the given cubic, we have merely to solve the quadratic $2x^2 - 2x - 6 = 0$, the roots of which are found by the quadratic formula to be $\frac{1}{2}(1 \pm \sqrt{13})$. These are real and irrational.

This last equation, $2x^2 - 2x - 6 = 0$, is called a **depressed equation.** After one rational root of a given equation has been found, in order to find the remaining roots, it is better to work with the depressed equation rather than with the original equation. This is particularly true if the given equation has a multiple root. For instance, in the example given above, if $-\frac{1}{2}$ were a multiple root, that fact would appear by substituting $-\frac{1}{2}$ in the depressed equation. Of course whenever a depressed equation is of degree not higher than two, all its roots are immediately obtainable.

In the particular case in which the coefficients of a polynomial equation are integers and the leading coefficient is ± 1, the only possible rational roots are those whose denominators are 1, and hence are integers. We therefore have the following corollary to Theorem 3.

▶ COROLLARY. *If the coefficients of a polynomial equation are integers, and if the leading coefficient is* ± 1, *the only possible rational roots are integral factors of the constant term.*

For example, the only possible rational roots of the cubic $x^3 - 5x - 4 = 0$ are the integers 1, 2, 4, and their negatives. By trial it is found that the only rational root is -1.

The criteria of Section 12.5 frequently save us much labor by furnishing upper and lower bounds for the roots.

EXERCISES

For each of the equations in Exercises 1 through 18 make a list of all possible rational roots and find by testing which, if any, are actually roots. If possible, find all the roots of the equation.

1. $2x^3 + x^2 - 2x - 1 = 0$
2. $x^3 - 6x^2 + 11x - 6 = 0$
3. $x^3 - 2x^2 - x + 2 = 0$
4. $3x^3 - x^2 - 12x + 4 = 0$
5. $x^3 - 3x^2 - 7x + 6 = 0$
6. $x^4 + 4x^3 - x - 4 = 0$
7. $3x^3 - 8x^2 + x + 2 = 0$
8. $x^4 + 3x^3 - 3x^2 - 7x + 6 = 0$
9. $2x^3 - 3x^2 + 3x - 1 = 0$
10. $3x^3 - 2x^2 - 2x - 5 = 0$
11. $x^3 - 2x^2 - 2x - 3 = 0$
12. $2x^3 + 5x^2 - 1 = 0$
13. $3x^3 - x^2 + x + 2 = 0$
14. $x^3 - 2x + 4 = 0$
15. $4x^3 - x^2 - 7x - 3 = 0$
16. $4x^3 - 5x - 2 = 0$
17. $x^3 - \frac{2}{3}x^2 + \frac{5}{3}x + \frac{2}{3} = 0$
18. $4x^4 + 5x^3 - 10x^2 - 5x + 6 = 0$
19. Use the theory of Section 12.9 to prove that $\sqrt{3}$ is irrational.

Factor the polynomials in Exercises 20 through 25, first allowing only factors with rational coefficients, then allowing factors with real coefficients, and finally allowing factors with complex coefficients.

20. $x^3 + 2x^2 - 5x - 6$
21. $x^3 + x^2 - 4x - 4$
22. $2x^3 - 3x^2 - 12x + 5$
23. $6x^3 + 11x^2 - 6x - 8$
24. $3x^4 + 2x^3 + 7x^2 + 8x - 20$
25. $2x^4 - 3x^3 - 2x + 3$

12.10 Irrational Roots by Linear Interpolation

After all rational roots, if any, of a given equation have been found and the corresponding factors have been divided out, it frequently happens that the depressed equation has one or more *real* roots. Such roots are, of course, irrational. They cannot be expressed exactly as decimals, although by a process of successive approximation they can be obtained to any desired degree of accuracy. One method of doing this is called **linear interpolation.** The method is best explained by an example.

Example

Find an irrational root of the equation

$$P(x) = x^3 - x^2 + 2x - 5 = 0,$$

correct to two decimal places.

SOLUTION: We use synthetic substitution to obtain the following table of values:

x				$P(x)$
0	1	−1	2	−5
1	1	0	2	−3
2	1	1	4	3
−1	1	−2	4	−9

By the criteria for upper and lower bounds, it is clear from the table that there is no root to the right of 2 nor to the left of -1, but there is at least one real root between 1 and 2. We plot a graph as shown in Fig. 12–2. Since the equation cannot have any rational roots other than ± 1, ± 5, the real root between 1 and 2 is irrational. As a first approximation we note from the graph that this root is about 1.6. By the use of tables of squares and cubes, a calculating machine, or direct computation, we find that

$$P(1.6) = 1.6^3 - 1.6^2 + 2(1.6) - 5 = 4.096 - 2.56 + 3.2 - 5 = -0.264,$$
$$P(1.7) = 1.7^3 - 1.7^2 + 2(1.7) - 5 = 4.913 - 2.89 + 3.4 - 5 = +0.423.$$

Since $P(1.6)$ and $P(1.7)$ have opposite signs, by the principle stated in Section 12.5 the graph crosses the horizontal axis between 1.6 and 1.7, so that the value of the root to two digits is $x = 1.6$.

To obtain a closer approximation we use the process of linear interpolation. To illustrate this we plot another graph on an enlarged scale as shown in Fig. 12–3, where the point S is at 1.6 on the x axis and P and Q are points on

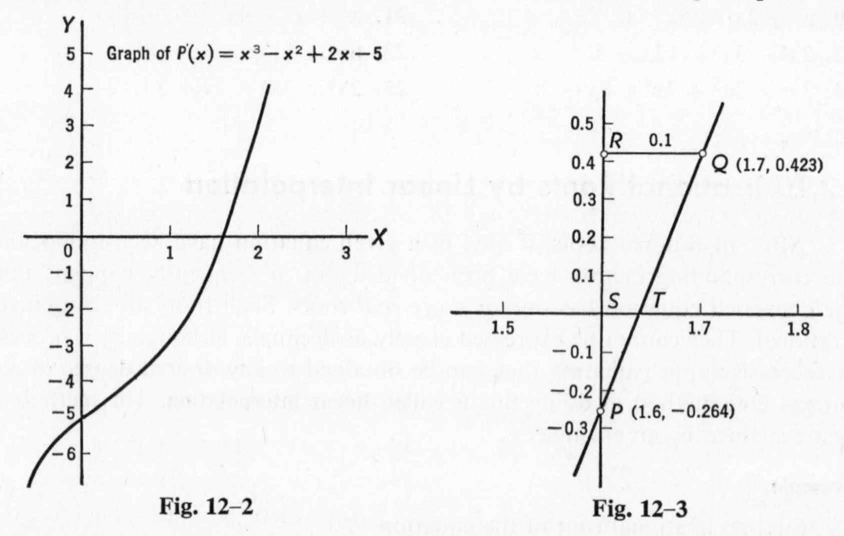

Fig. 12–2

Fig. 12–3

the graph corresponding to $x = 1.6$ and $x = 1.7$, respectively. Since it is relatively short, we may replace the *arc* PQ of the curve by the straight line PTQ without introducing a large error. If we denote the length of ST by d, the root of our equation is approximately $1.6 + d$. Now from similar triangles PTS and PQR we have

$$\frac{ST}{RQ} = \frac{PS}{PR} \quad \text{or} \quad \frac{d}{0.1} = \frac{0.264}{0.264 + 0.423} = \frac{0.264}{0.687}.$$

Hence,

$$d = \frac{0.0264}{0.687} = 0.03^+,$$

so that $x = 1.63$, approximately.

To obtain still greater accuracy, we compute

$$P(1.63) = 1.63^3 - 1.63^2 + 2(1.63) - 5$$
$$= 4.3307 - 2.6569 + 3.26 - 5 = -0.0662,$$

$$P(1.64) = 1.64^3 - 1.64^2 + 2(1.64) - 5$$
$$= 4.4109 - 2.6896 + 3.28 - 5 = +0.0013.$$

This shows that the root actually lies between 1.63 and 1.64. Also, on computing the next correction, we have

$$\frac{d}{0.01} = \frac{0.0662}{0.0675},$$

from which $d = 0.009^{+}$. The next approximation is therefore

$$x = 1.63 + 0.009 = 1.639.$$

This process can be continued as far as desired, although the work becomes more difficult as we proceed. Rounded off to two decimal places, the answer is $x = 1.64$.

EXERCISES

By the method of linear interpolation find the irrational roots of each of the equations in Exercises 1 through 18, correct to two decimal places.

1. $x^3 + x + 13 = 0$

2. $x^3 + 3x - 7 = 0$

3. $x^3 - x^2 + x - 7 = 0$

4. $x^3 - 4x^2 + 2x - 4 = 0$

5. $x^4 + x^3 - 4x^2 + x - 5 = 0$

6. $x^4 + 3x - 11 = 0$

7. $x^3 - 3x^2 + 3x - 14 = 0$

8. $x^3 + 3x^2 - 6x - 2 = 0$

9. $x^3 + 6x - 13 = 0$

10. $x^3 - 47 = 0$

11. $x^3 - 3x^2 + 2x - 11 = 0$

12. $x^3 - 3x^2 + 4x - 7 = 0$

13. $x^3 - 3x^2 + 4x - 5 = 0$

14. $2x^4 - x^3 - 2x^2 - 21x + 11 = 0$
Hint: First remove rational factor.

15. $4x^3 - 6x - 13 = 0$

16. $2x^4 + x^3 + 2x^2 - 9x - 5 = 0$

17. $x^4 - 5x^3 - x^2 - 5x - 2 = 0$

18. $x^3 - 3x^2 + 7x - 12 = 0$

19. A buoy is in the form of a sphere of radius r. If the specific gravity of the buoy is $s < 1$, the depth x to which it will sink in water is given by the smaller positive root of the equation $x^3 - 3rx^2 + 4r^3s = 0$. To what depth will a buoy whose radius is 2 ft and specific gravity 0.75 sink?

20. A box with open top is to be made from a sheet of tin 14 in. square by cutting equal squares from the corners and bending up the sides. If the box is to have a volume of 156 cu in., find the length of the side of the square to be cut out.

12.11 Further Remarks on Equations of Higher Degree

The quadratic formula

$$x = \frac{-b \pm \sqrt{b^2 - 4ac}}{2a}$$

expresses values for the roots of the general quadratic equation $ax^2 + bx + c = 0$ in terms of the coefficients a, b, and c. The formula involves only the four rational operations and the extraction of a square root. If the coefficients of a quadratic are known, its roots can be found by performing on the coefficients the operations indicated by the formula.

Similar formulas exist for the roots of the general cubic equation, $ax^3 + bx^2 + cx + d = 0$, and for the general quartic equation, $ax^4 + bx^3 + cx^2 + dx + e = 0$. These formulas are considerably more complicated than the quadratic formula, but they involve only rational operations and the extraction of roots.

It was thought for a long time that similar formulas existed for general polynomial equations of all degrees. Such, however, is not the case. In 1824, Niels Abel, the brilliant Norwegian mathematician, proved that for polynomial equations of degree greater than 4 no formulas such as the quadratic formula can exist. A criterion for determining when a given polynomial equation can be solved by a process involving only rational operations and the extraction of roots was discovered by the French mathematician Évariste Galois (1811–1832), an ill-starred genius who was killed in a duel before reaching the age of 21 and yet left to posterity a theory whose deep significance was not appreciated until many decades after his death.

Permutations, Combinations, and Probability ◄ 13

13.1 Meaning of Permutations and Combinations

Let us consider a set of four marbles of different colors. Designate the individual marbles by the letters a, b, c, and d, respectively. We now list the different *sets* consisting of three marbles each which can be chosen from the four marbles. They are:

$$abc, \quad abd, \quad acd, \quad bcd.$$

Each of these sets is called a **combination.** Two combinations are the same if they contain the same objects, the order in which the objects were selected and the arrangement of the objects within the combination being immaterial.

Let us now list the different *arrangements* of three marbles in a row which can be formed from the four marbles. They are:

$$\begin{array}{cccccc} a\,b\,c & a\,c\,b & b\,a\,c & b\,c\,a & c\,a\,b & c\,b\,a \\ a\,b\,d & a\,d\,b & b\,a\,d & b\,d\,a & d\,a\,b & d\,b\,a \\ a\,c\,d & a\,d\,c & c\,a\,d & c\,d\,a & d\,a\,c & d\,c\,a \\ b\,c\,d & b\,d\,c & c\,b\,d & c\,d\,b & d\,b\,c & d\,c\,b \end{array}$$

Each of these arrangements is called a **permutation.** Notice that each of the four distinct *combinations* gives rise to six different *permutations* by rearrangement of the order of the objects within the combination.

In general, by the different *combinations* obtainable from a set of n objects r at a time, we mean the distinct subsets of r objects each which can be selected from the n objects, the order of selection and the arrangement within the subset being of no significance.

By the different *permutations* of n objects r at a time we mean the distinct *arrangements* of r objects in a row that can be formed from the set of n objects.

To develop the theory of permutations and combinations—sometimes referred to as the theory of *choices*—we need the principle stated in the next section.

13.2 A Fundamental Principle

If a certain operation can be performed in $\mathbf{m}$ *ways and if, after this operation has been performed, a second operation can be performed in* $\mathbf{n}$ *ways, then the total number of ways in which the two operations can be performed in the order named is* $\mathbf{m \cdot n}$.

This basic principle of counting is equivalent to the following statement: If one set contains m elements and a second set contains n elements, there are exactly mn ordered pairs, with the first member of each pair an element of the first set and the second member of the pair an element of the second set.

Example 1

From 6 baseball pitchers and 3 catchers how many different batteries consisting of a pitcher and catcher can be formed?

SOLUTION: The pitcher can be selected in 6 ways and the catcher in 3 ways. Hence, the battery can be selected in $6 \cdot 3 = 18$ different ways.

The fundamental principle can be generalized to cases of three, four, or any number of operations. Thus, if a first operation can be performed in n_1 ways, and after this is done a second can be performed in n_2 ways, and after this is done a third can be performed in n_3 ways, etc., then the total number of ways in which the operations can be performed in the order named is $n_1 \cdot n_2 \cdot n_3 \cdots$.

Example 2

From panels of 7 men representing labor, 5 men representing management, and 4 men representing the public, how many different 3-man committees can be formed consisting of a representative from each of the three panels?

SOLUTION: The labor representative can be chosen in 7 ways, the management representative in 5 ways, and the public's representative in 4 ways. Hence, by the fundamental principle, the number of different committees is $7 \cdot 5 \cdot 4 = 140$.

EXERCISES

1. A manufacturer of prefabricated houses has one floor plan but secures variety by having 3 different colored roofs, attaching the garage in 4 different ways, and using 3 different types of entrances. Find the number of different-looking houses produced.
2. A college boy has 5 pairs of slacks, 3 sport coats, and 4 sweaters. How many different ensembles, each consisting of slacks, sport coat, and sweater, can he select?
3. A baseball manager has 4 pitchers and 2 players for each of the other 8 positions. Now many different teams could he put on the field?
4. From the digits 2, 5, 7, 9, how many different three-digit numbers could be written if no digits were repeated? If repetitions were allowed?
5. A freshman is to take 3 courses chosen as follows: one of 5 natural sciences, English or history, and one of 4 foreign languages. How many different study programs are possible?
6. A nominating committee for a club brings in a slate of 2 men for president, 3 for vice-president, and 4 for secretary-treasurer. How many different sets of officers can be elected from this slate?
7. If 9 different signal flags are available, how many different signal displays are possible using 4 flags in a row? Using 5 flags?
8. In how many ways may three prizes be won by 11 competitors if no person may win more than one prize? If there is no restriction on the number of prizes an individual may win?
9. If 2 cubical dice are tossed simultaneously, in how many different ways can they fall?
10. If types of airplanes are designated by two of the letters B, C, D, F, M, and P followed by one of the numerals 1 to 9, find the number of different possible designations, first if repetition of letters is permitted, and second if repetition is not permitted.
11. How many different automobile license-plate designations can be made using a letter followed by a positive integer consisting of not more than 5 digits?
12. In how many different ways can 5 people be seated in a room that contains 7 chairs?
13. From 4 married couples, in how many different ways can a pair of bridge partners consisting of a man and a woman be chosen if husband and wife are not to play together?
14. How many different positive even integers consisting of not more than three digits can be written using the digits 2, 5, 6, 7, and 8 without repetitions? If repetitions are allowed?

13.3 Number of Permutations of *n* Different Objects Taken *r* at a Time without Repetitions

In Section 13.1 we considered the number of linear arrangements, taken 3 at a time, that can be formed from 4 different-colored marbles. We found by listing them that there were 24 in all. The number of different permutations can be found without listing them. In forming any permutation the marble for the first position can be chosen in 4 ways, then the marble for the second position can be chosen in 3 ways, and then the marble for the third position can be chosen in 2 ways. Thus by the fundamental principle the choice for the permutation can be made in $4 \cdot 3 \cdot 2 = 24$ ways. Hence, 24 different permutations are possible.

This line of reasoning can be applied to the general case of the number of permutations possible from n different things taken r at a time without repetition. We shall refer to these as ***r*-permutations** and denote the number of them by P_r^n. The first element in an r-permutation may be selected in n ways, then the second may be selected in $n - 1$ ways, and so on. Thus by the fundamental principle, we have

$$P_r^n = n(n-1)(n-2) \cdots \textit{to r factors}. \qquad [13.1]$$

The last factor in this product is $n - r + 1$; so we may write

$$P_r^n = n(n-1)(n-2) \cdots (n-r+1). \qquad [13.2]$$

A special case occurs when $r = n$. In this case we have

$$P_n^n = n! \qquad [13.3]$$

Note: Other symbols which have the same meaning as P_r^n are $P_{n,r}$ and $P(n, r)$.

Example 1

From 10 Greek letters, how many fraternity designations of 3 different letters each may be formed?

SOLUTION: This is a case of the number of 3-permutations that can be formed from 10 objects. Applying [13.1], we get

$$P_3^{10} = 10 \cdot 9 \cdot 8 = 720.$$

Example 2

A student has a mathematics book, a history book, an English book, and a French book. In how many different ways can he arrange these books in a row on his desk?

SOLUTION: We seek here the number of 4-permutations of 4 objects. Applying [13.3] we have

$$P_4^4 = 4! = 24.$$

6 . 5 4

13.4 Permutations with Repetitions

Let us ask for the number of three-digit numbers that can be formed from the digits 3, 5, 7, and 8, if repetitions are allowed. The digit in the hundreds' place can be chosen in 4 ways, then the digit in the tens' place can be chosen in 4 ways, and finally the digit in the units' place can be chosen in 4 ways. Thus, altogether $4 \cdot 4 \cdot 4 = 4^3 = 64$ choices are possible.

In general, in forming the permutations of n things r at a time with unlimited repetitions allowed—the so-called ***r*-permutations with repetitions**—each of the r places in the permutation may be filled in n ways. Hence, the total number of r-permutations with repetitions is $\boldsymbol{n^r}$.

13.5 Permutations of a Set of Objects Not All Different

Let us consider the permutations that can be formed from the letters of the word *banana*, using all the letters each time. Let x denote the actual number of different permutations obtainable. Then let us temporarily suppose that the a's may be distinguished from each other by some such device as using subscripts and writing them a_1, a_2, a_3. Thus, for each of the x permutations mentioned above, there would be 3! different permutations arising from rearranging the a's among themselves. Hence, $3! \cdot x$ is the number of different permutations if we consider the a's as distinguishable from one another. Moreover, if we also consider the n's as distinguishable from each other, corresponding to each of these $3! \cdot x$ permutations are 2! permutations resulting from permuting the n's among themselves. Thus, under the supposition that the a's are distinguishable from one another and the n's are distinguishable from each other, the total number of different permutations is $2! \cdot 3! \cdot x$. But this supposition is the same as assuming all the original letters to be different from one another, and under this hypothesis the number of different permutations would be 6!. Hence we have

$$2! \cdot 3! \cdot x = 6! \qquad \text{or} \qquad x = \frac{6!}{2!\,3!}\cdot$$

The same line of reasoning applied to the general case yields the following result. *The number of different n-permutations that can be formed from n objects, of which u are alike of one kind, v are alike of another kind, w are alike of a third kind, etc., is given by*

$$P = \frac{n!}{u!\,v!\,w!\cdots}\cdot \qquad [13.4]$$

EXERCISES do

16! 1. In how many ways can 16 books be arranged on a shelf?

2. In how many ways can 10 books be arranged on a shelf if 3 of them are to be kept together? If 3 are to be kept together in a certain order?

3. A basketball coach has 9 first-string players, all of whom can play any of the five positions on the team. How many different teams can he form? (Teams are counted different if players play different positions even if the same 5 players are involved.)

4. How many different two-digit numbers can be formed using the digits 3, 6, 7, 8, and 9 without repetitions? How many if repetitions are allowed?

5. How many even three-digit numbers can be formed using the digits 2, 3, 5, 6, 7 without repetitions? With repetitions allowed?

6. With 8 seats from which to choose, in how many ways can 5 people be seated?

7. In how many ways can 4 men and 4 women be seated in a row if men and women are to occupy alternate seats?

8. In Exercise 7 how many seating arrangements are possible if the men and women are husbands and wives, and husbands and wives are to sit together, men and women occupying alternate seats?

9. The Greek alphabet contains 24 letters. How many fraternity names may be formed using 3 different letters? How many if repetitions are allowed?

10. How many 8-permutations can be formed from the letters of the word *hesitate?* In how many of these do the *e*'s occur together?

11. How many different arrangements can be made from the letters of the word *Mississippi*, using all the letters each time?

12. Find the total number of numbers that can be written using the digits 2, 3, 5, 7, 8, no digit being repeated in any number.

13. Find the number of numbers greater than 4000 that can be written using the digits 0, 3, 5, 6, 8 without repetitions.

14. A signalman has 4 identical sets of signal flags. Each set consists of 6 flags of different colors. How many different displays of 1 to 4 flags on a vertical staff can he make?

15. By rearranging the digits, how many different six-digit numbers can be formed from 346,474?

16. A student has 4 mathematics books, 5 history books, and 7 English books. In how many ways can he arrange them on a shelf if books on the same subject are to be kept together?

17. Three benches have 8 seats each. There are 5 men, 6 women, and 8 children to be seated. The men, women, and children are to occupy different benches. In how many ways may these people be seated?

18. In how many different ways may 12 people be seated at a round table, the *order only* being significant in determining different arrangements? *Hint:* The order is not changed if the entire group shifts 1, 2, · · · , 11 places.

19. Solve Exercise 18 if there are 6 men and 6 women and if the men and women are to be seated alternately.
20. A signalman has 3 red flags, 4 blue flags, and 2 yellow flags. How many different signal displays of 9 flags in a row can be formed?

13.6 Number of Combinations of *n* Different Objects Taken *r* at a Time

We recall that a *combination* is a subset of a given set. Two combinations are the same if, and only if, they contain the same objects. Obviously, from one combination we can get several permutations by rearranging the objects within the combination. In fact by [13.3], to each combination of r objects there correspond $r!$ permutations. Hence, if we denote by C_r^n the number of different combinations that can be formed from n different objects, taking them r at a time, we have

$$r!\,C_r^n = P_r^n.$$

Substituting the value of P_r^n from [13.2] and solving for C_r^n, we get

$$C_r^n = \frac{n(n-1)\cdots(n-r+1)}{r!}.$$

If we multiply both numerator and denominator by $(n-r)!$, we get the following compact formula:

$$C_r^n = \frac{n!}{r!\,(n-r)!} \qquad [13.5]$$

Note: Other symbols which have the same meaning as C_r^n are $C_{n,r}$, $C(n, r)$, and $\binom{n}{r}$.

Example

Squad A has 5 tennis players and squad B has 8 players. In how many ways can a doubles match be arranged between the two squads?

SOLUTION: The number of different doubles teams that can be formed by squad A is simply the number of combinations of 5 things taken 2 at a time. By [13.5] this is

$$C_2^5 = \frac{5!}{2!\,3!} = 10.$$

Similarly, the number of different doubles teams that squad B can form is

$$C_2^8 = \frac{8!}{2!\,6!} = 28.$$

Hence, by the fundamental principle, a doubles match can be arranged in

$$C_2^5 \cdot C_2^8 = 10 \cdot 28 = 280 \text{ different ways.}$$

13.7 Combinations and the Binomial Theorem

The expression $(a + b)^n$, where n is a positive integer, represents the product of n factors, each of which is $a + b$. To obtain a term in the expansion of this product, we take the product of the b's occurring in certain of the factors by the a's occurring in the remaining factors. Let r denote the number of factors from which b is taken. Then a must be taken from the remaining $n - r$ factors. The resulting product is $a^{n-r}b^r$. For a fixed integer r, $0 \leqq r \leqq n$, the r factors of $(a + b)^n$ from which the b's are to be taken can be chosen in C_r^n ways. Hence, the term $a^{n-r}b^r$ will occur C_r^n times. Thus, if we collect these, we see that the typical term in the expansion of $(a + b)^n$ is

$$C_r^n a^{n-r} b^r \qquad \text{or} \qquad \frac{n!}{r!\,(n-r)!}\, a^{n-r} b^r. \qquad [13.6]$$

This result is the same as that obtained in Section 7.3 and is correct even for the extreme cases $r = 0$ and $r = n$. Hence we have here a different proof of the binomial theorem. This theorem can be written in the following form, which is obtained from [13.6] by assigning to r successively the values $0, 1, 2, \cdots, n$ and adding the results.

$$(a + b)^n = C_0^n a^n + C_1^n a^{n-1} b + \cdots + C_r^n a^r b^{n-r} + \cdots + C_n^n b^n. \qquad [13.7]$$

If in [13.7] we let $a = b = 1$, we get

$$2^n = C_0^n + C_1^n + C_2^n + \cdots + C_r^n + \cdots + C_n^n.$$

The terms on the right represent the number of combinations of n objects taken 0 at a time, 1 at a time, 2 at a time, etc., up to n at a time. Thus the sum of these terms is the total number of combinations that can be formed from n objects, and we observe that this number is 2^n.

Thus, the total number of subsets of a set of n objects is $\mathbf{2^n}$.

EXERCISES

1. The winner of a contest can choose any 8 of 15 books. How many different selections can he make?
2. Find the number of different lines determined by 11 points, no three of which lie on the same line.
3. How many different bridge hands of 13 cards may be dealt from a deck of 52 cards? (Do not multiply out.)
4. Eight people are to play bridge. In how many ways may they be divided into two equal groups?

5. From a committee of 12 Democrats and 9 Republicans how many different subcommittees of 5 each may be formed if 3 are to be Democrats and 2 Republicans?

6. From 3 officers and 10 enlisted men, in how many ways can 8 persons be chosen to include exactly one officer? To include at least one officer?

7. From a penny, a nickel, a dime, a quarter, and a half-dollar, how many different sums of money can be formed?

8. A baseball league contains 8 teams. If each team is to play every other team 10 times, how many games are played in the league?

9. A student council is to consist of 4 seniors, 3 juniors, 2 sophomores, and 2 freshmen. How many councils may be elected from a slate of 8 seniors, 5 juniors, 7 sophomores, and 10 freshmen?

10. From a group of 12 men, in how many ways may a group of 5 be selected if a specific individual is to be included? If a specific individual is to be excluded?

11. There are 10 points in a plane, no three of which lie on the same straight line. How many different triangles may be formed using these points as vertices?

12. From 5 Americans, 4 Englishmen, 3 Frenchmen, and 6 Russians, how many committees of 9 members may be formed if each of the four nations is to be represented by at least 2 members?

13. From 5 generals, 3 admirals, and 7 civilians, a committee of 6 members is to be chosen to consist of 2 generals, 2 admirals, and 2 civilians. How many different committees may be chosen?

14. In how many ways can 12 objects be separated into three equal piles?

15. In how many ways can 12 books be equally distributed among three students?

16. From 9 novels and 6 biographies, in how many ways can 4 novels and 3 biographies be selected and arranged on a shelf?

17. How many different groups of five letters, each consisting of 3 consonants and 2 vowels, can be selected from the letters of the word *universal?* How many "code words" of five letters each can be formed from rearranging the letters within the groups in such a way that consonants and vowels alternate?

18. Find the number of different football teams of 11 players, 7 linemen and 4 backs, that may be selected from 18 players, 10 of whom are linemen and 8 of whom are backs, if (a) we count as different only teams containing different individuals; (b) we count as different, teams that are made up of the same individuals but in which assignments to positions are different, it being assumed that any lineman can play any position in the line and any back can play any position in the backfield?

19. How many different baseball line-ups can be formed from 2 catchers, 5 pitchers, 6 players who can play any position in the infield, and 4 players who can play any position in the outfield?

20. Prove that $C_r^n = C_{n-r}^n$.

21. Prove that $C_r^n + C_{r+1}^n = C_{r+1}^{n+1}$.

13.8 Meaning of Probability

In everyday conversation we often hear such expressions as: "It will probably rain today," "That student is likely to fail this course," "The chances are that the Democrats will win the next election," "The odds favor Candy Spots to win the Kentucky Derby next Saturday." These statements are all concerned with the probability that some specified event will happen. The term **probability** as used in mathematics denotes a measure, or index, of the likelihood that some stated event will take place. Before stating a formal definition of this concept, let us first consider an example.

If a card is drawn at random from a well-shuffled deck of 52, there is no a priori reason for thinking that any specific card will be drawn rather than some other card. We say that each card in the deck is **equally likely** to be drawn. Let us inquire into the likelihood that the card drawn is a king. The experiment of drawing a card has exactly 52 equally likely outcomes, of which 4 would result in drawing a king. Hence, it appears reasonable to take as a suitable measure of the likelihood of drawing a king the ratio of 4 to 52. Hence, we say that the probability of drawing a king is $4/52$ or $1/13$.

In general, let S be the set of all possible outcomes of a trial (or experiment). Suppose that S is finite and that each of the outcomes is equally likely to occur. Let E denote a subset of S and suppose a certain **event** is said to occur, provided the outcome of the trial belongs to E. Then the **probability** p that the event will occur is defined by

$$p = \frac{\text{number of elements in } E}{\text{number of elements in } S}.$$

Clearly, $0 \leqq p \leqq 1$, and $p = 0$ if and only if E is empty, and $p = 1$ if and only if $E = S$.

In the example given above, S contains 52 elements, since there are 52 cards in a deck, and E contains 4 elements, since there are 4 kings in a deck. The definition yields the same result as previously obtained, namely, $4/52$.

Example 1

The probability that a 3 is obtained on a single throw of a die is $1/6$, for the total number of outcomes of the trial of throwing a die is 6 and only one of these outcomes would result in a 3. Hence, the set S of outcomes contains

6 elements and the subset E corresponding to the event of throwing a 3 contains 1 element.

Example 2

If a ball is drawn at random from a bag containing 3 white and 4 black balls, the probability that the ball drawn is white is $3/7$. The student should supply the reasoning involved in the application of the definition to obtain this result.

Example 3

If 2 balls are drawn simultaneously from the bag in Example 2, let us find the probability that they are both white. Since there are 7 balls altogether in the bag, the total number of different pairs of balls that may be obtained is $C_2^7 = 21$. Thus, the set S of outcomes of the experiment consists of 21 equally likely members. Since there are 3 white balls in the bag, 2 white balls may be selected in $C_2^3 = 3$ different ways. Thus, the number of members in the subset E of outcomes resulting in 2 white balls being drawn is 3. Hence, the probability of drawing 2 white balls is $3/21$ or $1/7$.

The definition of probability given here applies only in situations where the outcomes of an experiment can be regarded as "equally likely." The concept of equally likely is not adequate for a more advanced development of probability theory. In more general situations, the elements of the set S of outcomes of a trial may not be equally likely and are assigned different measures for likelihood of occurrence. In this book we consider only situations in which the possible outcomes of a trial can be counted and are equally likely in the sense that there is no reason to expect one of them to occur in preference to any other one.

If the set S of possible outcomes of a trial contains n elements and the subset E corresponding to an event contains h elements, then the probability p that the event occurs is by our definition

$$p = \frac{h}{n}.$$

The event is said to fail to occur in case the outcome of a trial does not belong to E. The subset F of S corresponding to failure of the event contains $n - h$ elements, and thus the probability q that the event fails to occur is

$$q = \frac{n-h}{n}.$$

Then,

$$p + q = \frac{h}{n} + \frac{n-h}{n} = \frac{n}{n} = 1.$$

Thus, the sum of the probability that an event will occur and the probability that it will fail is 1.

If the probability that an event will happen is 1, then $h = n$, and the event is certain to occur. If the probability of occurrence is 0, then $h = 0$, and the event cannot occur.

These last two remarks are not necessarily true in situations involving probability where the set of outcomes of an experiment is infinite.

Example 4

Two cards are drawn at random from a deck of 52. Let us find the probability that both are not of the same suit. The total number of different pairs of cards that can be drawn is $C_2^{52} = 1326$. There are four suits of 13 cards each, so that the number of different pairs in which the two cards are of the same suit is $4 \cdot C_2^{13} = 312$. Thus, the set S of outcomes of the experiment contains 1326 members, of which 312 correspond to the occurrence of the event of drawing two cards of the same suit. Hence, the probability of drawing two cards of the same suit is $312/1326$ or $4/17$. Therefore, the probability that the two cards drawn are not of the same suit is $1 - 4/17 = 13/17$.

The approach to probability given here reflects the fact that the subject had its beginning in the study of games of chance. But the subject has now come to be of utmost importance in many fields of human welfare such as insurance, medicine, agriculture, quality control in industry, and in many branches of the natural and social sciences. We can give only a brief and somewhat idealized introduction to a few of its most elementary concepts.

13.9 Odds and Expectation

If from a bag containing 3 white balls and 2 black balls a ball is drawn at random, there are 3 outcomes that would result in a white ball being drawn and 2 outcomes in which a white ball would not be drawn. We say that the **odds** in favor of drawing a white ball are 3 to 2.

In general, if a trial has $h+f$ equally likely outcomes, h of which would result in the occurrence of a certain event and f of which would result in the nonoccurrence of the event, we say that the odds are h to f in favor of the event occurring if $h > f$, or that the odds are f to h against the occurrence of the event if $f > h$.

It is easy to see that the odds on an event can be obtained by taking the ratio of the probabilities of the occurrence and nonoccurrence of the event.

Example 1

If two people are selected at random from a group of 10 people containing only three married couples, let us find the odds against the pair being man and wife. The total number of different pairs of people that can be selected is

$C_2^{10} = 45$. Only 3 of these pairs are man and wife. Thus, the odds against the event are 42 to 3 or 14 to 1.

If the probability that an event will occur is p, and if the value to some individual of the occurrence of the event is M, then the **expectation** of that individual is defined to be $\boldsymbol{pM}$.

Example 2

In a raffle of an automobile worth \$2400, a man holds 7 chances out of a total of 3000. Let us find his expectation. The probability that the man will win the automobile is $7/3000$. Hence, his expectation is

$$7/3000(\$2400) = \$5.60.$$

Example 3

In a game of chance a man is to win a stake of \$72 in case he throws a 5 or 8 on a single throw with a pair of dice. Let us find the odds against the man's winning and his expectation.

A 5 may be obtained by throwing 1 and 4, 4 and 1, 2 and 3, 3 and 2. An 8 may be obtained by throwing 2 and 6, 6 and 2, 3 and 5, 5 and 3, 4 and 4. Hence, there are 9 outcomes of the throw which would result in a 5 or 8. There are $6 \cdot 6 = 36$ possible outcomes altogether. Hence, the odds against the man's winning are 27 to 9 or 3 to 1. The probability of his winning is $9/36$ or $1/4$. Therefore, his expectation is $1/4(\$72) = \$18$, which is the fair amount he should pay to play.

Expectation is defined as given in this section because a game conducted in accord with this definition would in the long run practically ensure no loss to the man conducting the game.

EXERCISES

1. A card is drawn at random from a full deck of 52. What is the probability that it is a club?

2. If two coins are tossed simultaneously, find the probability that they will both fall heads up.

3. What is the probability of obtaining a 5 or a 6 on a single throw of a die?

4. What is the probability of obtaining a total of 10 on a single throw with a pair of dice?

5. A bag contains 4 white balls, 3 blue balls, and 7 red balls. A ball is drawn at random.
   (a) What is the probability that it is white?
   (b) What is the probability that it is blue?
   (c) What is the probability that it is either red or blue?

6. Four cards are drawn at random from a deck of 52. Find the probability (a) that they are all hearts, (b) that they are all of the same suit.
7. From a deck of 52 cards, 5 cards are drawn at random. Find the probability that 4 are of the same denomination (that is, 4 aces or 4 kings, etc.).
8. A bag contains 5 white balls and 7 black balls. Three balls are drawn at random. Find the probability that they are all black.
9. Six people are seated at random in a row. Find the probability that two particular people will sit together.
10. The probability of an event happening is $5/8$. What are the odds in favor of it?
11. Odds against an event happening are 7 to 3. What is the probability that it will happen?
12. A man holds 6 lottery tickets out of a total of 2400. The prize is a $2000 automobile. What is his expectation?
13. A man is to draw two tickets at random from a hat containing ten tickets numbered 1, 3, · · ·, 10. If the sum of the numbers on the two tickets he draws is an even number, he will win $18. Find his expectation.
14. In a certain well-known game of chance, a man finds himself in the position of desiring to throw an 8 with a pair of dice before he throws a 7. Compare the respective probabilities of these two events on his first throw.
15. A man will win a prize of $432 if he obtains a total of 6 on a single throw of three dice. Find the odds against his winning, the probability that he will win, and his expectation.
16. In a game of dice a man wins on his first throw of two dice if he gets a 7 or 11. Find the odds against his winning on the first throw, the probability that he will win on this throw, and his expectation on this throw if the stake is $2.25.
17. A secretary writes 3 letters and addresses the corresponding envelopes. She then absent-mindedly places the letters in the envelopes at random. (a) What is the probability that each letter is in its proper envelope? (b) What is the probability that no letter is in the proper envelope?
18. A bag contains 6 white balls and 9 black balls. If 5 balls are drawn at random from the bag, what is the probability that 3 will be white and 2 black?
19. There are 250 tickets in a lottery, of which 3 are winners. If a man holds 2 tickets, what is his probability of winning something?
20. Six pennies are tossed at random. What is the probability that 3 fall heads and the other 3 tails?
21. Three brothers are in a group of ten draftees, 5 of whom are to be assigned by lot to the army and 5 to the navy. Find the probability that the three brothers will be assigned to the same branch of the service.

13.10 Independent Events

Let us consider two experiments: tossing a die and pitching a penny. Associate with the first experiment the event of having the die fall with an even-numbered face up, and associate with the second experiment the event of having the penny fall heads up. These two events are independent in the sense that the occurrence of one does not influence the occurrence of the other. Now let us consider the two experiments as a single *compound* experiment and the two events as a single *compound* event. We ask for the probability of the occurrence of the compound event, that is, the occurrence of *both* separate events comprising the compound event.

The set S of outcomes of the compound experiment can be enumerated as follows:

$$S = \{(1,\mathrm{H}),(1,\mathrm{T}),(2,\mathrm{H}),(2,\mathrm{T}),(3,\mathrm{H}),(3,\mathrm{T}),(4,\mathrm{H}),(4,\mathrm{T}),(5,\mathrm{H}),(5,\mathrm{T}),(6,\mathrm{H}),(6,\mathrm{T})\},$$

where the first member of each ordered pair denotes an outcome for the toss of the die and the second member denotes an outcome for the pitch of the penny. Each of these outcomes is equally likely, a fact we can regard as a fundamental property of independent events. The subset E of S corresponding to the occurrence of the compound event of obtaining an even number on the toss of the die and a head on the pitch of the penny is

$$E = \{(2, \mathrm{H}), (4, \mathrm{H}), (6, \mathrm{H})\}.$$

Thus, since S contains 12 elements and E contains 3 elements, the probability p of the occurrence of this compound event is $p = 3/12$. But we may write this result in the form

$$p = 3/6 \cdot 1/2,$$

and $3/6$ is the probability of obtaining an even number on the die and $1/2$ is the probability of obtaining a head with the penny. Thus, the probability that *both* independent events will occur is the product of their respective probabilities.

We have here an illustration of the following theorem.

▶ THEOREM 1. *If for two independent events the probability of the occurrence of the first is* p_1 *and the probability of the occurrence of the second is* p_2, *then the probability that both will occur is* $p_1 \cdot p_2$.

The proof of this theorem follows the line of reasoning employed in the illustration given above. Let the first event be associated with an experiment, with b_1 equally likely outcomes of which a_1 correspond to the occurrence of the first event. Let the second event be associated with an experiment, with

b_2 equally likely outcomes of which a_2 correspond to the occurrence of the second event. The respective probabilities of the occurrence of the two events are

$$p_1 = \frac{a_1}{b_1} \quad \text{and} \quad p_2 = \frac{a_2}{b_2}.$$

The set S of outcomes for the compound experiment consisting of the two experiments mentioned above has b_1b_2 equally likely members, of which a_1a_2 correspond to the occurrence of the compound event consisting of the two separate events mentioned above. Thus, the probability p of the occurrence of this compound event is

$$p = \frac{a_1a_2}{b_1b_2} = \frac{a_1}{b_1}\frac{a_2}{b_2} = p_1 \cdot p_2.$$

In more complex situations it may not be clear as to whether two events are independent or not. Indeed, the concept as we have described it is, strictly speaking, not a mathematical concept. In a more general development of probability, the property stated in Theorem 1 is taken as a *definition* of independence of two events.

Note: The set S of outcomes for the compound experiment is the Cartesian product $A \times B$ of the sets A and B of outcomes of the two experiments comprising the compound experiment. (Recall the definition of Cartesian product given in Section 1.2.)

Theorem 1 can be generalized to cover any finite number of independent events. Thus, if the probabilities of the individual occurrence of a set of independent events are $p_1, p_2, p_3, \cdots, p_r$, then the probability that they will all occur is $p_1 \cdot p_2 \cdot p_3 \cdots p_r$. This generalization is easily proved by mathematical induction. A special case of this occurs when the events consist of repetitions of the same event. Thus, if the probability of an event happening on one trial is p, the probability that it will happen r times in r trials is p^r.

Example 1

A bag contains 3 red, 4 green, and 5 blue balls. Three balls are drawn in succession and after each ball is drawn it is replaced in the bag. What is the probability that the three balls drawn are red, green, and blue *in that order?*

SOLUTION: Since the ball drawn is replaced after each drawing, the three events of drawing a red ball first, a green ball second, and a blue ball third are independent. Since on any drawing the probability of drawing a red ball is $3/12$, a green ball is $4/12$, and a blue ball is $5/12$, the probability of these three events taking place in the order named on three consecutive drawings is

$$p = 3/12 \cdot 4/12 \cdot 5/12 = 5/144.$$

Example 2

What is the probability of throwing heads on all 5 consecutive tosses of a coin?

SOLUTION: The probability of throwing heads on one toss of a coin is $1/2$. Hence, the probability of throwing heads on 5 consecutive tosses is $(1/2)^5$, or $1/32$.

Example 3

What is the probability of obtaining a 6 at least once on 3 consecutive throws of a die?

SOLUTION: This event will happen unless all 3 throws result in numbers different from 6. The probability of *not* throwing a 6 in a single throw is $5/6$. Hence, the probability of not throwing a 6 in 3 consecutive throws is $(5/6)^3$, or $125/216$. Since the probability of the failure of our event is $125/216$, the probability of its success is $1 - 125/216 = 91/216$.

13.11 Dependent Events

From a bag containing 3 white balls and 5 black balls, one ball is drawn at random and then a second ball is drawn at random. Let us find the probability that the first ball is white and the second ball black. These events are **dependent** as the occurrence of the first event affects the occurrence of the second.

The probability of drawing a white ball on the first draw is $p_1 = 3/8$. Now consider the experiment of drawing a ball from the bag, assuming that a white ball has already been drawn. There are 7 possible equally likely outcomes, of which 5 correspond to the event of drawing a black ball. Hence, the probability of drawing a black ball on the second draw (assuming that a white ball was obtained on the first draw) is $p_2 = 5/7$.

The compound experiment consisting of drawing a ball from the original bag and then drawing a ball from this bag with one white ball removed has $8 \cdot 7$ equally likely outcomes, of which $3 \cdot 5$ correspond to the compound event of drawing a white ball on the first draw and a black ball on the second. Thus, the probability p of the occurrence of this compound event is

$$p = \frac{3 \cdot 5}{8 \cdot 7} = \frac{3}{8} \cdot \frac{5}{7} = p_1 \cdot p_2.$$

This example illustrates the following theorem.

▶ THEOREM 2. *If the probability of the occurrence of one event is p_1, and if after this event has occurred the probability of the occurrence of a second event is p_2, then the probability of the occurrence of both events in the order named is $p_1 \cdot p_2$.*

The proof of this theorem follows the pattern of the example given above and is left to the reader. The theorem generalizes to more than two events, where the probability used for the occurrence of any event in a sequence is based on the supposition that the preceding events in the sequence have actually occurred.

13.12 Mutually Exclusive Events

Two events are called *mutually exclusive* if the occurrence of one of them means that the other one cannot occur. Thus, on a single throw of two dice, obtaining a total of 3 and obtaining a total of 9 are mutually exclusive events, for if one event occurs, the other is precluded from occurring. Now the set S of equally likely outcomes of the experiment of throwing the two dice contains 36 members. The subset E_1 of these outcomes yielding a total of 3 contains 2 elements. For a 3 is obtained if either die falls with 1 up and the other with 2 up, and thus a total of 3 can be obtained in two ways. Similarly, the subset E_2 of outcomes yielding a total of 9 can be seen to contain 4 members. Now the event of obtaining a 3 *or* a 9 occurs if the outcome belongs to the union $E_1 \cup E_2$. Since E_1 and E_2 have no members in common, the number of elements in the union is the sum of the numbers of elements in the separate sets, namely, $2 + 4$. Hence, the probability p that either a 3 or a 9 is obtained is

$$p = \frac{2+4}{36} = \frac{2}{36} + \frac{4}{36}.$$

But $2/36$ is the probability of throwing a 3 and $4/36$ is the probability of throwing a 9. Thus, in this example, the probability of the occurrence of one or the other of the two mutually exclusive events is the sum of the respective probabilities of the occurrence of the individual events.

Now, in general, suppose that A and B are mutually exclusive events associated with an experiment whose set S of equally likely outcomes contains n elements. Let a denote the number of elements in the subset E_1 of these outcomes corresponding to the occurrence of event A, and let b denote the number of elements in the subset E_2 of outcomes corresponding to the occurrence of event B. The subset that corresponds to the occurrence of A or B is the union $E_1 \cup E_2$. This set contains $a + b$ members, since E_1 and E_2 contain no members in common. Hence, the probability p of the occurrence of A or B is

$$p = \frac{a+b}{n} = \frac{a}{n} + \frac{b}{n}.$$

But a/n is the probability p_1 that A will occur and b/n is the probability p_2 that B will occur. Hence,

$$p = p_1 + p_2.$$

Thus, we have the following theorem.

▶ THEOREM 3. *If A and B are two mutually exclusive events whose respective probabilities of occurrence are p_1 and p_2, then the probability p that one or the other of the events will occur is the sum of their respective probabilities. That is,* $p = p_1 + p_2$.

The statement and proof of this theorem may be easily generalized to apply to more than two events. Thus, if $A_1, A_2, A_3, \cdots, A_n$ are mutually exclusive events whose respective probabilities of occurrence are $p_1, p_2, p_3, \cdots, p_r$, then the probability p that some one of these events will occur is given by

$$p = p_1 + p_2 + p_3 + \cdots + p_r.$$

If a certain event can happen in several different kinds of ways, and these kinds of ways are mutually exclusive, then the event happening in the first kind of way, the event happening in the second kind of way, etc., may be thought of as mutually exclusive events. An adaptation of the generalization of Theorem 3 to this situation yields the following.

▶ THEOREM 4. *If the probability of an event happening in one manner is p_1, the probability of its happening in a second manner is p_2, etc., and if these different manners of occurrence are mutually exclusive, then the probability p that the event will occur is*

$$p = p_1 + p_2 + \cdots.$$

Example

One purse contains 3 nickels, 2 dimes, 4 quarters, and 3 half-dollars. A second purse contains 2 nickels, 5 dimes, 3 quarters, and 1 half-dollar. One purse is selected at random and from that purse a coin is drawn at random. What is the probability that it is a quarter?

SOLUTION: The event of obtaining a quarter can materialize in two mutually exclusive manners—namely, by drawing it from the first purse or by drawing it from the second purse. The probability of selecting the first purse is $1/2$, and if the first purse is selected, then the probability that the coin drawn from it is a quarter is $4/12$. Then, by Theorem 2, the probability of selecting the first purse and then drawing a quarter from it is $1/2 \cdot 4/12 = 1/6$. Similarly, the probability of selecting the second purse and then drawing a quarter from it is $1/2 \cdot 3/11 = 3/22$. Hence, by Theorem 4, the probability of obtaining a quarter is

$$p = 1/6 + 3/22 = 20/66 = 10/33.$$

EXERCISES

1. Find the probability of obtaining a 7 on each of two successive throws of two dice.

2. A bag contains 3 white balls and 7 black balls. Two balls are drawn in succession from the bag. Find the probability that both are white (a) if the first ball is replaced before the second is drawn; (b) if the first ball is not replaced.
3. A bag contains 4 blue balls and 5 red balls. A ball is drawn at random, replaced, and a second ball is drawn. (a) Find the probability that the first ball drawn is blue and the second red. (b) Find the probability that the two balls drawn are of different colors.
4. What is the probability of throwing a deuce on the first only of two successive throws of a single die?
5. A coin is tossed 3 times in succession. What is the probability of obtaining 3 heads? At least 1 head?
6. A man holds 5 tickets on a lottery in which there are 100 tickets with one winner, and he will win in another game of chance if a wheel stops in a certain one of 25 equally likely positions. Find the probability (a) that he will win in both cases; (b) that he will lose in both cases; (c) that he will win in at least one case.
7. Each of 2 safes has 3 compartments. A document is in a compartment of one of the safes. One of the 2 safes is chosen at random and one of its compartments opened at random. What is the probability that it contains the document?
8. A man places bets on two horses in the same race. Assuming their respective probabilities of winning are $2/7$ and $3/25$, and neglecting the possibility of a tie, find the probability that one of the two horses will win.
9. In a certain horse race the odds against Arrat are 7 to 1 and against Canopus are 12 to 5. What is the probability that one of these two horses will win?
10. A hat contains 11 tickets numbered 1 to 11. Two tickets are drawn in succession. Find the probability that the first number drawn is even and the second one odd.
11. One urn contains 2 white balls and 3 blue balls. A second urn contains 3 white balls and 3 black balls. A ball is drawn at random from the first urn and placed in the second. Then a ball is drawn from the second urn. What is the probability that both balls drawn are white?
12. The odds in favor of A winning his match are 3 to 2 and the odds against B winning another match are 4 to 3. Find the probability (a) that both will win; (b) that both will lose; (c) that A will win and B lose.
13. A and B "match" coins to see who "matches" C for the privilege of paying for the drinks. Find their respective chances of securing this privilege.
14. An objective-type test consists of 10 questions, alongside each of which are listed 5 possible answers, only one of which is correct. The student is to select the correct answer. An ignorant student selects the answers at random.

What is the probability (a) that he answers the first two correctly; (b) that he fails to answer any of them correctly?

15. Four cards are drawn at random from an ordinary deck. Find the probability that (a) they are all spades; (b) they are all of the same suit; (c) they are a spade, a heart, a diamond, and a club in that order; (d) they are all of different suits.

16. The probability that one student can solve a problem is $2/3$ and the probability that another student can solve it is $3/5$. If both students try, what is the probability that the problem will be solved? *Hint:* The problem will be solved unless both boys fail.

17. One group of children consists of 5 boys and 3 girls. Another group consists of 4 boys and 4 girls. (a) One child is chosen by lot from each group. What is the probability that both are boys? (b) One of the groups is selected at random and from that group a child is selected at random. Find the probability that it is a boy.

18. One of two automobiles standing in front of a house has the key in the ignition, and the other one has the ignition locked. The key to the second automobile is one of three lying on a table. A man selects one of the three keys at random and then enters one of the two automobiles at random. What is the probability that he can drive off?

19. A beginner at golf has a probability of $1/2$ of getting a good shot if he uses the correct club and a probability of $1/4$ if he uses an incorrect club. If he chooses a club at random from 5 different clubs in his bag and takes a stroke, find the probability that he gets a good shot, assuming that only one club in his bag is the correct one for the shot in question.

20. A bag contains 3 white balls and 4 black balls. A man draws a ball at random and lays it aside without observing its color. Then a second ball is drawn. Under these circumstances, show that the probability of the second ball being black is the same as the probability of drawing a black ball on the first draw.

21. A punchboard contains four $1.00 prizes, two $5.00 prizes, one $10.00 prize, and 43 blanks. What is the value of the expectation on a single punch?

22. *A*, *B*, and *C* are playing a game in which the first person to draw a white ball from a bag containing 2 white balls and 3 black balls wins. If the drawing is in the order *A*, *B*, *C*, and is to continue until a white ball is drawn, what are their respective probabilities of winning?

23. An urn contains 3 white balls and 4 black balls. A second urn contains 2 white balls and 3 black balls. A man draws a ball at random from the first urn and, without observing its color, places it in the second urn. He then draws a ball at random from the second urn. What is the probability that the ball drawn from the second urn is white?

13.13 Repeated Trials

Suppose a single die is thrown five times in succession. What is the probability that a deuce will be obtained on exactly three of these throws? In order for this event to take place, a deuce must turn up on some three throws and fail to turn up on the remaining two. On any particular throw the probability p of obtaining a deuce is $\frac{1}{6}$ and the probability q of failing to obtain a deuce is $\frac{5}{6}$. Now, if we specify the *particular* throws for obtaining a deuce, such as the odd-numbered ones, the probability of the event happening in this way is, by the generalization of Theorem 1, $(\frac{1}{6})^3(\frac{5}{6})^2$. But there are C_3^5 ways in which the particular throws for obtaining a deuce can be specified. These C_3^5 different selections give rise to C_3^5 mutually exclusive ways in which the event we are considering can occur, and the probability for each of these ways is $(\frac{1}{6})^3(\frac{5}{6})^2$. Hence, by Theorem 4, the probability that exactly three of the five throws will result in deuces is $C_3^5(\frac{1}{6})^3(\frac{5}{6})^2$, or $\frac{125}{3888}$. This is an illustration of the following theorem.

▶ THEOREM 5. *If the probability of an event's occurring on any single trial is p and the probability of its failing is q, then in a set of n trials the probability that the event will occur exactly r times and fail to occur the remaining n − r times is* $C_r^n p^r q^{n-r}$.

The proof of this theorem follows exactly the same line of reasoning employed in the example given and is left for the student to supply.

Example 1

A card is drawn at random from a full deck and replaced, after which the deck is reshuffled. This process is repeated until 8 cards have been drawn. What is the probability that exactly 5 of them are spades?

SOLUTION: On any one trial the probability of drawing a spade is $\frac{1}{4}$ and the probability of failing to draw a spade is $\frac{3}{4}$. Hence, by Theorem 5, the probability of drawing exactly 5 spades in 8 trials is

$$C_5^8(\tfrac{1}{4})^5(\tfrac{3}{4})^3 = \tfrac{189}{8192}.$$

Referring to the form of the binomial formula stated in Section 13.7 and using the fact $C_r^n = C_{n-r}^n$, proved in Exercise 20 of Section 13.7, we may write the first $n - r + 1$ terms in the expansion of $(p + q)^n$ as follows, where p and q have the same meaning as in Theorem 5:

$$(p + q)^n = p^n + C_{n-1}^n p^{n-1}q + C_{n-2}^n p^{n-2}q^2 + \cdots + C_r^n p^r q^{n-r} + \cdots.$$

The successive terms of this expansion represent respectively the probabilities that the event will occur exactly n times, $n - 1$ times, and so on down to r times, all based on n trials. Hence, the sum of these $n - r + 1$ terms is the probability that the event will occur *at least r* times on n trials.

Example 2

If a coin is tossed 7 times, what is the probability that it will fall heads at least 4 times?

SOLUTION: Here $p = q = \frac{1}{2}$, $n = 7$, and $r = 4$. Hence, the sum of the first four terms in the expansion of $(\frac{1}{2} + \frac{1}{2})^7$ is the probability we seek. Thus, we have

$$p = (\tfrac{1}{2})^7 + 7(\tfrac{1}{2})^6(\tfrac{1}{2}) + 21(\tfrac{1}{2})^5(\tfrac{1}{2})^2 + 35(\tfrac{1}{2})^4(\tfrac{1}{2})^3 = \tfrac{1}{2}.$$

13.14 Statistical or Empirical Probability

Many events, such as the death of a given individual within the next ten years, the theft of an automobile, or the burning of a house within the next year, cannot be analyzed in the manner necessary for the application of the definition given for probability in Section 13.8. It is manifestly impossible to enumerate an exhaustive set of equally likely ways in which such events can happen or fail to happen. Another approach to the problem of getting a measure of the likelihood of the occurrence of such an event is through the concept of **statistical** or **empirical** probability. This measure of probability is based upon data obtained by observing a large number of specific cases. The concept may be approximately described as follows.

If for a sufficiently large number of cases N an event E has happened in m of the cases, the ratio m/N, called the **relative frequency,** may be taken as a measure of the probability that E will happen in a specific case of the kind studied, provided the circumstances are similar.

This statement obviously lacks precision. For example, what is meant by the expression "sufficiently large"? In general, we may say that the larger the number of cases included in the statistical data, the more confidence we should have in using the relative frequency as a measure of probability in a particular case.

The American Experience Mortality Table, compiled in 1860 and used by insurance companies until replaced recently by a more up-to-date table, is a classic example of statistical data used to compute probability. Based on the study of 100,000 individuals alive at age 10, the table lists the number alive at the end of each year thereafter. These data can be used to compute the probability that an individual of a given age will live to reach another specified age. It is clear that reasonably accurate calculations of such probabilities are absolutely essential for the operation of insurance companies.

EXERCISES

1. Five integers are chosen at random. What is the probability that exactly 4 of them are even?
2. A coin is tossed 10 times in succession. What is the probability of obtaining exactly 7 heads? At least 7 heads?
3. A die is thrown 4 times in succession. What is the probability of obtaining a 6 on exactly 2 of the throws? On at least 2 of the throws?
4. From a bag containing 2 white balls and 3 black balls, a ball is drawn and replaced in the bag. This operation is performed 6 times. Find the probability that on exactly 4 of the drawings the ball drawn is white.
5. A wheel used in a gambling game can stop in 18 equally likely positions numbered 1 to 18. A customer places bets on all the positions divisible by 3. What is the probability that he will win exactly 3 times on 8 whirls of the wheel?
6. What is the probability of obtaining 7 at least 4 times on 5 throws of two dice?
7. Eight coins are tossed simultaneously. What is the probability that at least half of them will fall heads?
8. Of two tennis players, A and B, the odds in favor of A's winning any given set from B are 2 to 1. Find the probability that out of 5 sets played, A will win (a) exactly 3 sets; (b) at least 3 sets.
9. A student can solve, on the average, one-half of the problems given him. He is required to solve 5 out of 7 problems on an examination to pass. What are his chances of passing?
10. In a certain battle area, an average of 1 out of every 10 airplanes sent on combat missions was lost. Of a group of 5 planes sent out, what is the probability that at least 4 will return safely?
11. A, B, and C in the order named are allowed one throw each with a pair of dice. The first one, if any, who throws a 7 gets $216. Find the expectation of each.
12. One urn contains 4 white balls and 1 black ball. A second urn contains 2 white balls. Three balls are drawn at random from the first urn and placed in the second, and then 4 balls are drawn at random from the second and placed in the first. Find the probability that the black ball is in the first urn after this operation is complete.
13. Write out a proof of Theorem 5.

Tables

TABLE I. POWERS—ROOTS—RECIPROCALS. 1–100

n	n^2	n^3	$\sqrt{n}$	$\sqrt[3]{n}$	$1/n$
1	1	1	1.000	1.000	1.0000
2	4	8	1.414	1.260	.5000
3	9	27	1.732	1.442	.3333
4	16	64	2.000	1.587	.2500
5	25	125	2.236	1.710	.2000
6	36	216	2.449	1.817	.1667
7	49	343	2.646	1.913	.1429
8	64	512	2.828	2.000	.1250
9	81	729	3.000	2.080	.1111
10	100	1,000	3.162	2.154	.1000
11	121	1,331	3.317	2.224	.0909
12	144	1,728	3.464	2.289	.0833
13	169	2,197	3.606	2.351	.0769
14	196	2,744	3.742	2.410	.0714
15	225	3,375	3.873	2.466	.0667
16	256	4,096	4.000	2.520	.0625
17	289	4,913	4.123	2.571	.0588
18	324	5,832	4.243	2.621	.0556
19	361	6,859	4.359	2.668	.0526
20	400	8,000	4.472	2.714	.0500
21	441	9,261	4.583	2.759	.0476
22	484	10,648	4.690	2.802	.0455
23	529	12,167	4.796	2.844	.0435
24	576	13,824	4.899	2.884	.0417
25	625	15,625	5.000	2.924	.0400
26	676	17,576	5.099	2.962	.0385
27	729	19,683	5.196	3.000	.0370
28	784	21,952	5.292	3.037	.0357
29	841	24,389	5.385	3.072	.0345
30	900	27,000	5.477	3.107	.0333
31	961	29,791	5.568	3.141	.0323
32	1,024	32,768	5.657	3.175	.0312
33	1,089	35,937	5.745	3.208	.0303
34	1,156	39,304	5.831	3.240	.0294
35	1,225	42,875	5.916	3.271	.0286
36	1,296	46,656	6.000	3.302	.0278
37	1,369	50,653	6.083	3.332	.0270
38	1,444	54,872	6.164	3.362	.0263
39	1,521	59,319	6.245	3.391	.0256
40	1,600	64,000	6.325	3.420	.0250
41	1,681	68,921	6.403	3.448	.0244
42	1,764	74,088	6.481	3.476	.0238
43	1,849	79,507	6.557	3.503	.0233
44	1,936	85,184	6.633	3.530	.0227
45	2,025	91,125	6.708	3.557	.0222
46	2,116	97,336	6.782	3.583	.0217
47	2,209	103,823	6.856	3.609	.0213
48	2,304	110,592	6.928	3.634	.0208
49	2,401	117,649	7.000	3.659	.0204
50	2,500	125,000	7.071	3.684	.0200
51	2,601	132,651	7.141	3.708	.0196
52	2,704	140,608	7.211	3.733	.0192
53	2,809	148,877	7.280	3.756	.0189
54	2,916	157,464	7.348	3.780	.0185
55	3,025	166,375	7.416	3.803	.0182
56	3,136	175,616	7.483	3.826	.0179
57	3,249	185,193	7.550	3.849	.0175
58	3,364	195,112	7.616	3.871	.0172
59	3,481	205,379	7.681	3.893	.0169
60	3,600	216,000	7.746	3.915	.0167
61	3,721	226,981	7.810	3.936	.0164
62	3,844	238,328	7.874	3.958	.0161
63	3,969	250,047	7.937	3.979	.0159
64	4,096	262,144	8.000	4.000	.0156
65	4,225	274,625	8.062	4.021	.0154
66	4,356	287,496	8.124	4.041	.0152
67	4,489	300,763	8.185	4.062	.0149
68	4,624	314,432	8.246	4.082	.0147
69	4,761	328,509	8.307	4.102	.0145
70	4,900	343,000	8.367	4.121	.0143
71	5,041	357,911	8.426	4.141	.0141
72	5,184	373,248	8.485	4.160	.0139
73	5,329	389,017	8.544	4.179	.0137
74	5,476	405,224	8.602	4.198	.0135
75	5,625	421,875	8.660	4.217	.0133
76	5,776	438,976	8.718	4.236	.0132
77	5,929	456,533	8.775	4.254	.0130
78	6,084	474,552	8.832	4.273	.0128
79	6,241	493,039	8.888	4.291	.0127
80	6,400	512,000	8.944	4.309	.0125
81	6,561	531,441	9.000	4.327	.0123
82	6,724	551,368	9.055	4.344	.0122
83	6,889	571,787	9.110	4.362	.0120
84	7,056	592,704	9.165	4.380	.0119
85	7,225	614,125	9.220	4.397	.0118
86	7,396	636,056	9.274	4.414	.0116
87	7,569	658,503	9.327	4.431	.0115
88	7,744	681,472	9.381	4.448	.0114
89	7,921	704,969	9.434	4.465	.0112
90	8,100	729,000	9.487	4.481	.0111
91	8,281	753,571	9.539	4.498	.0110
92	8,464	778,688	9.592	4.514	.0109
93	8,649	804,357	9.644	4.531	.0108
94	8,836	830,584	9.695	4.547	.0106
95	9,025	857,375	9.747	4.563	.0105
96	9,216	884,736	9.798	4.579	.0104
97	9,409	912,673	9.849	4.595	.0103
98	9,604	941,192	9.899	4.610	.0102
99	9,801	970,299	9.950	4.626	.0101
100	10,000	1,000,000	10.000	4.642	.0100

TABLE II. VALUES OF FUNCTIONS AND RADIANS

Degrees	Radians	Sin	Csc	Tan	Cot	Sec	Cos		
0° 0′	.0000	.0000	——	.0000	——	1.000	1.0000	1.5708	90° 0′
10′	029	029	343.8	029	343.8	000	000	679	50′
20′	058	058	171.9	058	171.9	000	000	650	40′
30′	.0087	.0087	114.6	.0087	114.6	1.000	1.0000	1.5621	30′
40′	116	116	85.95	116	85.94	000	.9999	592	20′
50′	145	145	68.76	145	68.75	000	999	563	10′
1° 0′	.0175	.0175	57.30	.0175	57.29	1.000	.9998	1.5533	89° 0′
10′	204	204	49.11	204	49.10	000	998	504	50′
20′	233	233	42.98	233	42.96	000	997	475	40′
30′	.0262	.0262	38.20	.0262	38.19	1.000	.9997	1.5446	30′
40′	291	291	34.38	291	34.37	000	996	417	20′
50′	320	320	31.26	320	31.24	001	995	388	10′
2° 0′	.0349	.0349	28.65	.0349	28.64	1.001	.9994	1.5359	88° 0′
10′	378	378	26.45	378	26.43	001	993	330	50′
20′	407	407	24.56	407	24.54	001	992	301	40′
30′	.0436	.0436	22.93	.0437	22.90	1.001	.9990	1.5272	30′
40′	465	465	21.49	466	21.47	001	989	243	20′
50′	495	494	20.23	495	20.21	001	988	213	10′
3° 0′	.0524	.0523	19.11	.0524	19.08	1.001	.9986	1.5184	87° 0′
10′	553	552	18.10	553	18.07	002	985	155	50′
20′	582	581	17.20	582	17.17	002	983	126	40′
30′	.0611	.0610	16.38	.0612	16.35	1.002	.9981	1.5097	30′
40′	640	640	15.64	641	15.60	002	980	068	20′
50′	669	669	14.96	670	14.92	002	978	039	10′
4° 0′	.0698	.0698	14.34	.0699	14.30	1.002	.9976	1.5010	86° 0′
10′	727	727	13.76	729	13.73	003	974	981	50′
20′	756	756	13.23	758	13.20	003	971	952	40′
30′	.0785	.0785	12.75	.0787	12.71	1.003	.9969	1.4923	30′
40′	814	814	12.29	816	12.25	003	967	893	20′
50′	844	843	11.87	846	11.83	004	964	864	10′
5° 0′	.0873	.0872	11.47	.0875	11.43	1.004	.9962	1.4835	85° 0′
10′	902	901	11.10	904	11.06	004	959	806	50′
20′	931	929	10.76	934	10.71	004	957	777	40′
30′	.0960	.0958	10.43	.0963	10.39	1.005	.9954	1.4748	30′
40′	989	987	10.13	992	10.08	005	951	719	20′
50′	.1018	.1016	9.839	.1022	9.788	005	948	690	10′
6° 0′	.1047	.1045	9.567	.1051	9.514	1.006	.9945	1.4661	84° 0′
10′	076	074	9.309	080	9.255	006	942	632	50′
20′	105	103	9.065	110	9.010	006	939	603	40′
30′	.1134	.1132	8.834	.1139	8.777	1.006	.9936	1.4573	30′
40′	164	161	8.614	169	8.556	007	932	544	20′
50′	193	190	8.405	198	8.345	007	929	515	10′
7° 0′	.1222	.1219	8.206	.1228	8.144	1.008	.9925	1.4486	83° 0′
10′	251	248	8.016	257	7.953	008	922	457	50′
20′	280	276	7.834	287	7.770	008	918	428	40′
30′	.1309	.1305	7.661	.1317	7.596	1.009	.9914	1.4399	30′
40′	338	334	7.496	346	7.429	009	911	370	20′
50′	367	363	7.337	376	7.269	009	907	341	10′
8° 0′	.1396	.1392	7.185	.1405	7.115	1.010	.9903	1.4312	82° 0′
10′	425	421	7.040	435	6.968	010	899	283	50′
20′	454	449	6.900	465	6.827	011	894	254	40′
30′	.1484	.1478	6.765	.1495	6.691	1.011	.9890	1.4224	30′
40′	513	507	6.636	524	6.561	012	886	195	20′
50′	542	536	6.512	554	6.435	012	881	166	10′
9° 0′	.1571	.1564	6.392	.1584	6.314	1.012	.9877	1.4137	81° 0′
		Cos	Sec	Cot	Tan	Csc	Sin	Radians	Degrees

TABLE II. VALUES OF FUNCTIONS AND RADIANS (*Cont.*)

Degrees	Radians	Sin	Csc	Tan	Cot	Sec	Cos		
9° 0′	.1571	.1564	6.392	.1584	6.314	1.012	.9877	1.4137	81° 0′
10′	600	593	277	614	197	013	872	108	50′
20′	629	622	166	644	6.084	013	868	079	40′
30′	.1658	.1650	6.059	.1673	5.976	1.014	.9863	1.4050	30′
40′	687	679	5.955	703	871	014	858	1.4021	20′
50′	716	708	855	733	769	015	853	1.3992	10′
10° 0′	.1745	.1736	5.759	.1763	5.671	1.015	.9848	1.3963	80° 0′
10′	774	765	665	793	576	016	843	934	50′
20′	804	794	575	823	485	016	838	904	40′
30′	.1833	.1822	5.487	.1853	5.396	1.017	.9833	1.3875	30′
40′	862	851	403	883	309	018	827	846	20′
50′	891	880	320	914	226	018	822	817	10′
11° 0′	.1920	.1908	5.241	.1944	5.145	1.019	.9816	1.3788	79° 0′
10′	949	937	164	.1974	5.066	019	811	759	50′
20′	978	965	089	.2004	4.989	020	805	730	40′
30′	.2007	.1994	5.016	.2035	4.915	1.020	.9799	1.3701	30′
40′	036	.2022	4.945	065	843	021	793	672	20′
50′	065	051	876	095	773	022	787	643	10′
12° 0′	.2094	.2079	4.810	.2126	4.705	1.022	.9781	1.3614	78° 0′
10′	123	108	745	156	638	023	775	584	50′
20′	153	136	682	186	574	024	769	555	40′
30′	.2182	.2164	4.620	.2217	4.511	1.024	.9763	1.3526	30′
40′	211	193	560	247	449	025	757	497	20′
50′	240	221	502	278	390	026	750	468	10′
13° 0′	.2269	.2250	4.445	.2309	4.331	1.026	.9744	1.3439	77° 0′
10′	298	278	390	339	275	027	737	410	50′
20′	327	306	336	370	219	028	730	381	40′
30′	.2356	.2334	4.284	.2401	4.165	1.028	.9724	1.3352	30′
40′	385	363	232	432	113	029	717	323	20′
50′	414	391	182	462	061	030	710	294	10′
14° 0′	.2443	.2419	4.134	.2493	4.011	1.031	.9703	1.3265	76° 0′
10′	473	447	086	524	3.962	031	696	235	50′
20′	502	476	4.039	555	914	032	689	206	40′
30′	.2531	.2504	3.994	.2586	3.867	1.033	.9681	1.3177	30′
40′	560	532	950	617	821	034	674	148	20′
50′	589	560	906	648	776	034	667	119	10′
15° 0′	.2618	.2588	3.864	.2679	3.732	1.035	.9659	1.3090	75° 0′
10′	647	616	822	711	689	036	652	061	50′
20′	676	644	782	742	647	037	644	032	40′
30′	.2705	.2672	3.742	.2773	3.606	1.038	.9636	1.3003	30′
40′	734	700	703	805	566	039	628	1.2974	20′
50′	763	728	665	836	526	039	621	945	10′
16° 0′	.2793	.2756	3.628	.2867	3.487	1.040	.9613	1.2915	74° 0′
10′	822	784	592	899	450	041	605	886	50′
20′	851	812	556	931	412	042	596	857	40′
30′	.2880	.2840	3.521	.2962	3.376	1.043	.9588	1.2828	30′
40′	909	868	487	.2994	340	044	580	799	20′
50′	938	896	453	.3026	305	045	572	770	10′
17° 0′	.2967	.2924	3.420	.3057	3.271	1.046	.9563	1.2741	73° 0′
10′	996	952	388	089	237	047	555	712	50′
20′	.3025	.2979	357	121	204	048	546	683	40′
30′	.3054	.3007	3.326	.3153	3.172	1.048	.9537	1.2654	30′
40′	083	035	295	185	140	049	528	625	20′
50′	113	062	265	217	108	050	520	595	10′
18° 0′	.3142	.3090	3.236	.3249	3.078	1.051	.9511	1.2566	72° 0′
		Cos	Sec	Cot	Tan	Csc	Sin	Radians	Degrees

TABLE II. VALUES OF FUNCTIONS AND RADIANS (*Cont.*)

Degrees	Radians	Sin	Csc	Tan	Cot	Sec	Cos		
18° 0′	.3142	.3090	3.236	.3249	3.078	1.051	.9511	1.2566	**72° 0′**
10′	171	118	207	281	047	052	502	537	50′
20′	200	145	179	314	3.018	053	492	508	40′
30′	.3229	.3173	3.152	.3346	2.989	1.054	.9483	1.2479	30′
40′	258	201	124	378	960	056	474	450	20′
50′	287	228	098	411	932	057	465	421	10′
19° 0′	.3316	.3256	3.072	.3443	2.904	1.058	.9455	1.2392	**71° 0′**
10′	345	283	046	476	877	059	446	363	50′
20′	374	311	3.021	508	850	060	436	334	40′
30′	.3403	.3338	2.996	.3541	2.824	1.061	.9426	1.2305	30′
40′	432	365	971	574	798	062	417	275	20′
50′	462	393	947	607	773	063	407	246	10′
20° 0′	.3491	.3420	2.924	.3640	2.747	1.064	.9397	1.2217	**70° 0′**
10′	520	448	901	673	723	065	387	188	50′
20′	549	475	878	706	699	066	377	159	40′
30′	.3578	.3502	2.855	.3739	2.675	1.068	.9367	1.2130	30′
40′	607	529	833	772	651	069	356	101	20′
50′	636	557	812	805	628	070	346	072	10′
21° 0′	.3665	.3584	2.790	.3839	2.605	1.071	.9336	1.2043	**69° 0′**
10′	694	611	769	872	583	072	325	1.2014	50′
20′	723	638	749	906	560	074	315	1.1985	40′
30′	.3752	.3665	2.729	.3939	2.539	1.075	.9304	1.1956	30′
40′	782	692	709	.3973	517	076	293	926	20′
50′	811	719	689	.4006	496	077	283	897	10′
22° 0′	.3840	.3746	2.669	.4040	2.475	1.079	.9272	1.1868	**68° 0′**
10′	869	773	650	074	455	080	261	839	50′
20′	898	800	632	108	434	081	250	810	40′
30′	.3927	.3827	2.613	.4142	2.414	1.082	.9239	1.1781	30′
40′	956	854	595	176	394	084	228	752	20′
50′	985	881	577	210	375	085	216	723	10′
23° 0′	.4014	.3907	2.559	.4245	2.356	1.086	.9205	1.1694	**67° 0′**
10′	043	934	542	279	337	088	194	665	50′
20′	072	961	525	314	318	089	182	636	40′
30′	.4102	.3987	2.508	.4348	2.300	1.090	.9171	1.1606	30′
40′	131	.4014	491	383	282	092	159	577	20′
50′	160	041	475	417	264	093	147	548	10′
24° 0′	.4189	.4067	2.459	.4452	2.246	1.095	.9135	1.1519	**66° 0′**
10′	218	094	443	487	229	096	124	490	50′
20′	247	120	427	522	211	097	112	461	40′
30′	.4276	.4147	2.411	.4557	2.194	1.099	.9100	1.1432	30′
40′	305	173	396	592	177	100	088	403	20′
50′	334	200	381	628	161	102	075	374	10′
25° 0′	.4363	.4226	2.366	.4663	2.145	1.103	.9063	1.1345	**65° 0′**
10′	392	253	352	699	128	105	051	316	50′
20′	422	279	337	734	112	106	038	286	40′
30′	.4451	.4305	2.323	.4770	2.097	1.108	.9026	1.1257	30′
40′	480	331	309	806	081	109	013	228	20′
50′	509	358	295	841	066	111	.9001	199	10′
26° 0′	.4538	.4384	2.281	.4877	2.050	1.113	.8988	1.1170	**64° 0′**
10′	567	410	268	913	035	114	975	141	50′
20′	596	436	254	950	020	116	962	112	40′
30′	.4625	.4462	2.241	.4986	2.006	1.117	.8949	1.1083	30′
40′	654	488	228	.5022	1.991	119	936	054	20′
50′	683	514	215	059	977	121	923	1.1025	10′
27° 0′	.4712	.4540	2.203	.5095	1.963	1.122	.8910	1.0996	**63° 0′**
		Cos	Sec	Cot	Tan	Csc	Sin	Radians	Degrees

TABLE II. VALUES OF FUNCTIONS AND RADIANS (*Cont.*)

Degrees	Radians	Sin	Csc	Tan	Cot	Sec	Cos		
27° 0′	.4712	.4540	2.203	.5095	1.963	1.122	.8910	1.0996	**63° 0′**
10′	741	566	190	132	949	124	897	966	50′
20′	771	592	178	169	935	126	884	937	40′
30′	.4800	.4617	2.166	.5206	1.921	1.127	.8870	1.0908	30′
40′	829	643	154	243	907	129	857	879	20′
50′	858	669	142	280	894	131	843	850	10′
28° 0′	.4887	.4695	2.130	.5317	1.881	1.133	.8829	1.0821	**62° 0′**
10′	916	720	118	354	868	134	816	792	50′
20′	945	746	107	392	855	136	802	763	40′
30′	.4974	.4772	2.096	.5430	1.842	1.138	.8788	1.0734	30′
40′	.5003	797	085	467	829	140	774	705	20′
50′	032	823	074	505	816	142	760	676	10′
29° 0′	.5061	.4848	2.063	.5543	1.804	1.143	.8746	1.0647	**61° 0′**
10′	091	874	052	581	792	145	732	617	50′
20′	120	899	041	619	780	147	718	588	40′
30′	.5149	.4924	2.031	.5658	1.767	1.149	.8704	1.0559	30′
40′	178	950	020	696	756	151	689	530	20′
50′	207	.4975	010	735	744	153	675	501	10′
30° 0′	.5236	.5000	2.000	.5774	1.732	1.155	.8660	1.0472	**60° 0′**
10′	265	025	1.990	812	720	157	646	443	50′
20′	294	050	980	851	709	159	631	414	40′
30′	.5323	.5075	1.970	.5890	1.698	1.161	.8616	1.0385	30′
40′	352	100	961	930	686	163	601	356	20′
50′	381	125	951	.5969	675	165	587	327	10′
31° 0′	.5411	.5150	1.942	.6009	1.664	1.167	.8572	1.0297	**59° 0′**
10′	440	175	932	048	653	169	557	268	50′
20′	469	200	923	088	643	171	542	239	40′
30′	.5498	.5225	1.914	.6128	1.632	1.173	.8526	1.0210	30′
40′	527	250	905	168	621	175	511	181	20′
50′	556	275	896	208	611	177	496	152	10′
32° 0′	.5585	.5299	1.887	.6249	1.600	1.179	.8480	1.0123	**58° 0′**
10′	614	324	878	289	590	181	465	094	50′
20′	643	348	870	330	580	184	450	065	40′
30′	.5672	.5373	1.861	.6371	1.570	1.186	.8434	1.0036	30′
40′	701	398	853	412	560	188	418	1.0007	20′
50′	730	422	844	453	550	190	403	.9977	10′
33° 0′	.5760	.5446	1.836	.6494	1.540	1.192	.8387	.9948	**57° 0′**
10′	789	471	828	536	530	195	371	919	50′
20′	818	495	820	577	520	197	355	890	40′
30′	.5847	.5519	1.812	.6619	1.511	1.199	.8339	.9861	30′
40′	876	544	804	661	501	202	323	832	20′
50′	905	568	796	703	1.492	204	307	803	10′
34° 0′	.5934	.5592	1.788	.6745	1.483	1.206	.8290	.9774	**56° 0′**
10′	963	616	781	787	473	209	274	745	50′
20′	992	640	773	830	464	211	258	716	40′
30′	.6021	.5664	1.766	.6873	1.455	1.213	.8241	.9687	30′
40′	050	688	758	916	446	216	225	657	20′
50′	080	712	751	.6959	437	218	208	628	10′
35° 0′	.6109	.5736	1.743	.7002	1.428	1.221	.8192	.9599	**55° 0′**
10′	138	760	736	046	419	223	175	570	50′
20′	167	783	729	089	411	226	158	541	40′
30′	.6196	.5807	1.722	.7133	1.402	1.228	.8141	.9512	30′
40′	225	831	715	177	393	231	124	483	20′
50′	254	854	708	221	385	233	107	454	10′
36° 0′	.6283	.5878	1.701	.7265	1.376	1.236	.8090	.9425	**54° 0′**
		Cos	Sec	Cot	Tan	Csc	Sin	Radians	Degrees

TABLE II. VALUES OF FUNCTIONS AND RADIANS (*Cont.*)

Degrees	Radians	Sin	Csc	Tan	Cot	Sec	Cos		
36° 0′	.6283	.5878	1.701	.7265	1.376	1.236	.8090	.9425	**54° 0′**
10′	312	901	695	310	368	239	073	396	50′
20′	341	925	688	355	360	241	056	367	40′
30′	.6370	.5948	1.681	.7400	1.351	1.244	.8039	.9338	30′
40′	400	972	675	445	343	247	021	308	20′
50′	429	.5995	668	490	335	249	.8004	279	10′
37° 0′	.6458	.6018	1.662	.7536	1.327	1.252	.7986	.9250	**53° 0′**
10′	487	041	655	581	319	255	969	221	50′
20′	516	065	649	627	311	258	951	192	40′
30′	.6545	.6088	1.643	.7673	1.303	1.260	.7934	.9163	30′
40′	574	111	636	720	295	263	916	134	20′
50′	603	134	630	766	288	266	898	105	10′
38° 0′	.6632	.6157	1.624	.7813	1.280	1.269	.7880	.9076	**52° 0′**
10′	661	180	618	860	272	272	862	047	50′
20′	690	202	612	907	265	275	844	.9018	40′
30′	.6720	.6225	1.606	.7954	1.257	1.278	.7826	.8988	30′
40′	749	248	601	.8002	250	281	808	959	20′
50′	778	271	595	050	242	284	790	930	10′
39° 0′	.6807	.6293	1.589	.8098	1.235	1.287	.7771	.8901	**51° 0′**
10′	836	316	583	146	228	290	753	872	50′
20′	865	338	578	195	220	293	735	843	40′
30′	.6894	.6361	1.572	.8243	1.213	1.296	.7716	.8814	30′
40′	923	383	567	292	206	299	698	785	20′
50′	952	406	561	342	199	302	679	756	10′
40° 0′	.6981	.6428	1.556	.8391	1.192	1.305	.7660	.8727	**50° 0′**
10′	.7010	450	550	441	185	309	642	698	50′
20′	039	472	545	491	178	312	623	668	40′
30′	.7069	.6494	1.540	.8541	1.171	1.315	.7604	.8639	30′
40′	098	517	535	591	164	318	585	610	20′
50′	127	539	529	642	157	322	566	581	10′
41° 0′	.7156	.6561	1.524	.8693	1.150	1.325	.7547	.8552	**49° 0′**
10′	185	583	519	744	144	328	528	523	50′
20′	214	604	514	796	137	332	509	494	40′
30′	.7243	.6626	1.509	.8847	1.130	1.335	.7490	.8465	30′
40′	272	648	504	899	124	339	470	436	20′
50′	301	670	499	.8952	117	342	451	407	10′
42° 0′	.7330	.6691	1.494	.9004	1.111	1.346	.7431	.8378	**48° 0′**
10′	359	713	490	057	104	349	412	348	50′
20′	389	734	485	110	098	353	392	319	40′
30′	.7418	.6756	1.480	.9163	1.091	1.356	.7373	.8290	30
40′	447	777	476	217	085	360	353	261	20′
50′	476	799	471	271	079	364	333	232	10′
43° 0′	.7505	.6820	1.466	.9325	1.072	1.367	.7314	.8203	**47° 0′**
10′	534	841	462	380	066	371	294	174	50′
20′	563	862	457	435	060	375	274	145	40′
30′	.7592	.6884	1.453	.9490	1.054	1.379	.7254	.8116	30′
40′	621	905	448	545	048	382	234	087	20′
50′	650	926	444	601	042	386	214	058	10′
44° 0′	.7679	.6947	1.440	.9657	1.036	1.390	.7193	.8029	**46° 0′**
10′	709	967	435	713	030	394	173	.7999	50′
20′	738	.6988	431	770	024	398	153	970	40′
30′	.7767	.7009	1.427	.9827	1.018	1.402	.7133	.7941	30′
40′	796	030	423	884	012	406	112	912	20′
50′	825	050	418	.9942	006	410	092	883	10′
45° 0′	.7854	.7071	1.414	1.000	1.000	1.414	.7071	.7854	**45° 0′**
		Cos	Sec	Cot	Tan	Csc	Sin	Radians	Degrees

TABLE III. LOGARITHMS OF NUMBERS

n	0	1	2	3	4	5	6	7	8	9
10	0000	0043	0086	0128	0170	0212	0253	0294	0334	0374
11	0414	0453	0492	0531	0569	0607	0645	0682	0719	0755
12	0792	0828	0864	0899	0934	0969	1004	1038	1072	1106
13	1139	1173	1206	1239	1271	1303	1335	1367	1399	1430
14	1461	1492	1523	1553	1584	1614	1644	1673	1703	1732
15	1761	1790	1818	1847	1875	1903	1931	1959	1987	2014
16	2041	2068	2095	2122	2148	2175	2201	2227	2253	2279
17	2304	2330	2355	2380	2405	2430	2455	2480	2504	2529
18	2553	2577	2601	2625	2648	2672	2695	2718	2742	2765
19	2788	2810	2833	2856	2878	2900	2923	2945	2967	2989
20	3010	3032	3054	3075	3096	3118	3139	3160	3181	3201
21	3222	3243	3263	3284	3304	3324	3345	3365	3385	3404
22	3424	3444	3464	3483	3502	3522	3541	3560	3579	3598
23	3617	3636	3655	3674	3692	3711	3729	3747	3766	3784
24	3802	3820	3838	3856	3874	3892	3909	3927	3945	3962
25	3979	3997	4014	4031	4048	4065	4082	4099	4116	4133
26	4150	4166	4183	4200	4216	4232	4249	4265	4281	4298
27	4314	4330	4346	4362	4378	4393	4409	4425	4440	4456
28	4472	4487	4502	4518	4533	4548	4564	4579	4594	4609
29	4624	4639	4654	4669	4683	4698	4713	4728	4742	4757
30	4771	4786	4800	4814	4829	4843	4857	4871	4886	4900
31	4914	4928	4942	4955	4969	4983	4997	5011	5024	5038
32	5051	5065	5079	5092	5105	5119	5132	5145	5159	5172
33	5185	5198	5211	5224	5237	5250	5263	5276	5289	5302
34	5315	5328	5340	5353	5366	5378	5391	5403	5416	5428
35	5441	5453	5465	5478	5490	5502	5514	5527	5539	5551
36	5563	5575	5587	5599	5611	5623	5635	5647	5658	5670
37	5682	5694	5705	5717	5729	5740	5752	5763	5775	5786
38	5798	5809	5821	5832	5843	5855	5866	5877	5888	5899
39	5911	5922	5933	5944	5955	5966	5977	5988	5999	6010
40	6021	6031	6042	6053	6064	6075	6085	6096	6107	6117
41	6128	6138	6149	6160	6170	6180	6191	6201	6212	6222
42	6232	6243	6253	6263	6274	6284	6294	6304	6314	6325
43	6335	6345	6355	6365	6375	6385	6395	6405	6415	6425
44	6435	6444	6454	6464	6474	6484	6493	6503	6513	6522
45	6532	6542	6551	6561	6571	6580	6590	6599	6609	6618
46	6628	6637	6646	6656	6665	6675	6684	6693	6702	6712
47	6721	6730	6739	6749	6758	6767	6776	6785	6794	6803
48	6812	6821	6830	6839	6848	6857	6866	6875	6884	6893
49	6902	6911	6920	6928	6937	6946	6955	6964	6972	6981
50	6990	6998	7007	7016	7024	7033	7042	7050	7059	7067
51	7076	7084	7093	7101	7110	7118	7126	7135	7143	7152
52	7160	7168	7177	7185	7193	7202	7210	7218	7226	7235
53	7243	7251	7259	7267	7275	7284	7292	7300	7308	7316
54	7324	7332	7340	7348	7356	7364	7372	7380	7388	7396

TABLE III. LOGARITHMS OF NUMBERS (*Cont.*)

n	0	1	2	3	4	5	6	7	8	9
55	7404	7412	7419	7427	7435	7443	7451	7459	7466	7474
56	7482	7490	7497	7505	7513	7520	7528	7536	7543	7551
57	7559	7566	7574	7582	7589	7597	7604	7612	7619	7627
58	7634	7642	7649	7657	7664	7672	7679	7686	7694	7701
59	7709	7716	7723	7731	7738	7745	7752	7760	7767	7774
60	7782	7789	7796	7803	7810	7818	7825	7832	7839	7846
61	7853	7860	7868	7875	7882	7889	7896	7903	7910	7917
62	7924	7931	7938	7945	7952	7959	7966	7973	7980	7987
63	7993	8000	8007	8014	8021	8028	8035	8041	8048	8055
64	8062	8069	8075	8082	8089	8096	8102	8109	8116	8122
65	8129	8136	8142	8149	8156	8162	8169	8176	8182	8189
66	8195	8202	8209	8215	8222	8228	8235	8241	8248	8254
67	8261	8267	8274	8280	8287	8293	8299	8306	8312	8319
68	8325	8331	8338	8344	8351	8357	8363	8370	8376	8382
69	8388	8395	8401	8407	8414	8420	8426	8432	8439	8445
70	8451	8457	8463	8470	8476	8482	8488	8494	8500	8506
71	8513	8519	8525	8531	8537	8543	8549	8555	8561	8567
72	8573	8579	8585	8591	8597	8603	8609	8615	8621	8627
73	8633	8639	8645	8651	8657	8663	8669	8675	8681	8686
74	8692	8698	8704	8710	8716	8722	8727	8733	8739	8745
75	8751	8756	8762	8768	8774	8779	8785	8791	8797	8802
76	8808	8814	8820	8825	8831	8837	8842	8848	8854	8859
77	8865	8871	8876	8882	8887	8893	8899	8904	8910	8915
78	8921	8927	8932	8938	8943	8949	8954	8960	8965	8971
79	8976	8982	8987	8993	8998	9004	9009	9015	9020	9025
80	9031	9036	9042	9047	9053	9058	9063	9069	9074	9079
81	9085	9090	9096	9101	9106	9112	9117	9122	9128	9133
82	9138	9143	9149	9154	9159	9165	9170	9175	9180	9186
83	9191	9196	9201	9206	9212	9217	9222	9227	9232	9238
84	9243	9248	9253	9258	9263	9269	9274	9279	9284	9289
85	9294	9299	9304	9309	9315	9320	9325	9330	9335	9340
86	9345	9350	9355	9360	9365	9370	9375	9380	9385	9390
87	9395	9400	9405	9410	9415	9420	9425	9430	9435	9440
88	9445	9450	9455	9460	9465	9469	9474	9479	9484	9489
89	9494	9499	9504	9509	9513	9518	9523	9528	9533	9538
90	9542	9547	9552	9557	9562	9566	9571	9576	9581	9586
91	9590	9595	9600	9605	9609	9614	9619	9624	9628	9633
92	9638	9643	9647	9652	9657	9661	9666	9671	9675	9680
93	9685	9689	9694	9699	9703	9708	9713	9717	9722	9727
94	9731	9736	9741	9745	9750	9754	9759	9763	9768	9773
95	9777	9782	9786	9791	9795	9800	9805	9809	9814	9818
96	9823	9827	9832	9836	9841	9845	9850	9854	9859	9863
97	9868	9872	9877	9881	9886	9890	9894	9899	9903	9908
98	9912	9917	9921	9926	9930	9934	9939	9943	9948	9952
99	9956	9961	9965	9969	9974	9978	9983	9987	9991	9996

TABLE IV. LOGARITHMS OF TRIGONOMETRIC FUNCTIONS *

Angle	L Sin	d 1′	L Tan	cd 1′	L Cot	d 1′	L Cos	
0° 0′	——		——		——		10.0000	**90°** 0′
10′	7.4637		7.4637		12.5363	.0	.0000	50′
20′	.7648	301.1	.7648	301.1	.2352	.0	.0000	40′
30′	7.9408	176.0	7.9409	176.1	12.0591	.0	.0000	30′
40′	8.0658	125.0	8.0658	124.9	11.9342	.0	.0000	20′
50′	.1627	96.9	.1627	96.9	.8373	.0	10.0000	10′
1° 0′	8.2419	79.2	8.2419	79.2	11.7581	.1	9.9999	**89°** 0′
10′	.3088	66.9	.3089	67.0	.6911	.0	.9999	50′
20′	.3668	58.0	.3669	58.0	.6331	.0	.9999	40′
30′	.4179	51.1	.4181	51.2	.5819	.0	.9999	30′
40′	.4637	45.8	.4638	45.7	.5362	.1	.9998	20′
50′	.5050	41.3	.5053	41.5	.4947	.0	.9998	10′
2° 0′	8.5428	37.8	8.5431	37.8	11.4569	.1	9.9997	**88°** 0′
10′	.5776	34.8	.5779	34.8	.4221	.0	.9997	50′
20′	.6097	32.1	.6101	32.2	.3899	.1	.9996	40′
30′	.6397	30.0	.6401	30.0	.3599	.0	.9996	30′
40′	.6677	28.0	.6682	28.1	.3318	.1	.9995	20′
50′	.6940	26.3	.6945	26.3	.3055	.0	.9995	10′
3° 0′	8.7188	24.8	8.7194	24.9	11.2806	.1	9.9994	**87°** 0′
10′	.7423	23.5	.7429	23.5	.2571	.1	.9993	50′
20′	.7645	22.2	.7652	22.3	.2348	.0	.9993	40′
30′	.7857	21.2	.7865	21.3	.2135	.1	.9992	30′
40′	.8059	20.2	.8067	20.2	.1933	.1	.9991	20′
50′	.8251	19.2	.8261	19.4	.1739	.1	.9990	10′
4° 0′	8.8436	18.5	8.8446	18.5	11.1554	.1	9.9989	**86°** 0′
10′	.8613	17.7	.8624	17.8	.1376	.0	.9989	50′
20′	.8783	17.0	.8795	17.1	.1205	.1	.9988	40′
30′	.8946	16.3	.8960	16.5	.1040	.1	.9987	30′
40′	.9104	15.8	.9118	15.8	.0882	.1	.9986	20′
50′	.9256	15.2	.9272	15.4	.0728	.1	.9985	10′
5° 0′	8.9403	14.7	8.9420	14.8	11.0580	.2	9.9983	**85°** 0′
10′	.9545	14.2	.9563	14.3	.0437	.1	.9982	50′
20′	.9682	13.7	.9701	13.8	.0299	.1	.9981	40′
30′	.9816	13.4	.9836	13.5	.0164	.1	.9980	30′
40′	8.9945	12.9	8.9966	13.0	11.0034	.1	.9979	20′
50′	9.0070	12.5	9.0093	12.7	10.9907	.2	.9977	10′
6° 0′	9.0192	12.2	9.0216	12.3	10.9784	.1	9.9976	**84°** 0′
10′	.0311	11.9	.0336	12.0	.9664	.1	.9975	50′
20′	.0426	11.5	.0453	11.7	.9547	.2	.9973	40′
30′	.0539	11.3	.0567	11.4	.9433	.1	.9972	30′
40′	.0648	10.9	.0678	11.1	.9322	.1	.9971	20′
50′	.0755	10.7	.0786	10.8	.9214	.2	.9969	10′
7° 0′	9.0859	10.4	9.0891	10.5	10.9109	.1	9.9968	**83°** 0′
10′	.0961	10.2	.0995	10.4	.9005	.2	.9966	50′
20′	.1060	9.9	.1096	10.1	.8904	.2	.9964	40′
30′	.1157	9.7	.1194	9.8	.8806	.1	.9963	30′
40′	.1252	9.5	.1291	9.7	.8709	.2	.9961	20′
50′	.1345	9.3	.1385	9.4	.8615	.2	.9959	10′
8° 0′	9.1436	9.1	9.1478	9.3	10.8522	.1	9.9958	**82°** 0′
10′	.1525	8.9	.1569	9.1	.8431	.2	.9956	50′
20′	.1612	8.7	.1658	8.9	.8342	.2	.9954	40′
30′	.1697	8.5	.1745	8.7	.8255	.2	.9952	30′
40′	.1781	8.4	.1831	8.6	.8169	.2	.9950	20′
50′	.1863	8.2	.1915	8.4	.8085	.2	.9948	10′
9° 0′	9.1943	8.0	9.1997	8.2	10.8003	.2	9.9946	**81°** 0′
	L Cos	d 1′	L Cot	cd 1′	L Tan	1 d′	L Sin	Angle

* Subtract 10 from each entry in this table to obtain the proper logarithm of the indicated trigonometric function.

TABLE IV. LOGARITHMS OF TRIGONOMETRIC FUNCTIONS (*Cont.*)

Angle	L Sin	d 1′	L Tan	cd 1′	L Cot	d 1′	L Cos	
9° 0′	9.1943		9.1997		10.8003		9.9946	**81° 0′**
10′	.2022	7.9	.2078	8.1	.7922	.2	.9944	50′
20′	.2100	7.8	.2158	8.0	.7842	.2	.9942	40′
30′	.2176	7.6	.2236	7.8	.7764	.2	.9940	30′
40′	.2251	7.5	.2313	7.7	.7687	.2	.9938	20′
50′	.2324	7.3	.2389	7.6	.7611	.2	.9936	10′
10° 0′	9.2397	7.3	9.2463	7.4	10.7537	.2	9.9934	**80° 0′**
10′	.2468	7.1	.2536	7.3	.7464	.3	.9931	50′
20′	.2538	7.0	.2609	7.3	.7391	.2	.9929	40′
30′	.2606	6.8	.2680	7.1	.7320	.2	.9927	30′
40′	.2674	6.8	.2750	7.0	.7250	.3	.9924	20′
50′	.2740	6.6	.2819	6.9	.7181	.2	.9922	10′
11° 0′	9.2806	6.6	9.2887	6.8	10.7113	.3	9.9919	**79° 0′**
10′	.2870	6.4	.2953	6.6	.7047	.2	.9917	50′
20′	.2934	6.4	.3020	6.7	.6980	.3	.9914	40′
30′	.2997	6.3	.3085	6.5	.6915	.2	.9912	30′
40′	.3058	6.1	.3149	6.4	.6851	.3	.9909	20′
50′	.3119	6.1	.3212	6.3	.6788	.2	.9907	10′
12° 0′	9.3179	6.0	9.3275	6.3	10.6725	.3	9.9904	**78° 0′**
10′	.3238	5.9	.3336	6.1	.6664	.3	.9901	50′
20′	.3296	5.8	.3397	6.1	.6603	.2	.9899	40′
30′	.3353	5.7	.3458	6.1	.6542	.3	.9896	30′
40′	.3410	5.7	.3517	5.9	.6483	.3	.9893	20′
50′	.3466	5.6	.3576	5.9	.6424	.3	.9890	10′
13° 0′	9.3521	5.5	9.3634	5.8	10.6366	.3	9.9887	**77° 0′**
10′	.3575	5.4	.3691	5.7	.6309	.3	.9884	50′
20′	.3629	5.4	.3748	5.7	.6252	.3	.9881	40′
30′	.3682	5.3	.3804	5.6	.6196	.3	.9878	30′
40′	.3734	5.2	.3859	5.5	.6141	.3	.9875	20′
50′	.3786	5.2	.3914	5.5	.6086	.3	.9872	10′
14° 0′	9.3837	5.1	9.3968	5.4	10.6032	.3	9.9869	**76° 0′**
10′	.3887	5.0	.4021	5.3	.5979	.3	.9866	50′
20′	.3937	5.0	.4074	5.3	.5926	.3	.9863	40′
30′	.3986	4.9	.4127	5.3	.5873	.4	.9859	30′
40′	.4035	4.9	.4178	5.1	.5822	.3	.9856	20′
50′	.4083	4.8	.4230	5.2	.5770	.3	.9853	10′
15° 0′	9.4130	4.7	9.4281	5.1	10.5719	.4	9.9849	**75° 0′**
10′	.4177	4.7	.4331	5.0	.5669	.3	.9846	50′
20′	.4223	4.6	.4381	5.0	.5619	.3	.9843	40′
30′	.4269	4.6	.4430	4.9	.5570	.4	.9839	30′
40′	.4314	4.5	.4479	4.9	.5521	.3	.9836	20′
50′	.4359	4.5	.4527	4.8	.5473	.4	.9832	10′
16° 0′	9.4403	4.4	9.4575	4.8	10.5425	.4	9.9828	**74° 0′**
10′	.4447	4.4	.4622	4.7	.5378	.3	.9825	50′
20′	.4491	4.4	.4669	4.7	.5331	.4	.9821	40′
30′	.4533	4.2	.4716	4.7	.5284	.4	.9817	30′
40′	.4576	4.3	.4762	4.6	.5238	.3	.9814	20′
50′	.4618	4.2	.4808	4.6	.5192	.4	.9810	10′
17° 0′	9.4659	4.1	9.4853	4.5	10.5147	.4	9.9806	**73° 0′**
10′	.4700	4.1	.4898	4.5	.5102	.4	.9802	50′
20′	.4741	4.1	.4943	4.5	.5057	.4	.9798	40′
30′	.4781	4.0	.4987	4 4	.5013	.4	.9794	30′
40′	.4821	4.0	.5031	4.4	.4969	.4	.9790	20′
50′	.4861	4.0	.5075	4.4	.4925	.4	.9786	10′
18° 0′	9.4900	3.9	9.5118	4.3	10.4882	.4	9.9782	**72° 0′**
	L Cos	**d 1′**	**L Cot**	**cd 1′**	**L Tan**	**d 1′**	**L Sin**	**Angle**

TABLE IV. LOGARITHMS OF TRIGONOMETRIC FUNCTIONS (*Cont.*)

Angle	L Sin	d 1′	L Tan	cd 1′	L Cot	d 1′	L Cos	
18° 0′	9.4900		9.5118		10.4882		9.9782	**72° 0′**
10′	.4939	3.9	.5161	4.3	.4839	.4	.9778	50′
20′	.4977	3.8	.5203	4.2	.4797	.4	.9774	40′
30′	.5015	3.8	.5245	4.2	.4755	.4	.9770	30′
40′	.5052	3.7	.5287	4.2	.4713	.5	.9765	20′
50′	.5090	3.8	.5329	4.2	.4671	.4	.9761	10′
19° 0′	9.5126	3.6	9.5370	4.1	10.4630	.4	9.9757	**71° 0′**
10′	.5163	3.7	.5411	4.1	.4589	.5	.9752	50′
20′	.5199	3.6	.5451	4.0	.4549	.4	.9748	40′
30′	.5235	3.6	.5491	4.0	.4509	.5	.9743	30′
40′	.5270	3.5	.5531	4.0	.4469	.4	.9739	20′
50′	.5306	3.6	.5571	4.0	.4429	.5	.9734	10′
20° 0′	9.5341	3.5	9.5611	4.0	10.4389	.4	9.9730	**70° 0′**
10′	.5375	3.4	.5650	3.9	.4350	.5	.9725	50′
20′	.5409	3.4	.5689	3.9	.4311	.4	.9721	40′
30′	.5443	3.4	.5727	3.8	.4273	.5	.9716	30′
40′	.5477	3.4	.5766	3.9	.4234	.5	.9711	20′
50′	.5510	3.3	.5804	3.8	.4196	.5	.9706	10′
21° 0′	9.5543	3.3	9.5842	3.8	10.4158	.4	9.9702	**69° 0′**
10′	.5576	3.3	.5879	3.7	.4121	.5	.9697	50′
20′	.5609	3.3	.5917	3.8	.4083	.5	.9692	40′
30′	.5641	3.2	.5954	3.7	.4046	.5	.9687	30′
40′	.5673	3.2	.5991	3.7	.4009	.5	.9682	20′
50′	.5704	3.1	.6028	3.7	.3972	.5	.9677	10′
22° 0′	9.5736	3.2	9.6064	3.6	10.3936	.5	9.9672	**68° 0′**
10′	.5767	3.1	.6100	3.6	.3900	.5	.9667	50′
20′	.5798	3.1	.6136	3.6	.3864	.6	.9661	40′
30′	.5828	3.0	.6172	3.6	.3828	.5	.9656	30′
40′	.5859	3.1	.6208	3.6	.3792	.5	.9651	20′
50′	.5889	3.0	.6243	3.5	.3757	.5	.9646	10′
23° 0′	9.5919	3.0	9.6279	3.6	10.3721	.6	9.9640	**67° 0′**
10′	.5948	2.9	.6314	3.5	.3686	.5	.9635	50′
20′	.5978	3.0	.6348	3.4	.3652	.6	.9629	40′
30′	.6007	2.9	.6383	3.5	.3617	.5	.9624	30′
40′	.6036	2.9	.6417	3.4	.3583	.6	.9618	20′
50′	.6065	2.9	.6452	3.5	.3548	.5	.9613	10′
24° 0′	9.6093	2.8	9.6486	3.4	10.3514	.6	9.9607	**66° 0′**
10′	.6121	2.8	.6520	3.4	.3480	.5	.9602	50′
20′	.6149	2.8	.6553	3.3	.3447	.6	.9596	40′
30′	.6177	2.8	.6587	3.4	.3413	.6	.9590	30′
40′	.6205	2.8	.6620	3.3	.3380	.6	.9584	20′
50′	.6232	2.7	.6654	3.4	.3346	.5	.9579	10′
25° 0′	9.6259	2.7	9.6687	3.3	10.3313	.6	9.9573	**65° 0′**
10′	.6286	2.7	.6720	3.3	.3280	.6	.9567	50′
20′	.6313	2.7	.6752	3.2	.3248	.6	.9561	40′
30′	.6340	2.7	.6785	3.3	.3215	.6	.9555	30′
40′	.6366	2.6	.6817	3.2	.3183	.6	.9549	20′
50′	.6392	2.6	.6850	3.3	.3150	.6	.9543	10′
26° 0′	9.6418	2.6	9.6882	3.2	10.3118	.6	9.9537	**64° 0′**
10′	.6444	2.6	.6914	3.2	.3086	.7	.9530	50′
20′	.6470	2.6	.6946	3.2	.3054	.6	.9524	40′
30′	.6495	2.5	.6977	3.1	.3023	.6	.9518	30′
40′	.6521	2.6	.7009	3.2	.2991	.6	.9512	20′
50′	.6546	2.5	.7040	3.1	.2960	.7	.9505	10′
27° 0′	9.6570	2.4	9.7072	3.2	10.2928	.6	9.9499	**63° 0′**
	L Cos	d 1′	L Cot	cd 1′	L Tan	d 1′	L Sin	Angle

TABLE IV. LOGARITHMS OF TRIGONOMETRIC FUNCTIONS (*Cont.*)

Angle	L Sin	d 1′	L Tan	cd 1′	L Cot	d 1′	L Cos	
27° 0′	9.6570		9.7072		10.2928		9.9499	**63° 0′**
10′	.6595	2.5	.7103	3.1	.2897	.7	.9492	50′
20′	.6620	2.5	.7134	3.1	.2866	.6	.9486	40′
30′	.6644	2.4	.7165	3.1	.2835	.7	.9479	30′
40′	.6668	2.4	.7196	3.1	.2804	.6	.9473	20′
50′	.6692	2.4	.7226	3.0	.2774	.7	.9466	10′
28° 0′	9.6716	2.4	9.7257	3.1	10.2743	.7	9.9459	**62° 0′**
10′	.6740	2.4	.7287	3.0	.2713	.6	.9453	50′
20′	.6763	2.3	.7317	3.0	.2683	.7	.9446	40′
30′	.6787	2.4	.7348	3.1	.2652	.7	.9439	30′
40′	.6810	2.3	.7378	3.0	.2622	.7	.9432	20′
50′	.6833	2.3	.7408	3.0	.2592	.7	.9425	10′
29° 0′	9.6856	2.3	9.7438	3.0	10.2562	.7	9.9418	**61° 0′**
10′	.6878	2.2	.7467	2.9	.2533	.7	.9411	50′
20′	.6901	2.3	.7497	3.0	.2503	.7	.9404	40′
30′	.6923	2.2	.7526	2.9	.2474	.7	.9397	30′
40′	.6946	2.3	.7556	3.0	.2444	.7	.9390	20′
50′	.6968	2.2	.7585	2.9	.2415	.7	.9383	10′
30° 0′	9.6990	2.2	9.7614	2.9	10.2386	.8	9.9375	**60° 0′**
10′	.7012	2.2	.7644	3.0	.2356	.7	.9368	50′
20′	.7033	2.1	.7673	2.9	.2327	.7	.9361	40′
30′	.7055	2.2	.7701	2.8	.2299	.8	.9353	30′
40′	.7076	2.1	.7730	2.9	.2270	.7	.9346	20′
50′	.7097	2.1	.7759	2.9	.2241	.8	.9338	10′
31° 0′	9.7118	2.1	9.7788	2.9	10.2212	.7	9.9331	**59° 0′**
10′	.7139	2.1	.7816	2.8	.2184	.8	.9323	50′
20′	.7160	2.1	.7845	2.9	.2155	.8	.9315	40′
30′	.7181	2.1	.7873	2.8	.2127	.7	.9308	30′
40′	.7201	2.0	.7902	2.9	.2098	.8	.9300	20′
50′	.7222	2.1	.7930	2.8	.2070	.8	.9292	10′
32° 0′	9.7242	2.0	9.7958	2.8	10.2042	.8	9.9284	**58° 0′**
10′	.7262	2.0	.7986	2.8	.2014	.8	.9276	50′
20′	.7282	2.0	.8014	2.8	.1986	.8	.9268	40′
30′	.7302	2.0	.8042	2.8	.1958	.8	.9260	30′
40′	.7322	2.0	.8070	2.8	.1930	.8	.9252	20′
50′	.7342	2.0	.8097	2.7	.1903	.8	.9244	10′
33° 0′	9.7361	1.9	9.8125	2.8	10.1875	.8	9.9236	**57° 0′**
10′	.7380	1.9	.8153	2.8	.1847	.8	.9228	50′
20′	.7400	2.0	.8180	2.7	.1820	.9	.9219	40′
30′	.7419	1.9	.8208	2.8	.1792	.8	.9211	30′
40′	.7438	1.9	.8235	2.7	.1765	.8	.9203	20′
50′	.7457	1.9	.8263	2.8	.1737	.9	.9194	10′
34° 0′	9.7476	1.9	9.8290	2.7	10.1710	.8	9.9186	**56° 0′**
10′	.7494	1.8	.8317	2.7	.1683	.9	.9177	50′
20′	.7513	1.9	.8344	2.7	.1656	.8	.9169	40′
30′	.7531	1.8	.8371	2.7	.1629	.9	.9160	30′
40′	.7550	1.9	.8398	2.7	.1602	.9	.9151	20′
50′	.7568	1.8	.8425	2.7	.1575	.9	.9142	10′
35° 0′	9.7586	1.8	9.8452	2.7	10.1548	.8	9.9134	**55° 0′**
10′	.7604	1.8	.8479	2.7	.1521	.9	.9125	50′
20′	.7622	1.8	.8506	2.7	.1494	.9	.9116	40′
30′	.7640	1.8	.8533	2.7	.1467	.9	.9107	30′
40′	.7657	1.7	.8559	2.6	.1441	.9	.9098	20′
50′	.7675	1.8	.8586	2.7	.1414	.9	.9089	10′
36° 0′	9.7692	1.7	9.8613	2.7	10.1387	.9	9.9080	**54° 0′**
	L Cos	d 1′	L Cot	cd 1′	L Tan	d 1′	L Sin	Angle

TABLE IV. LOGARITHMS OF TRIGONOMETRIC FUNCTIONS (*Cont.*)

Angle	L Sin	d 1′	L Tan	cd 1′	L Cot	d 1′	L Cos	
36° 0′	9.7692		9.8613		10.1387		9.9080	**54° 0′**
10′	.7710	1.8	.8639	2.6	.1361	1.0	.9070	50′
20′	.7727	1.7	.8666	2.7	.1334	.9	.9061	40′
30′	.7744	1.7	.8692	2.6	.1308	.9	.9052	30′
40′	.7761	1.7	.8718	2.6	.1282	1.0	.9042	20′
50′	.7778	1.7	.8745	2.7	.1255	.9	.9033	10′
37° 0′	9.7795	1.7	9.8771	2.6	10.1229	1.0	9.9023	**53° 0′**
10′	.7811	1.6	.8797	2.6	.1203	.9	.9014	50′
20′	.7828	1.7	.8824	2.7	.1176	1.0	.9004	40′
30′	.7844	1.6	.8850	2.6	.1150	.9	.8995	30′
40′	.7861	1.7	.8876	2.6	.1124	1.0	.8985	20′
50′	.7877	1.6	.8902	2.6	.1098	1.0	.8975	10′
38° 0′	9.7893	1.6	9.8928	2.6	10.1072	1.0	9.8965	**52° 0′**
10′	.7910	1.7	.8954	2.6	.1046	1.0	.8955	50′
20′	.7926	1.6	.8980	2.6	.1020	1.0	.8945	40′
30′	.7941	1.5	.9006	2.6	.0994	1.0	.8935	30′
40′	.7957	1.6	.9032	2.6	.0968	1.0	.8925	20′
50′	.7973	1.6	.9058	2.6	.0942	1.0	.8915	10′
39° 0′	9.7989	1.6	9.9084	2.6	10.0916	1.0	9.8905	**51° 0′**
10′	.8004	1.5	.9110	2.6	.0890	1.0	.8895	50′
20′	.8020	1.6	.9135	2.5	.0865	1.1	.8884	40′
30′	.8035	1.5	.9161	2.6	.0839	1.0	.8874	30′
40′	.8050	1.5	.9187	2.6	.0813	1.0	.8864	20′
50′	.8066	1.6	.9212	2.5	.0788	1.1	.8853	10′
40° 0′	9.8081	1.5	9.9238	2.6	10.0762	1.0	9.8843	**50° 0′**
10′	.8096	1.5	.9264	2.6	.0736	1.1	.8832	50′
20′	.8111	1.5	.9289	2.5	.0711	1.1	.8821	40′
30′	.8125	1.4	.9315	2.6	.0685	1.1	.8810	30′
40′	.8140	1.5	.9341	2.6	.0659	1.0	.8800	20′
50′	.8155	1.5	.9366	2.5	.0634	1.1	.8789	10′
41° 0′	9.8169	1.4	9.9392	2.6	10.0608	1.1	9.8778	**49° 0′**
10′	.8184	1.5	.9417	2.5	.0583	1.1	.8767	50′
20′	.8198	1.4	.9443	2.6	.0557	1.1	.8756	40′
30′	.8213	1.5	.9468	2.5	.0532	1.1	.8745	30′
40′	.8227	1.4	.9494	2.6	.0506	1.2	.8733	20′
50′	.8241	1.4	.9519	2.5	.0481	1.1	.8722	10′
42° 0′	9.8255	1.4	9.9544	2.5	10.0456	1.1	9.8711	**48° 0′**
10′	.8269	1.4	.9570	2.6	.0430	1.2	.8699	50′
20′	.8283	1.4	.9595	2.5	.0405	1.1	.8688	40′
30′	.8297	1.4	.9621	2.6	.0379	1.2	.8676	30′
40′	.8311	1.4	.9646	2.5	.0354	1.1	.8665	20′
50′	.8324	1.3	.9671	2.5	.0329	1.2	.8653	10′
43° 0′	9.8338	1.4	9.9697	2.6	10.0303	1.2	9.8641	**47° 0′**
10′	.8351	1.3	.9722	2.5	.0278	1.2	.8629	50′
20′	.8365	1.4	.9747	2.5	.0253	1.1	.8618	40′
30′	.8378	1.3	.9772	2.5	.0228	1.2	.8606	30′
40′	.8391	1.3	.9798	2.6	.0202	1.2	.8594	20′
50′	.8405	1.4	.9823	2.5	.0177	1.2	.8582	10′
44° 0′	9.8418	1.3	9.9848	2.5	10.0152	1.3	9.8569	**46° 0′**
10′	.8431	1.3	.9874	2.6	.0126	1.2	.8557	50′
20′	.8444	1.3	.9899	2.5	.0101	1.2	.8545	40′
30′	.8457	1.3	.9924	2.5	.0076	1.3	.8532	30′
40′	.8469	1.2	.9949	2.5	.0051	1.2	.8520	20′
50′	.8482	1.3	9.9975	2.6	.0025	1.3	.8507	10′
45° 0′	9.8495	1.3	10.0000	2.5	10.0000	1.2	9.8495	**45° 0′**
	L Cos	d 1′	L Cot	cd 1′	L Tan	d 1′	L Sin	Angle

Answers to Odd-Numbered Exercises

ANSWERS TO ODD–NUMBERED EXERCISES

Section 1.3. Page 5

1. Yes, yes; no, yes.

7. (a) $\{x \mid x$ is a rational number$\}$, (b) $\{t \mid t$ is a right triangle$\}$.

9. $\{p\}$, $\{q\}$, $\{r\}$, $\{s\}$, $\{p, q\}$, $\{p, r\}$, $\{p, s\}$, $\{q, r\}$, $\{q, s\}$, $\{r, s\}$, $\{p, q, r\}$, $\{p, q, s\}$, $\{p, r, s\}$, $\{q, r, s\}$, $\{p, q, r, s\}$, ϕ.

15. $\{(x, p), (x, q), (x, r), (y, p), (y, q), (y, r)\}$, no. **17.** (b), (c), (d).

19. Set of even integers.

Section 1.4. Page 9

1. $\{1, 2, 3, 5\}$, $\{2, 3\}$. **3.** $\{x \mid x$ is a positive integer less than 15$\}$, $\{6, 7, 8, 9\}$.

5. $\{p, q, r, s\}$.

Section 1.7. Page 16

1. (a) $\{6, 12, 18, 24\}$. (b) $\{28, 29, 30, 31\}$. (c) $\{28, 29\}$. (d) $\{100\}$. (e) $\{x \mid x$ a real number, x greater than or equal to 32, x less than or equal to 212$\}$. **3.** (a) 13. (b) $\frac{15}{4}$. (c) -3. (d) $-\frac{97}{27}$. (e) Not defined.

5. (b) and (c). **7.** Domain: $\{0, 1, 2, 3, 4, 5\}$; range: $\{0, 2, 4, 6, 8, 10\}$; *Rule:* $f(x) = 2x$, one-to-one.

9. Domain: $\{0, 1, 2, 3, 4\}$; range: $\{1, 3, 5, 7, 9\}$; *Rule:* $f(x) = 2x + 1$, one-to-one.

11. Domain: set of integers; range: set of perfect square integers; *Rule:* $f(x) = x^2$, not one-to-one. **13.** Domain: set of real numbers; range: set of real numbers; *Rule:* $f(x) = 3x$, one-to-one. **15.** Domain: $\{0, 1, 2, 3, 4\}$; range: $\{3, 4, 5, 7\}$, not one-to-one. **17.** Not a function.

19. Domain: $\{1, 2, 3, 4, 5, 6, 7, 8, 9, 10, 11\}$; range: $\{1, 8, 27, 64, 125, 216, 343, 512, 729, 1000, 1331\}$, one-to-one.

29. Domain: all positive real numbers; range: all positive real numbers; $r = \sqrt{\frac{q_1 q_2}{F}}$; domain: all positive real numbers.

31. Domain: set of real numbers from -5 to 5, inclusive; range: set of real numbers from 0 to $\frac{25}{2}a$, inclusive, maximum when $x = \pm 5$, minimum when $x = 0$.

Section 1.8. Page 19

1. $g(f)(x) = (2x + 1)^3$; domain: set of nonnegative integers.

3. $g(f)(x) = 5x - 7$; domain: set of perfect square integers.

5. $g(f)(x) = -2\sqrt{x}$; domain: set of nonnegative real numbers; $f(g)(x) = \sqrt{-2x}$; domain: set of nonpositive real numbers. **7.** $r = 4 + 0.01t$, domain: set of real numbers 0 to 60, inclusive; $A = \pi r^2$, domain: set of real numbers 4 to 4.6, inclusive; $A = \pi(4 + 0.01t)^2$, domain: set of real numbers 0 to 60 inclusive.

9. $x = 60t$, $y = \sqrt{8100 + x^2}$, $y = 10\sqrt{81 + 36t^2}$.
11. $\{(1, 5), (3, 9), (5, 13)\}$.

Section 3.2. Page 33

1. -3. **3.** $\frac{2}{9}$. **5.** $\frac{11}{2}$. **7.** 28. **9.** $-\frac{3}{4}$. **11.** $-\frac{14}{3}$. **13.** 1. **15.** -4. **17.** 2. **19.** 26. **21.** $-\frac{10}{11}$. **23.** $-\frac{4}{3}$. **25.** $-\frac{5}{13}$. **27.** $-\frac{1}{2}$. **29.** $\frac{13}{2}$. **31.** $\frac{1}{11}$. **33.** $a = \frac{F}{m}$. **35.** $h = \frac{v^2}{2g}$. **37.** $V_2 = \frac{P_1V_1}{P_2}$. **39.** $g = \frac{v - v_0}{t}$. **41.** $F = \frac{9}{5}C + 32$. **43.** $q = \frac{\pi m}{Bt}$. **45.** $v = \frac{2s - v_0t}{t}$. **47.** $t = \frac{R - R_0}{aR_0}$. **49.** $r = \frac{E - ir'}{i}$. **51.** $\beta = \frac{P_t - P_0}{tP_0}$. **53.** $r_2 = \frac{Rr_1}{r_1 - R}$. **55.** $r = \frac{S - a}{S - l}$. **57.** $r = \frac{2u'}{Yuu' + 1}$. **59.** $M = \frac{l}{lt + 1}$. **61.** $u = \frac{bfv}{av - cf}$. **63.** $b = \frac{Qa}{Q - Kav_1 + Kav_2}$. **65.** $E = \frac{He^2 - FM_2}{2e}$. **67.** $N = \frac{Ct + 0.0885KS}{0.0885KS}$.

Section 3.3. Page 36

1. $z = kx^2$. **3.** $V = \frac{k}{P}$. **5.** $F = k\frac{mM}{d^2}$. **7.** $A = 6x^2$, 600 sq in. **9.** $s = 16t^2$, $\frac{15}{2}$ sec. **11.** $187\frac{1}{2}$ ft-lb. **13.** $T = \frac{1}{180}\frac{x^2}{p}$. **15.** $\frac{16}{27}$ ohm. **17.** 11.86 yr.

Section 3.4. Page 39

1. 4, -1. **3.** 3, $\frac{1}{2}$. **5.** 1, $-\frac{4}{3}$. **7.** -1, $\frac{7}{2}$. **9.** $\frac{3}{5}$, $-\frac{1}{2}$. **11.** $-2 \pm \sqrt{10}$. **13.** $\frac{1 \pm \sqrt{5}}{2}$. **15.** $\frac{2 \pm \sqrt{10}}{3}$. **17.** $\frac{-7 \pm \sqrt{73}}{6}$. **19.** 1.32, -0.57. **21.** -0.43, -2.32. **23.** 0.17, -3.57. **25.** 0.42, 0.22. **27.** $\frac{-5 \pm \sqrt{93}}{2}$. **29.** Two, real, rational. **31.** Two, real, irrational. **33.** One, real, rational. **35.** Two, imaginary. **37.** -4. **39.** $\frac{3}{4}$. **41.** 2, $-\frac{2}{3}$.

Section 3.5. Page 42

1. 9. **3.** 1. **5.** 0, 3. **7.** 0. **9.** 2. **11.** 5. **13.** 1.

Section 4.2. Page 50

1. $x < 2$. **3.** $x > \frac{11}{5}$. **5.** $x < -3$. **7.** $x < \frac{19}{6}$. **9.** $x < 1$. **11.** $x > -\frac{3}{8}$. **13.** $-1 < x < 2$. **15.** $-\frac{3}{2} < x < 2$. **17.** $x < -\frac{2}{3}$ or $x > 5$. **19.** $x < -4$ or $x > -\frac{3}{2}$. **21.** $x < -6$ or $x > -\frac{2}{3}$.

23. $\frac{3-\sqrt{37}}{2} < x < \frac{3+\sqrt{37}}{2}$. **25.** $k \leqq \frac{1}{3}$. **27.** $k \geqq -\frac{49}{32}$.
29. k any real number. **31.** $n > \frac{1}{6}$ or $n < 0$.

Section 4.3. Page 53

3. $1 < x < 5$. **5.** $2 < x < 3$. **7.** $-\frac{7}{3} < x < -1$.
9. $1 < x < 3$ or $-3 < x < -1$. **11.** $\sqrt{2} < x < 2$ or $-2 < x < -\sqrt{2}$.
13. $\sqrt{3} < x < \sqrt{13}$ or $-\sqrt{13} < x < -\sqrt{3}$. **15.** $\frac{2}{3} < x < 4$.
17. $-6 < x < -\frac{4}{5}$. **21.** $\frac{1}{1+k} < x < \frac{1}{1-k}$.

Section 5.2. Page 58

1. 1, −4. **3.** −0.2, −2.8. **5.** −1.2, 3.4. **7.** 1.7, 0.2. **9.** −2, 1.5.
11. No solution. **13.** Infinitely many solutions. **15.** No solution.

Section 5.3. Page 60

1. 1, 2. **3.** −3, 3. **5.** $-\frac{5}{3}, \frac{2}{3}$. **7.** $\frac{13}{14}, -\frac{9}{7}$. **9.** $\frac{7}{3}, -\frac{2}{5}$. **11.** $\frac{7}{16}, \frac{37}{16}$.
13. $\frac{3p+q}{5m}, \frac{2p-q}{5n}$. **15.** $\frac{c_1b_2 - c_2b_1}{a_1b_2 - a_2b_1}, \frac{a_1c_2 - a_2c_1}{a_1b_2 - a_2b_1}$. **17.** 60 ft, 20 ft.
19. 300 mph, 25 mph. **21.** 40 lb of copper and 80 lb of magnesium. **23.** 85.

Section 5.4. Page 63

1. 1, 2, 3. **3.** 4, −2, 1. **5.** $-\frac{1}{2}, \frac{1}{2}, \frac{7}{2}$. **7.** 3, −2, $\frac{1}{2}$. **9.** $-\frac{3}{2}, \frac{3}{4}, -\frac{1}{2}$.
11. No solution. **13.** $\frac{15}{7} - \frac{16}{7}k, \frac{10}{7}k - \frac{19}{7}, k$. **15.** $-k, \frac{1}{2}k, k$. **17.** $-k, 4k, k$.
19. 18 lb, 12 lb. **21.** 142. **23.** 2, 3, −8. **25.** −3, −4, 7.

Section 5.5. Page 67

1. Yes. **3.** No. **5.** No. **19.** $2x + 5y \leqq 20$, $x \geqq 0$, $y \geqq 1$, {(0, 1), (0, 2), (0, 3), (0, 4), (1, 1), (1, 2), (1, 3), (2, 1), (2, 2), (2, 3), (3, 1), (3, 2), (4, 1), (4, 2), (5, 1), (5, 2), (6, 1), (7, 1)}.

Section 6.1. Page 71

1. 1, 2. **3.** 2, −3. **5.** $\frac{5}{2}$, −3. **7.** $\frac{14}{19}, -\frac{36}{19}$. **9.** No solution. **11.** 7, −22, 39.
13. 2, −1, −2. **15.** $\frac{2}{3} + \frac{2}{3}k, \frac{4}{3} - \frac{2}{3}k, k$.

Section 6.2. Page 73

1. $\begin{pmatrix} 5 & 3 \\ 1 & 6 \end{pmatrix}$. **3.** $\begin{pmatrix} 5 & 1 & -1 \\ 5 & -3 & 1 \end{pmatrix}$. **5.** $\begin{pmatrix} 1 & 6 & 2 \\ 6 & 2 & 3 \\ -3 & -1 & 8 \end{pmatrix}$. **7.** $\begin{pmatrix} 4 & -5 \\ 6 & -11 \end{pmatrix}$.

9. $\begin{pmatrix} 0 & 0 \\ 0 & 0 \end{pmatrix}$. **11.** $\begin{pmatrix} 7 & -1 & 0 \\ -5 & 8 & 12 \\ -23 & -3 & 2 \end{pmatrix}$. **13.** $\begin{pmatrix} 1 \\ 7 \end{pmatrix}$. **15.** $\begin{pmatrix} -1 & -17 \\ 9 & 28 \end{pmatrix}$.

17. $(-1 \quad 5 \quad -2)$.

Section 6.3. Page 77

9. $\begin{pmatrix} 2 & -1 \\ -3 & 2 \end{pmatrix}$. **11.** $\begin{pmatrix} 2 & -\frac{5}{2} \\ -1 & \frac{3}{2} \end{pmatrix}$. **13.** $\begin{pmatrix} \frac{3}{5} & \frac{1}{5} \\ -\frac{2}{5} & \frac{1}{5} \end{pmatrix}$. **15.** $\begin{pmatrix} 0 & \frac{1}{3} \\ -\frac{1}{2} & \frac{5}{6} \end{pmatrix}$.
17. 2, −3. **19.** −5, 2. **21.** $-\frac{6}{11}, -\frac{19}{11}$.

Section 6.4. Page 80

1. 3, 4. **3.** 2, −1. **5.** −3, 2. **7.** $-\frac{9}{17}, -\frac{46}{17}$. **9.** $\frac{26}{11}, -\frac{17}{11}$. **11.** $\frac{11}{26}, -\frac{27}{26}$.
13. $\frac{11}{4}, -\frac{13}{8}$. **15.** $\frac{55}{17}, -\frac{35}{34}$. **17.** $\frac{625}{137}, \frac{140}{137}$. **19.** $-\frac{13}{15}, -\frac{26}{23}$.
21. $\dfrac{b_2 - b_1}{m_1 - m_2}, \dfrac{m_1 b_2 - m_2 b_1}{m_1 - m_2}$.

Section 6.7. Page 84

1. (a) 17, −7, 4; (b) 17, 7, 4; (c) 7, −8, −3; (d) 4, −14, −8. **7.** 125.
9. −9, 23, −107.

Section 6.8. Page 88

1. 2, −1, 1. **3.** 0, $\frac{2}{3}, \frac{1}{3}$. **5.** $-\frac{2}{39}, \frac{100}{39}, \frac{73}{39}$. **7.** $-\frac{8}{7}, -\frac{5}{7}, -\frac{9}{7}$.
9. $-\frac{209}{116}, \frac{275}{116}, \frac{13}{4}$. **11.** $\frac{351}{32}, \frac{376}{32}, -\frac{199}{32}$.

Section 6.9. Page 90

1. $\frac{28}{13}, -\frac{66}{13}, -\frac{29}{13}$. **3.** −29, 1, 24. **5.** $-\frac{256}{161}, \frac{11}{7}, \frac{90}{161}$. **7.** 1, 2, −2. **9.** 2, −1, 3.
11. $\frac{14}{45}, -\frac{164}{45}, -\frac{211}{45}$. **13.** $-\frac{77}{120}, -\frac{97}{60}, -\frac{19}{8}$.
15. $\dfrac{k(a-d)(a-b-c+d)}{D}, \dfrac{k(a-c)(a-b+c-d)}{D}, \dfrac{k(a-b)(a+b-c-d)}{D}$,
where $D = a^3 - ab^2 - ac^2 - ad^2 + 2bdc$.

Section 6.10. Page 94

11. 155. **13.** −68.

Section 6.11. Page 97

1. −85. **3.** 386. **5.** −221. **7.** −104. **11.** 1, 2, −3, −1. **13.** 2, −1, $\frac{1}{2}$, 1.

Section 7.2. Page 104

1. $x^4 + 4x^3y + 6x^2y^2 + 4xy^3 + y^4$ **3.** $x^8 + 12x^6y + 54x^4y^2 + 108x^2y + 81y^4$.
5. $x^5 - 5x^4y + 10x^3y^2 - 10x^2y^3 + 5xy^4 - y^5$.
7. $m^7 + 7m^6n + 21m^5n^2 + 35m^4n^3 + 35m^3n^4 + 21m^2n^5 + 7mn^6 + n^7$.
9. $a^8 - 4a^6b + 6a^4b^2 - 4a^2b^3 + b^4$.
11. $243x^5 - 405x^4y + 270x^3y^2 - 90x^2y^3 + 15xy^4 - y^5$.
13. $x^{15} + 10x^{12}y + 40x^9y^2 + 80x^6y^3 + 80x^3y^4 + 32y^5$.
15. $729x^{12} - 486x^9 + 135x^6 - 20x^3 + \dfrac{5}{3} - \dfrac{2}{27x^3} + \dfrac{1}{729x^6}$.
17. $x^{18} + 12x^{13} + 60x^8 + 160x^3 + \dfrac{240}{x^2} + \dfrac{192}{x^7} + \dfrac{64}{x^{12}}$.

19. $2187a^{14} - 5103\dfrac{a^{12}}{b} + 5103\dfrac{a^{10}}{b^2} - 2835\dfrac{a^8}{b^3} + 945\dfrac{a^6}{b^4} - 189\dfrac{a^4}{b^5} + 21\dfrac{a^2}{b^6} - \dfrac{1}{b^7}$.

21. $128x^7 + 448x^6\sqrt{x} + 672x^6 + 560x^5\sqrt{x} + 280x^5 + 84x^4\sqrt{x} + 14x^4 + x^3\sqrt{x}$.

23. $a^{16} + 4a^{13}\sqrt{a} + 7a^{11} + 7a^8\sqrt{a} + \dfrac{35}{8}a^6 + \dfrac{7}{4}a^3\sqrt{a} + \dfrac{7}{16}a + \dfrac{1}{16a\sqrt{a}} + \dfrac{1}{256a^4}$.

25. $512x^{27} - 1152x^{23}\sqrt{x} + 1152x^{20} - 672x^{16}\sqrt{x} + 252x^{13} - 63x^9\sqrt{x} + \dfrac{21}{2}x^6 - \dfrac{9}{8}x^2\sqrt{x} + \dfrac{9}{128x} - \dfrac{1}{512x^4\sqrt{x}}$.

27. $1024a^{10} + 2560a^8\sqrt{a} + 2880a^7 + 1920a^5\sqrt{a} + 840a^4 + 252a^2\sqrt{a} + \dfrac{105}{2}a + \dfrac{15}{2\sqrt{a}} + \dfrac{45}{64a^2} + \dfrac{5}{128a^3\sqrt{a}} + \dfrac{1}{1024a^5}$.

29. $x^{20} - 20x^{19}y + 190x^{18}y^2 - 1140x^{17}y^3 + \cdots$.

31. $x^{32} + 8x^{29} + 30x^{26} + 70x^{23} + \cdots$.

33. $a^{33} - \frac{11}{3}a^{29} + \frac{55}{9}a^{25} - \frac{55}{9}a^{21} + \cdots$. **35.** $x^8 + 8x^7 + 30x^6 + 70x^5 + \cdots$.

Section 7.5. Page 108

1. $220a^9x^3$. **3.** $-2002x^9y^5$. **5.** $31{,}824a^7x^{11}$. **7.** $-2{,}562{,}560a^{12}b^9$.

9. $\dfrac{25!}{10!\,15!}p^{30}\left(\dfrac{q}{2}\right)^{10}$. **11.** $31{,}824x^{11}y^7$. **13.** $-220x^9y^3$. **15.** $3276x^{50}y^9$.

17. $184{,}756x^{30}y^{10}$. **19.** $a^{-1} + a^{-2}b + a^{-3}b^2 + a^{-4}b^3 + \cdots$.

21. $x^{\frac{2}{3}} + \frac{2}{3}x^{-\frac{1}{3}}y - \frac{1}{9}x^{-\frac{4}{3}}y^2 + \frac{4}{81}x^{-\frac{7}{3}}y^3 + \cdots$.

23. $a^{-\frac{2}{3}} + 2a^{-\frac{5}{3}} + 5a^{-\frac{8}{3}} + \frac{40}{3}a^{-\frac{11}{3}} + \cdots$.

25. $x^3 - \frac{3}{2}xy + \frac{3}{8}x^{-1}y^2 + \frac{1}{16}x^{-3}y^3 + \cdots$.

27. $a^{-\frac{3}{5}} - \frac{6}{5}a^{-\frac{8}{5}}b + \frac{48}{25}a^{-\frac{13}{5}}b^2 - \frac{416}{125}a^{-\frac{18}{5}}b^3 + \cdots$.

29. $\dfrac{1}{8x^3} - \dfrac{3y}{64x^5} + \dfrac{15y^2}{1024x^7} - \dfrac{35y^3}{8192y^9} + \cdots$.

31. 1.27. **33.** 0.82. **35.** 4.80. **37.** 4.64. **39.** 0.87. **41.** 0.35.

Section 7.6. Page 111

1. 1, 3, 5, 7. **3.** 2, 2, 2. **5.** −5, −33, −88. **7.** $\frac{1}{6}$, 5, $77\frac{1}{2}$.

9. $4\frac{1}{7}$, $6\frac{2}{7}$, $8\frac{3}{7}$, $10\frac{4}{7}$, $12\frac{5}{7}$, $14\frac{6}{7}$. **11.** $2\frac{2}{3}$, $3\frac{1}{3}$, 4, $4\frac{2}{3}$, $5\frac{1}{3}$. **13.** 6, $5\frac{1}{3}$, $4\frac{2}{3}$.

15. 1, 3, 5. **17.** $27,750. **19.** 12 days. **21.** 63. **25.** $\frac{1}{4}$, $\frac{1}{8}$.

27. 12, 14. **29.** $\frac{16}{81}$, $\frac{32}{243}$. **31.** 0.00000063, 0.0000000063. **33.** $-\frac{1}{9}$, $20\frac{2}{9}$.

35. $-\frac{4}{3}$, $-\frac{5}{2}$. **37.** $2\sqrt{2}$, 4, $4\sqrt{2}$. **39.** ±6. **41.** 256. **43.** $\dfrac{b^2}{a}$, $\dfrac{b^3}{a^2}$.

45. 9.41×10^{19}. **47.** 26.21%, 10.74%. **49.** 2 in., π sq in.

Section 7.7. Page 116

1. 27. **3.** $\frac{125}{9}$. **5.** 50. **17.** $\frac{5}{9}$. **19.** $\frac{5}{33}$. **21.** $\frac{704}{111}$. **23.** $\frac{41}{74}$. **25.** $\frac{8}{11}$.

27. 60 ft, $57\frac{1}{2}$ ft.

Section 8.3. Page 121

1. 1. **3.** 4. **5.** $\frac{2}{3}$. **7.** 5. **9.** $\frac{a}{b^5}$. **11.** $\frac{1}{8x^3}$. **13.** $\frac{a^2}{b^2c^4}$. **15.** $\frac{1}{y^2z^2}$. **17.** $\frac{b^2}{4a^2}$.
19. $\frac{1}{9x^4}$. **21.** 1. **23.** $\frac{3}{v^3}$. **25.** -1. **27.** $\frac{1}{ab}$. **29.** 25. **31.** $\frac{a+b}{a^2b^2(b-a)}$.
33. $x+1$ **35.** $\frac{b}{y}$. **37.** $ab(a-b)$. **39.** 1. **49.** 3×10^{10}. **51.** 4.50×10^{-3}.
53. 2.662×10^5. **55.** 6.61×10^3. **57.** 9.10×10^3. **59.** 4.6×10^{-4}.
61. 0.14 in. **63.** 7.6×10^{23} molecules.

Section 8.5. Page 126

1. $\frac{1}{4}$. **3.** 4. **5.** $\frac{1}{2}$. **7.** $\frac{1}{5}$. **9.** $\frac{27}{8}$. **11.** $\frac{1}{8}$. **13.** 1. **15.** 125. **17.** $\frac{3}{2}$. **19.** 1.
21. $\frac{1}{25}$. **23.** $\frac{1}{3}$. **25.** $\frac{1}{13}$. **27.** 5. **29.** $\frac{1}{a}$. **31.** $2ax$. **33.** $2\frac{y^3}{x^3}$. **35.** $4a^2b^4$.
37. $\frac{x^2}{2a}$. **39.** $\frac{b^2}{2a^2}$. **41.** ax^2. **43.** x^2y. **45.** $x-y$. **47.** $8\frac{b^2c^3}{a}$. **49.** $27x^6$.
51. 3. **53.** 1. **55.** $\frac{xy}{x+y}$. **57.** $\frac{a^2b^2}{a^2-ab+b^2}$. **59.** $\frac{y^4}{4x^2}$. **61.** $x-y$.
63. $x-y$. **65.** $x+4+\frac{4}{x}$.

Section 8.9. Page 130

33. 0.6020. **35.** 0.7781. **37.** 0.3980. **39.** 0.1505. **41.** 0.9030. **43.** 0.1193.

Section 8.12. Page 135

33. 1.45. **35.** 9.47. **37.** 29,200. **39.** 178. **41.** 8.73. **43.** 1.95. **45.** 2800.
47. 4,190,000. **49.** 1400. **51.** 41,900,000. **53.** 1.23. **55.** 6.30×10^{11}.
57. 2.71. **59.** 6.45. **61.** 0.208. **63.** 51.8.

Section 8.13. Page 138

1. 0.5884. **3.** 1.3585. **5.** 2.9418. **7.** 0.8775 – 2. **9.** 1.4610. **11.** 3.6870.
13. 5.0948. **15.** 0.9898 – 1. **17.** 8.904. **19.** 2914. **21.** 0.02792. **23.** 73,650.
25. 0.05821. **27.** 0.5486. **29.** 73.27. **31.** 483,900. **33.** 155.8. **35.** 126.7.
37. 22.37. **39.** 138.4. **41.** 488.2. **43.** 6.988. **45.** 4.017. **47.** 9.418×10^{-7}.
49. 11.29. **51.** 14.63. **53.** 570.0 **55.** 174.0. **57.** 1812.

Section 8.15. Page 142

1. 34.05. **3.** 865.4. **5.** 0.07182. **7.** 0.4625. **9.** 0.3391. **11.** 0.002593.
13. 22.55. **15.** 0.3241. **17.** 3013. **19.** 4013. **21.** 0.08402. **23.** 0.003663.
25. 2.088. **27.** 15.15. **29.** 75.08. **31.** 0.06654. **33.** 7,888,000 cu ft.
35. 430.7 sq in. **37.** 1.099. **39.** 2.485. **41.** 4.095. **43.** 5.546.

Section 8.19. Page 148

1. $g(y) = 1 - y$, set of real numbers. **3.** $g(y) = \sqrt[3]{y}$, set of real numbers.
5. (a) $g = \{(1, 0), (-1, 1), (2, 2), (-2, 3), (3, 4)\}$; domain $= \{-2, -1, 1, 2, 3\}$; (b) no inverse; (c) no inverse. **7.** No inverse.
9. $\begin{pmatrix} x & 0 \\ 0 & x^2 \end{pmatrix} \rightarrow x$, domain: set of matrices of the form $\begin{pmatrix} x & 0 \\ 0 & x^2 \end{pmatrix}$ with x an integer.
11. Set of real numbers, set of positive real numbers.
13. Set of real numbers, set of positive real numbers.
15. Set of positive real numbers, set of real numbers.
17. Set of positive real numbers, set of real numbers.
19. 6. **21.** 8. **23.** 0.8562. **25.** 0. **27.** 18.86. **29.** 49.54. **31.** 5.812. **33.** 5.
35. 4. **37.** 1001. **39.** $\frac{99}{298}$.

Section 9.6. Page 162

Exercises	$\sin\theta$	$\cos\theta$	$\tan\theta$	$\cot\theta$	$\sec\theta$	$\csc\theta$
1.		$\pm\frac{3}{5}$	$\pm\frac{4}{3}$	$\pm\frac{3}{4}$	$\pm\frac{5}{3}$	$\frac{5}{4}$
3.	$\pm\frac{3}{13}\sqrt{13}$	$\mp\frac{2}{13}\sqrt{13}$		$-\frac{2}{3}$	$\mp\frac{1}{2}\sqrt{13}$	$\pm\frac{1}{3}\sqrt{13}$
5.	$-\frac{4}{7}$	$\mp\frac{1}{7}\sqrt{33}$	$\pm\frac{4}{33}\sqrt{33}$	$\pm\frac{1}{4}\sqrt{33}$	$\mp\frac{7}{33}\sqrt{33}$	
7.	$\frac{3}{5}$	$-\frac{4}{5}$	$-\frac{3}{4}$		$-\frac{5}{4}$	$\frac{5}{3}$
9.	$-\frac{15}{17}$	$\frac{8}{17}$	$-\frac{15}{8}$	$-\frac{8}{15}$		$-\frac{17}{15}$
11.	$-\frac{2}{5}\sqrt{5}$	$-\frac{1}{5}\sqrt{5}$		$\frac{1}{2}$	$-\sqrt{5}$	$-\frac{1}{2}\sqrt{5}$
13.	$\frac{n}{m}$	$\frac{\sqrt{m^2 - n^2}}{m}$	$\frac{n}{\sqrt{m^2 - n^2}}$	$\frac{\sqrt{m^2 - n^2}}{n}$	$\frac{m}{\sqrt{m^2 - n^2}}$	

15. $-\frac{24}{25}$. **17.** $\frac{3}{4}$.

Exercises	Angle	sin	cos	tan	cot	sec	csc
19.	60°	$\frac{1}{2}\sqrt{3}$	$\frac{1}{2}$	$\sqrt{3}$	$\frac{1}{3}\sqrt{3}$	2	$\frac{2}{3}\sqrt{3}$
21.	225°	$-\frac{1}{2}\sqrt{2}$	$-\frac{1}{2}\sqrt{2}$	1	1	$-\sqrt{2}$	$-\sqrt{2}$
23.	150°	$\frac{1}{2}$	$-\frac{1}{2}\sqrt{3}$	$-\frac{1}{3}\sqrt{3}$	$-\sqrt{3}$	$-\frac{2}{3}\sqrt{3}$	2
25.	180°	0	-1	0	—	-1	—
27.	315°	$-\frac{1}{2}\sqrt{2}$	$\frac{1}{2}\sqrt{2}$	-1	-1	$\sqrt{2}$	$-\sqrt{2}$
29.	0°	0	1	0	—	1	—
31.	450°	1	0	—	0	—	1
33.	$-225°$	$\frac{1}{2}\sqrt{2}$	$-\frac{1}{2}\sqrt{2}$	-1	-1	$-\sqrt{2}$	$\sqrt{2}$

35. (a) $\frac{1}{2}\sqrt{3}$; (b) $1 - \frac{1}{2}\sqrt{3}$; (c) $\sqrt{3} - 2$; (d) $2 + \sqrt{3}$.
37. (a) 60°, 240°; (b) 45°, 315°; (c) 210°, 330°; (d) 135°, 225°; (e) 270°; (f) 150°, 330°.

Section 9.10. Page 167

1. (a) $22° 30'$; (b) $55°$; (c) $20°$. **5.** 112.8. **7.** 27.07. **9.** $b = 151.2$, $c = 174.3$. **11.** 15.12 ft. **13.** 6.98 ft. **15.** 32.40 miles, 15.96 miles. **17.** 1464 ft. **19.** 476.3 yd.

Section 9.13. Page 171

1. (a) 0.4648; (b) 0.8146; (c) 2.513; (d) 1.258; (e) 3.114; (f) 1.187.
3. (a) $29° 52'$; (b) $67° 23'$; (c) $14° 58'$; (d) $54° 6'$; (e) $75° 44'$; (f) $22° 57'$.
5. 241.8. **7.** $B = 61° 6'$; $b = 507.1$; $c = 579.6$.
9. $B = 48° 33'$; $a = 12.46$; $b = 14.11$. **11.** $45° 47'$.
13. $A = 38° 27'$; $B = 51° 33'$; $c = 688.2$.
15. $A = 60° 47'$; $B = 29° 13'$; $a = 33.08$. **17.** $4°$. **19.** 3333 ft. **21.** 7494 ft.
23. 686.7 ft.

Section 9.14. Page 175

1. 1450 ft north, 1378 ft west. **3.** 16.94 miles. **5.** 11.33 in. **7.** N 32° E.
9. 1648 ft. **11.** 129.0 ft. **13.** 1.075 miles. **15.** 18,448 ft.

Section 9.15. Page 179

1. (a) 61.04 lb; $55° 1'$; (b) 50.48 lb, $33° 41'$; (c) 265.6 lb, $48° 49'$; (d) 360.4 lb, $29° 3'$.
3. (a) 229.8 lb, 192.8 lb; (b) 200.8 lb, 101.6 lb; (c) 56.80 lb, 40.92 lb; (d) 48.09 lb, 142.1 lb. **5.** 275.6 mph southward, 172.2 mph westward.
7. 1844 lb, $49° 24'$ with 1200-lb force. **9.** $11°$, 183.4 mph.
11. $194° 42'$, 223.5 mph. **13.** 154.6 lb, $44° 42'$. **15.** 145.5 lb.
17. $(3\sqrt{2}, 135°)$, $(4, 150°)$, $(5, 306° 52')$. **19.** $x^2 + y^2 - 3x = 0$.
21. (a) $(\frac{5}{3}, \frac{2}{3})$, $(\frac{1}{3}\sqrt{29}, 21° 48')$; (b) $(0, 1)$, $(1, 90°)$; (c) no intersection; (d) $(\frac{1}{2}, \pm\frac{1}{2}\sqrt{3})$, $(1, \pm 60°)$; (e) $(1, -1)$, $(\sqrt{2}, 315°)$.

Section 9.17. Page 186

1. 0.6691. **3.** −0.3584. **5.** −0.8391. **7.** −1.556. **9.** −0.3746. **11.** 0.4540.
13. 1.423. **15.** 1.375. **17.** −0.9520. **19.** −1.675. **21.** −0.9271. **23.** −0.4467.
25. 1. **27.** 1.269. **29.** −2.130. **31.** −0.8829. **33.** 0.7536. **35.** −0.5150.
37. 1.624. **39.** 1.327. **41.** −1.122. **43.** $-\tan\theta$. **45.** $\csc\theta$. **47.** $-\sin\theta$.
49. $-\cos\theta$. **51.** $\cos\theta$. **53.** $-\cot\theta$. **55.** $\sec\theta$. **57.** $-\tan\theta$. **59.** $\tan\theta$.
61. $\cot\theta$. **63.** $-\cot\theta$. **65.** $-\cos\theta$.

Section 9.19. Page 189

1. 60°, 120°. **3.** 135°, 315°. **5.** 45°, 315°. **7.** 22°, 202°. **9.** 112°, 248°.
11. $34° 10'$, $214° 10'$. **13.** $122° 40'$, $237° 20'$. **15.** $215° 35'$, $324° 25'$.
17. $158° 25'$, $338° 25'$. **19.** 9.9061 − 10. **21.** 9.6573 − 10. **23.** 9.8581 − 10.
25. 9.9852 − 10. **27.** 9.6454 − 10. **29.** 9.6059 − 10. **31.** $54° 20'$.
33. $25° 26'$. **35.** $52° 27'$. **37.** $49° 23'$. **39.** $78° 33'$. **41.** $16° 32'$.

Section 9.20. Page 192

1. $A = 83° 57'$, $a = 10.94$, $b = 8.814$. **3.** $B = 60° 47'$, $a = 259.1$, $c = 196.4$. **5.** $A = 65° 20'$, $a = 18.24$, $c = 16.14$. **7.** $C = 62° 2'$, $b = 37.19$, $c = 34.64$. **9.** $B = 107° 35'$, $a = 4222$, $c = 1387$. **11.** $AP = 188.6$ yd, $BP = 146.5$ yd. **13.** 12.48 miles, 16.49 miles. **15.** 9558 yd.

Section 9.21. Page 195

1. No triangle. **3.** $B = 41° 24'$, $A = 86° 22'$, $a = 484.0$.
5. $C = 81° 50'$, $A = 25° 33'$, $a = 38.96$; $C' = 98° 10'$, $A' = 9° 13'$, $a' = 14.46$.
7. $C = 49° 34'$, $A = 17° 44'$, $a = 1872$.
9. $C = 82° 40'$, $B = 33°$, $b = 2.375$; $C' = 97° 20'$, $B' = 18° 20'$, $b' = 1.372$.
11. $A = 56° 34'$, $C = 66° 52'$, $c = 59.92$. **13.** 1822 ft.

Section 9.23. Page 200

1. $c = 13.73$, $A = 79° 53'$, $B = 64° 7'$. **3.** $a = 13$, $B = 32° 12'$, $C = 27° 48'$. **5.** $c = 5.085$, $A = 39° 17'$, $B = 108° 16'$. **7.** $c = 8.218$, $A = 110° 15'$, $B = 25° 15'$. **9.** $A = 34° 3'$, $B = 44° 25'$, $C = 101° 32'$. **11.** $A = 82° 49'$, $B = 55° 46'$, $C = 41° 25'$. **13.** $A = 61° 56'$, $B = 90°$, $C = 28° 4'$. **15.** $A = 15° 18'$, $B = 20° 35'$, $C = 144° 7'$. **17.** 124.9 lb, 16° 6′. **19.** 39.84 lb, 62° 17′. **21.** 223.6 mph, 162° 11′. **23.** 285.4 mph, 312° 18′.

Section 10.1. Page 203

9. Values of t	$\frac{1}{4}\pi$	$-\frac{2}{3}\pi$	$\frac{7}{6}\pi$	$\frac{3}{2}\pi$	2π
$\sin t$	$\frac{1}{2}\sqrt{2}$	$-\frac{1}{2}\sqrt{3}$	$-\frac{1}{2}$	-1	0
$\cos t$	$\frac{1}{2}\sqrt{2}$	$-\frac{1}{2}$	$-\frac{1}{2}\sqrt{3}$	0	1
$\tan t$	1	$\sqrt{3}$	$\frac{1}{3}\sqrt{3}$	—	0

11. The same except possibly for sign.

Section 10.3. Page 207

1. 0.4077. **3.** 0.9394. **5.** 2.650. **7.** −0.7946. **13.** 10.58 in. **15.** 29.12 ft. **17.** $\sqrt{2 - 2\cos t}$. **19.** $\frac{4}{3}\pi$, 240°, $\frac{4}{3}\pi$. **21.** 225°, or $\frac{5}{4}\pi$ radians; 315°, or $\frac{7}{4}\pi$ radians. **23.** 1.4 radians. **25.** 42° 58′. **27.** $\frac{4}{3}$ radians. **29.** 6000 ft. **31.** 146,616 miles.

Section 10.4. Page 214

1. 2π, 3. **3.** $\frac{2}{3}\pi$, 1. **5.** 4π, 2. **7.** 2π, 2, $-\frac{1}{2}\pi$. **9.** π, 1, $-\frac{1}{4}\pi$. **11.** 4π, 3, $\frac{2}{3}\pi$. **13.** 2π, $\sqrt{2}$. **15.** 4π, 2.1.

Section 10.5. Page 218

1. −30°, $-\frac{1}{6}\pi$. **3.** 60°, $\frac{1}{3}\pi$. **5.** 0°, 0. **7.** 0°, 0. **9.** 180°, π. **11.** 59°, 1.0297. **13.** 46°22′, 0.8093. **15.** 70°45′, 1.2348. **17.** 60°, or $\frac{1}{3}\pi$. **19.** 2. **21.** 180°, or π. **23.** $-\frac{8}{15}$. **25.** $\frac{3}{5}$. **27.** $-\frac{12}{5}$. **29.** yes, no. **31.** 35° 16′, or 0.6155. **33.** 24° 53′, or 0.4343.

Section 10.6. Page 223

1. $\sin u = \frac{4}{5}$, $\cos u = \frac{3}{5}$, $\tan u = \frac{4}{3}$, $\sec u = \frac{5}{3}$, $\csc u = \frac{5}{4}$.
3. $\sin t = -\frac{15}{17}$, $\cos t = -\frac{8}{17}$, $\tan t = \frac{15}{8}$, $\cot t = \frac{8}{15}$, $\sec t = -\frac{17}{8}$.
5. $\dfrac{1}{\pm\sqrt{1 - \sin^2 u}}$. **7.** $\dfrac{\pm\sqrt{1 + \tan^2 t}}{\tan t}$.
9. $\sin \theta = \pm\sqrt{1 - \cos^2 \theta}$, $\tan \theta = \dfrac{\pm\sqrt{1 - \cos^2 \theta}}{\cos \theta}$, $\cot \theta = \dfrac{\cos \theta}{\pm\sqrt{1 - \cos^2 \theta}}$,
$\sec \theta = \dfrac{1}{\cos \theta}$, $\csc \theta = \dfrac{1}{\pm\sqrt{1 - \cos^2 \theta}}$.
11. 1. **13.** $\tan t$. **15.** $\sec t$. **17.** $\dfrac{1}{\cos \theta}$. **19.** $\sin \theta$.

Section 10.7. Page 227

1. $\frac{1}{4}\pi, \frac{3}{4}\pi$. **3.** $\frac{2}{3}\pi, \frac{5}{3}\pi$. **5.** $\frac{1}{2}\pi, \frac{3}{2}\pi$. **7.** $\frac{5}{4}\pi, \frac{7}{4}\pi$. **9.** 0. **11.** $\frac{1}{3}\pi, \frac{1}{2}\pi, \frac{3}{2}\pi, \frac{5}{3}\pi$.
13. $\frac{1}{4}\pi, \frac{3}{4}\pi, \frac{5}{4}\pi, \frac{7}{4}\pi$. **15.** 0.8411, 5.4421, π. **17.** 0°, 135°, 180°, 315°.
19. 90°, 270°. **21.** 0°, 180°. **23.** 41° 49′, 138° 11′, 270°.
25. 71° 34′, 135°, 251° 34′, 315°. **27.** 114° 28′, 245° 32′. **29.** 60°, 300°.
31. 0°, 36° 52′. **33.** 1.4711, 4.6127. **35.** No solution.
37. 0.6674, 5.6158, 2.4742, 3.8090. **39.** All values of t with $0 \leqq t < 2\pi$.

Section 10.11. Page 233

9. $\frac{63}{65}$. **11.** $\frac{13}{85}$. **13.** $-\frac{16}{65}, \frac{63}{65}, -\frac{16}{63}, \frac{56}{33}$. **15.** $-\frac{33}{65}, \frac{56}{65}, -\frac{33}{56}, \frac{63}{65}, -\frac{16}{65}, -\frac{63}{16}$.

Section 10.13. Page 237

7. $\frac{120}{169}, -\frac{119}{169}, -\frac{120}{119}$. **15.** $-\frac{527}{625}$. **17.** $\frac{4}{5}$. **19.** $-\frac{4}{3}$. **21.** $\frac{40}{9}$. **23.** $\frac{5}{26}\sqrt{26}$.
25. $\frac{5}{34}\sqrt{34}$. **27.** 0°, 60°, 180°, 300°. **29.** 60°, 180°, 300°. **45.** $\frac{16}{65}$. **47.** $\frac{2}{11}$.

Section 10.15. Page 240

1. $\frac{1}{2}[\cos 40° + \cos 20°]$. **3.** $\frac{1}{2}[\sin 75° - \sin 25°]$. **5.** $-\frac{1}{2}[\cos 4\theta - \cos 2\theta]$.
7. $\frac{1}{2}[\sin 2\theta + \sin \theta]$. **9.** $2 \sin 24° \cos 8°$. **11.** $-2 \sin 50° \sin 20°$.
13. $2 \cos 5\theta \cos \theta$. **15.** $2 \cos 3t \sin t$. **17.** 1. **19.** $-\frac{1}{3}\sqrt{3}$.

Section 11.3. Page 246

15. $(1, -4)$. **17.** $(-1, 1)$. **19.** $2i, -2i$. **21.** $-\frac{1}{2} + \frac{1}{2}\sqrt{3}i, -\frac{1}{2} - \frac{1}{2}\sqrt{3}i$.

Section 11.5. Page 250

9. $7 + 5i$. **11.** $-2 - 3i$. **13.** $(1, -\sqrt{3})$. **15.** $(-\frac{5}{2}\sqrt{2}, \frac{5}{2}\sqrt{2})$. **17.** (4, 60°).
19. (4, 180°). **21.** $2\sqrt{2}(\cos 225° + i \sin 225°)$. **23.** $\cos 90° + i \sin 90°$.
25. $3(\cos 180° + i \sin 180°)$. **27.** $2(\cos 60° + i \sin 60°)$.
29. $3\sqrt{2}(\cos 135° + i \sin 135°)$. **31.** $\cos 120° + i \sin 120°$. **33.** $\frac{5}{2}\sqrt{3} + \frac{5}{2}i$.
35. $-\frac{7}{2}\sqrt{2} + \frac{7}{2}\sqrt{2}i$. **37.** $-6i$. **39.** $4 - 4\sqrt{3}i$. **43.** $r = |a|$.
45. $r^2 \sin 2\theta = 14$. **47.** $3(r^2 \cos^2 \theta - 8r \cos \theta + 12) - r^2 \sin^2 \theta = 0$.
49. $x^2 + y^2 = 2y$. **51.** $(x^2 + y^2)^{\frac{3}{2}} = 4(x^2 - y^2)$. **53.** $\sqrt{x^2 + y^2} - 2x - 6 = 0$.

Section 11.7. Page 253

1. $-3+3\sqrt{3}i$. **3.** $2\sqrt{2}(\cos 105° + i \sin 105°)$. **5.** $\sqrt{2}(\cos 75° + i \sin 75°)$. **7.** $\sqrt{2}(\cos 165° + i \sin 165°)$. **9.** $-\sqrt{3} - i$. **11.** $\sqrt{2}(\cos 15° + i \sin 15°)$. **13.** -1. **15.** $-16\sqrt{3} - 16i$. **17.** $-16 + 16\sqrt{3}i$. **19.** 8.

Section 11.8. Page 255

1. $\pm\left(\frac{3}{2}+\frac{3\sqrt{3}}{2}i\right)$.
3. $1.532 + 1.2856i$; $-0.7492 + 1.8544i$; $-1.9952 - 0.1396i$; $-0.4838 - 1.9406i$; $1.696 - 1.0598i$.
5. $\pm\left(\frac{\sqrt{2}}{2}+\frac{\sqrt{2}}{2}i\right)$.
7. $\sqrt[6]{2}\left(\frac{\sqrt{2}}{2}+\frac{\sqrt{2}}{2}i\right)$; $\sqrt[6]{2}(-0.9659 + 0.2588i)$; $\sqrt[6]{2}(0.2588 - 0.9659i)$.
9. $\pm\left(\frac{\sqrt{6}}{2}+\frac{\sqrt{2}}{2}i\right)$; $\pm\sqrt{2}i$, $\pm\left(\frac{\sqrt{6}}{2}-\frac{\sqrt{2}}{2}i\right)$. **11.** $\pm(1 - \sqrt{3}i)$, $\pm(\sqrt{3} + i)$.
13. $\sqrt{2} + \sqrt{2}i$; $-0.9080 + 1.7820i$; $-1.9754 - 0.3128i$; $-0.3128 - 1.9754i$; $1.7820 - 0.9080i$.
15. $3, -\frac{3}{2} \pm \frac{3\sqrt{3}}{2}i$. **17.** $-1, 0.90 \pm 0.43i, 0.22 \pm 0.97i, -0.62 \pm 0.78i$.
19. $\sqrt[6]{5}(-0.78 - 0.63i)$, $\sqrt[6]{5}(0.93 - 0.36i)$, $\sqrt[6]{5}(-0.16 + 0.99i)$.
21. $0.309 \pm 0.9511i, -0.809 \pm 0.5878i$.

Section 12.3. Page 260

1. $Q(x) = 2x - 5$, $R(x) = 7x + 10$. **3.** -1. **5.** 3. **7.** 5. **9.** $(x - 2)(3x + 2)$.
11. $6(x + \frac{5}{2})(x - \frac{2}{3})$. **13.** $\left(x - \frac{3+\sqrt{5}}{2}\right)\left(x - \frac{3-\sqrt{5}}{2}\right)$.
15. $\left(x + \frac{3-\sqrt{23}i}{8}\right)\left(x + \frac{3+\sqrt{23}i}{8}\right)$. **21.** 2. **23.** ± 1. **25.** $-\frac{1}{2}$, 1.
27. $-4, 2; 3x - 1$. **29.** $x^3 - 4x^2 + x + 6$. **31.** $3x^2 - 12x + 15$.

Section 12.5. Page 266

1. $x^2 - 2x - 10, -23$. **3.** $x^3 - 3x^2 + x + 1, -13$.
5. $3x^3 + 11x^2 - 41x + 89, -183$. **7.** $x^2 - 0.2x + 0.05, 0$.
9. $x^2 + 0.05x + 0.0018, 0.00005$. **11.** 43, 100, 4.171. **13.** -0.5, 3.
15. -2, 1, 3. **17.** -2, 1. **19.** $\pm 1, \pm 3$. **21.** ± 1. **23.** -5.1, 0.2, 3.4.
25. -1.8, 1.2. **27.** -2, 0, 3. **29.** -0.97.

Section 12.8. Page 272

1. $x^3 - 6x^2 + 11x - 6 = 0$. **3.** $x^3 - 5x^2 + 8x - 4 = 0$.
5. $x^3 - 6x^2 + 12x - 8 = 0$. **7.** $9x^4 - 45x^3 + 65x^2 - 35x + 6 = 0$.

9. $x^3 - 6x^2 + 9x - 2 = 0$. **11.** $x^3 + x^2 - 4x + 6 = 0$. **13.** $1 \pm 2i, \frac{1}{2}$.
15. $-1 \pm i, 2, -1$. **17.** $x^4 - 10x^3 + 39x^2 - 70x + 50 = 0$.
19. $(x-1)(3x+2)$. **21.** Irreducible. **23.** $(x - 2\sqrt{2})(x + 2\sqrt{2})$.
25. Irreducible. **27.** $(x-2)(2x^2 + 2x + 3)$. **29.** $b = 4, c = 12$.

Section 12.9. Page 276

1. $\pm 1, -\frac{1}{2}$. **3.** $\pm 1, 2$. **5.** $-2, \dfrac{5 \pm \sqrt{13}}{2}$. **7.** $\frac{2}{3}, 1 \pm \sqrt{2}$. **9.** $\frac{1}{2}, \dfrac{1 \pm \sqrt{3}i}{2}$.

11. $3, \dfrac{-1 \pm \sqrt{3}i}{2}$. **13.** $-\frac{2}{3}, \dfrac{1 \pm \sqrt{3}i}{2}$. **15.** $-\frac{3}{4}, \dfrac{1 \pm \sqrt{5}}{2}$. **17.** $-\frac{1}{3}, \dfrac{1 \pm \sqrt{7}i}{2}$.

21. $(x+1)(x-2)(x+2)$.

23. $(x+2)(6x^2 - x - 4), (x+2)\left(x - \dfrac{1 + \sqrt{97}}{12}\right)\left(x - \dfrac{1 - \sqrt{97}}{12}\right)$.

25. $(x-1)(2x-3)(x^2 + x + 1), (x-1)(2x-3)\left(x + \dfrac{1 + \sqrt{3}i}{2}\right)\left(x + \dfrac{1 - \sqrt{3}i}{2}\right)$.

Section 12.10. Page 279

1. -2.21. **3.** 2.10. **5.** 1.79, -2.79. **7.** 3.35. **9.** 1.55. **11.** 3.37.
13. 2.21. **15.** 1.81. **17.** 5.37, -0.37. **19.** 2.695 ft.

Section 13.2. Page 283

1. 36. **3.** 1024. **5.** 40. **7.** 3024, 15,120. **9.** 36. **11.** 2,599,974. **13.** 12.

Section 13.5. Page 285

1. 16!. **3.** 15,120. **5.** 24, 50. **7.** 1152. **9.** 12,144; 13,824.
11. 34,650. **13.** 168. **15.** 120. **17.** $\frac{1}{2}(8!)^3$. **19.** 86,400.

Section 13.7. Page 288

1. 6435. **3.** $\dfrac{32!}{(13!)(39!)}$. **5.** 7920. **7.** 31. **9.** 661,500.

11. 120. **13.** 630. **15.** 34,650. **17.** 60,720. **19.** 86,400.

Section 13.9. Page 293

1. $\frac{1}{4}$. **3.** $\frac{1}{3}$. **5.** (a) $\frac{2}{7}$; (b) $\frac{3}{14}$; (c) $\frac{5}{7}$. **7.** $\frac{1}{4165}$. **9.** $\frac{1}{3}$. **11.** $\frac{3}{10}$.
13. \$8.00. **15.** 103 to 5, $\frac{5}{108}$, \$20. **17.** (a) $\frac{1}{6}$; (b) $\frac{1}{3}$. **19.** $\frac{248}{10,375}$. **21.** $\frac{1}{6}$.

Section 13.12. Page 299

1. $\frac{1}{36}$. **3.** (a) $\frac{20}{81}$; (b) $\frac{40}{81}$. **5.** $\frac{1}{8}, \frac{7}{8}$. **7.** $\frac{1}{6}$. **9.** $\frac{57}{136}$. **11.** $\frac{8}{35}$.
13. $\frac{1}{4}, \frac{1}{4}, \frac{1}{2}$. **15.** (a) $\frac{11}{4165}$; (b) $\frac{44}{4165}$; (c) $\frac{2197}{499,800}$; (d) $\frac{2197}{20,825}$.
17. (a) $\frac{5}{16}$; (b) $\frac{9}{16}$. **19.** $\frac{3}{10}$. **21.** 48 cents. **23.** $\frac{17}{42}$.

Section 13.14. Page 304

1. $\frac{5}{32}$. **3.** $\frac{25}{216}, \frac{19}{144}$. **5.** $\frac{1792}{6561}$. **7.** $\frac{163}{256}$. **9.** $\frac{29}{128}$. **11.** \$36, \$30, \$25.

Index

Index

(The numbers refer to pages)